mathematical theory of switching circuits
and automata

mathematical theory of
switching circuits and automata

by

SZE-TSEN HU

UNIVERSITY OF CALIFORNIA PRESS
BERKELEY AND LOS ANGELES 1968

University of California Press
Berkeley and Los Angeles, California

Cambridge University Press
London, England

Library of Congress Catalog Card Number: 68-18370

Manufactured in the United States of America

PREFACE

Interchanges between mathematics and technology always benefit both fields. Historical examples are numerous. The experiences of surveyors in ancient Egypt led to the creation of Greek geometry, which very much improved surveying. Studies in dynamics led to the discovery of calculus, which made modern astronomy and physics possible. While more and more advanced mathematics were applied to sciences and engineering with success, Einstein's theory of relativity vitalized modern differential geometry, and quantum mechanics suggested the notion of distribution which revolutionized the theory of differential equations.

By applying Boolean algebra to circuit design techniques, C. E. Shannon practically created the switching theory necessary to the development of electronic computers. During the three decades that have followed the birth of this theory, much research has been carried out by numerous engineers and a few mathematicians. As a result, most of the major problems have been solved; and recent interest has been concentrated on the purely theoretical aspect of the theory, rather than on its application to logical design.

It seems to me that now is the time to organize these results as a branch of pure mathematics and to simplify the theory not obscured by the complexity of hardware, and to do so is the purpose of this book. Within it, I have organized known results as a simple branch of pure mathematics with uniformized notation and terminology. My objective is a book that both mathematicians and engineers will find readable. Because of this duality, much effort has been made to strip away all hardware considerations, as well as all unnecessary advanced mathematics.

To mathematicians, I wish to show one can organize a body to technical or scientific knowledge and bring it up to the standard of pure mathematics. Whoever reads this book does not have to worry about the hardware and technical difficulties of which he might be completely ignorant. Now it is up to the pure mathematicians to dig up deeper results of purely mathematical interest free from the utilitarian point of view presented in most engineering works.

To engineers, I wish to show the simplicity of the theory when it is stripped of hardware considerations, technical difficulties, and unnecessary advanced mathematics brought in by some contemporary workers. Because of the uniformity requirement, my notation and terminology may vary considerably in some places from what is customary; therefore, established engineers are advised to read with reasonable patience. It is up to them to apply the approach outlined here to the more specialized results not covered in this book.

As to mathematical prerequisites, all the reader must know are the fundamentals about sets, functions, and relations covered by most high school "new mathematics" programs. To those who are not sufficiently familiar with these fundamentals, I recommend the first chapter of my *Introduction to Contempory Mathematics* [H2], listed in the bibliography at the end of this volume. Although I occasionally mention "group," "semigroup," or "monoid," those who are not familiar with these terms may neglect them without serious inconvenience. Those who want to become familiar with these and other useful algebraic terms can do so by reading the third chapter of [H2].

Although there is no engineering prerequisite for this book, engineering students are advised to study the first chapter of McCluskey's *Introduction to the Theory of Switching Circuits* [Mc] to discover the technical motivation behind the theory.

The present book is designed as a text for courses on computing machines offered in mathematics departments. It may also be used as a text for courses in switching theory for engineers provided the students are required to read the first chapters of [H2] and [Mc] before beginning this volume.

Within this book there are four chapters of approximately equal length. The first three chapters cover combinational circuits, and the final chapter takes up sequential circuits. These are loosely connected in their natural order and, therefore, may be read independently without serious inconvenience.

Because of my dual purpose, I have attempted to present mathematical theories in a somewhat leisurly manner, hoping that nonmathematicians may be able to follow without too much effort. In giving proofs, I include details that might ordinarily be omitted, preferring intelligibility to brevity. Mathematical proofs are mostly indicated by *Proof* at their beginning and by the symbol ‖ at their end. Engineers who are interested only in the formulations and statements of the results may certainly omit all proof without serious loss of continuity.

Illustrative examples are given with detailed explanations and sometimes even with descriptions of the blank tables to be used. Because of these, the solutions given are frequently much longer than the customary form of worked-out examples. These extra details should be helpful to the average student.

The exercises at the end of each chapter are carefully chosen. After a few routine problems, exercises offering more coverage of results are presented so that the good student may find a challenge sufficient to induce him to participate further in the development of the theory. No exercise is used later in the text; therefore, busy readers may skip all exercises.

The bibliography at the end of the book has been reduced to the minimum essential to the text and the exercises. References to this bibliography are given in brackets by letters and numbers for books, and by authors' last names and numbers for papers. These references are given for the benefit of the reader, not for the record of discovery. Those readers who are interested in the history of the results covered in this book can easily find applicable accounts in the existing books on the subject.

Cross-references are given in the form (I, 7.8), where "I" stands for Chapter I and "7.8" for the numbering of the statement in the chapter. The chapter numeral is omitted when reference is made within a chapter to material in that same chapter. I give as many cross-references as necessary. Furthermore, I frequently recall definitions not given immediately before to help those readers who might already have forgotten.

The index contains every term that is either defined or italicized in text or exercises. A list of special symbols and abbreviations used in this book immediately follows the contents page. In particular, I have used the symbol $*$ as the "don't care" sign when it is neither a subscript nor a superscript, and the abbreviation "iff" for the phrase "if and only if."

This manuscript was prepared during a sabbatical year made possible by a grant from the Air Force Office of Scientific Research. I wish to acknowledge my indebtedness to the AFOSR, and to thank the University of California Press and the printer for their courtesy and cooperation.

Sze-Tsen Hu

CONTENTS

SPECIAL SYMBOLS AND ABBREVIATIONS

(Numbers indicate the page on which the symbol first appears and the page on which it is discussed or defined)

§	section (of a chapter)	1
Q	set that consists of the two values of the classical two-valued logic	1
1, 0	two integers used for definiteness to denote the two members of Q;	1
	also used to denote the constant functions of n variables, the unit function and the zero function, respectively, when there is no danger of ambiguity	10
$<$	is less than	1
$=$	equals; is equal to	2
n	arbitrarily given positive integer	2
Q^n	Cartesian product of n copies of Q; called the n-cube	2
$x_1 x_2 \cdots x_3$	2^n ordered n-tuples that are members of Q^n and are called its points; frequently called combinations	2
i, j, k	notations to denote integers	2
$\leq$	is less than or equal to	2
R	set of all real numbers	2
R^n	n-dimensional Euclidean space	3
I	closed unit interval	3
iff	if and only if	3
$\neq$	does not equal; is not equal to	4
N	set of the first n positive integers	4
M	subset of N	4
$\in$	is a member of	4
$\setminus$	set-theoretic difference	4

T_n	infinite set of all possible input tapes of n variables into the set $Q = \{0, 1\}$	196
$A : T_n \to Q$	an automaton of n variables	197
$A(\tau) \in Q$	corresponding output of the automaton A	197
A_f	a function that is an automaton of n variables; referred to as the induced automaton	198
f_A	switching function referred to as the restriction of the automaton A on the n-cube Q^n	199
$M : S \times Q^n \to S$	a function from the Cartesian product $S \times Q^n$ into the set S; called transition function; used to denote sequential machine itself	202
$f : S \to Q$	arbitrarily given output function for sequential machine	203
M_a	component machine	206
$h : R \to S$	a homomorphism; a function from the set R of states in the machine L into the set S of states in the machine M	208
$i : R \to S$	inclusion function; referred to as the inclusion homomorphism	208
$\mathrm{Im}(h)$	image of the homomorphism h	209
$F_n : T_n \times Q^n \to T_n$	free sequential machine	209
$L^* = L/{\sim}$	quotient machine of the given machine L over the invariant equivalence relation $\sim$ in R	213
$p : R \to R^*$	natural projection of the given machine L onto its quotient machine L^*	213
$g = h(f)$	output function induced from f by the epimorphism h	218
$\underset{f}{\sim}$	the maximal invariant equivalence relation in R that preserves output with respect to $f : R \to Q$	219
$L_f = L/\underset{f}{\sim}$	minimal quotient machine of L with respect to the output function $f : R \to Q$	220
$i^{-1} : S \to R^*$	inverse isomorphism	221
Ω_n	set of all automata of n variables	230
Φ_n	set of all finite automata of n variables	230
S_f	set of all equivalence classes in S with respect to the equivalence relation $\underset{f}{\sim}$	235
$S^2 = S \times S$	Cartesian square	237
e_1, e_2	two switching functions; usually called the excitation functions of the machine M	246

Chapter I

SWITCHING FUNCTIONS

This opening chapter introduces the reader to switching functions and their various representations. By a switching function of n variables, we mean simply a two-valued function f defined on the vertices of the unit cube in the n-dimensional Euclidean space. The two values of f will always be denoted by the integers 1 and 0. The Boolean operations on switching functions are defined in §4 and are studied with the set-theoretic operations in §5. Then, in §6, we precisely define Boolean expressions of any given switching function f, with the elementary functions playing the role of variables. In §7, we study functional completeness. This notion is important because a network of manufactured gates realizing the switching functions in a functionally complete set can be used to mechanize any switching function. The notion of "don't care" points, which is explored in greater depth in Chapters II and III, is introduced in §8 of this first chapter. The classification of switching functions into equivalence classes called symmetry types is described in §9. The importance of this classification may be explained by the fact that switching functions in the same symmetry type can be mechanized by the same network with an appropriate permutation and/or a few complementations of the variables. The last three sections of this chapter are devoted to three important kinds of special switching functions.

1. The n-Cube Q^n

Throughout this book, let Q denote the set that consists of the two values of the classical two-valued logic. In the literature, the two members of the set Q are denoted by various notations, such as T and F, H and L, 1 and -1, or 1 and 0. For definiteness, the two members of Q are denoted by the two integers 1 and 0 throughout this book.

Since 1 and 0 are merely the integers one and zero, 0 is less than 1, as usual, and this value relationship may be expressed in symbols as

$$0 < 1.$$

Furthermore, the usual arithmetic operations, such as addition, subtraction, and multiplication, can be applied to these two integers 1 and 0.

In most instances, the result of such an operation is again one of these two integers. Precisely, we have

$$0 + 0 = 0, \quad 0 + 1 = 1, \quad 1 + 0 = 1,$$
$$0 - 0 = 0, \quad 1 - 0 = 1, \quad 1 - 1 = 0,$$
$$0 \times 0 = 0, \quad 1 \times 0 = 0, \quad 0 \times 1 = 0, \quad 1 \times 1 = 1.$$

We shall frequently make use of these arithmetic operations, and, in so doing, deviate from the traditional Boolean algebraic attitude in switching theory.

Now let n denote an arbitrarily given positive integer. Consider the Cartesian power

$$Q^n = Q \times \cdots \times Q$$

which is the Cartesian product of n sets $Q, \cdots, Q$. By definition [H2, p. 25], the members of Q^n are the 2^n ordered n-tuples

$$(x_1, x_2, \cdots, x_n),$$

where the k-th coordinate x_k is a member of the set Q for every integer $k = 1, 2, \cdots, n$.

Throughout the present book, Q^n is called the *n-cube*, and its 2^n members, its *points*. In the literature of switching theory, these points of Q^n are frequently called *combinations*.

Because the n coordinates $x_1, x_2, \cdots, x_n$ of the points of the n-cube Q^n are either 1 or 0, there is no danger of ambiguity if we delete the commas between the coordinates, as well as the parentheses at both ends. Consequently, every point of Q^n may be represented by a sequence

$$x_1 x_2 \cdots x_n$$

of n juxtaposed binary digits, and hence corresponds to an integer x satisfying

$$0 \leq x \leq 2^n - 1.$$

For example, if $n = 4$, the sixteen points of Q^4 are shown in Table I-1-1, where the sixteen corresponding integers are represented in the decimal basis.

In the literature of switching theory, the 2^n integers that correspond to the 2^n points of the n-cube Q^n are often represented in the octal basis because integers can be conveniently transformed to this basis from the binary basis and back again.

Next let us consider the n-cube Q^n from another point of view. Since Q is a subset of the set R of all real numbers, the n-cube Q^n is a subset of the

TABLE I-1-1

x	x_1	x_2	x_3	x_4
0	0	0	0	0
1	0	0	0	1
2	0	0	1	0
3	0	0	1	1
4	0	1	0	0
5	0	1	0	1
6	0	1	1	0
7	0	1	1	1
8	1	0	0	0
9	1	0	0	1
10	1	0	1	0
11	1	0	1	1
12	1	1	0	0
13	1	1	0	1
14	1	1	1	0
15	1	1	1	1

n-dimensional Euclidean space R^n. Precisely, Q^n consists of the 2^n vertices of the *real n-cube*

$$I^n = I \times \cdots \times I$$

which is the Cartesian product of n copies of the closed unit interval $I = [0, 1]$ of real numbers t satisfying $0 \le t \le 1$. This geometric interpretation of the n-cube Q^n is used frequently in the sequel.

For $n = 1, 2,$ and 3, the n-cube Q^n may be illustrated as in Figure I-1-2. Two distinct points $x = x_1x_2 \cdots x_n$ and $y = y_1y_2 \cdots y_n$ of the n-cube Q^n are said to be *adjacent* iff they differ in precisely one coordinate. In other

FIGURE I-1-2

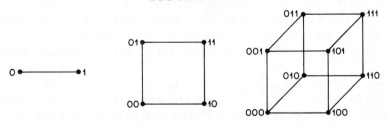

words, x and y are adjacent iff there exists an integer k, $(1 \leq k \leq n)$, such that

$$x_i = y_i, \qquad (\text{if } i \neq k).$$

Since the points x and y are distinct, we must have $x_k \neq y_k$ and hence

$$y_k = 1 - x_k.$$

In Figure I-1-2, adjacent points are joined by a line segment.

For additional convenience, we shall introduce another notation for the points of Q^n. Let

$$N = \{1, 2, \cdots, n\}$$

denote the set of the first n positive integers. For every subset M of N, we shall denote by v_M the point

$$v_M = x_1 x_2 \cdots x_n$$

of the n-cube Q^n such that

$$x_k = \begin{cases} 1 & (\text{if } k \in M), \\ 0 & (\text{if } k \in N \backslash M), \end{cases}$$

where $N \backslash M$ denotes the *set-theoretic difference*. If $M = \square$ is the empty subset of N, then we denote

$$v_0 = v_{\square}.$$

This point v_0 of the n-cube Q^n will be referred to as the *origin* of Q^n. If $M = \{i\}$ consists of a single integer $i \in N$, we denote

$$v_i = v_{\{i\}}.$$

Similar notations will be used where M consists of two or more integers of N.

For example, the sixteen points of Q^4 can be written in the v_M notation as shown in Table I-1-3.

Finally, for $n \leq 4$, the points of Q^n can be conveniently exhibited by means of the *Karnaugh maps*. For the trivial case $n = 1$, Q^n consists of two points 0 and 1 which are adjacent. Hence let us begin with the case $n = 2$. The Karnaugh map of Q^2 is given in Table I-1-4. The decimal integers in the four squares for x correspond to the points of Q^2 with coordinates $x_1 x_2$. Observe that any two points of Q^2 are adjacent iff they are located in adjacent squares, that is, squares with a common side.

The Karnaugh map of Q^3 is given in Table I-1-5. The decimal integers in the eight squares for x correspond to the points of Q^3 with coordinates $x_1 x_2 x_3$. The left boundary of the column of squares headed by 00 is to be

TABLE I-1-3

x	x_1	x_2	x_3	x_4	v_M
0	0	0	0	0	v_0
1	0	0	0	1	v_4
2	0	0	1	0	v_3
3	0	0	1	1	$v_{3,4}$
4	0	1	0	0	v_2
5	0	1	0	1	$v_{2,4}$
6	0	1	1	0	$v_{2,3}$
7	0	1	1	1	$v_{2,3,4}$
8	1	0	0	0	v_1
9	1	0	0	1	$v_{1,4}$
10	1	0	1	0	$v_{1,3}$
11	1	0	1	1	$v_{1,3,4}$
12	1	1	0	0	$v_{1,2}$
13	1	1	0	1	$v_{1,2,4}$
14	1	1	1	0	$v_{1,2,3}$
15	1	1	1	1	$v_{1,2,3,4}$

TABLE I-1-4

x_1 \ x \ x_2	0	1
0	0	1
1	2	3

TABLE I-1-5

x_1 \ x \ $x_2 x_3$	00	01	11	10
0	0	1	3	2
1	4	5	7	6

identified with the right boundary of the column of squares headed by 10. Thus, the eight squares for x are on a cylinder instead of a rectangle. Then the squares 0 and 2 are adjacent, and so are the squares 4 and 6. With this understanding, one can easily verify that any two points of Q^3 are adjacent iff they are located in adjacent squares.

The Karnaugh map of Q^4 is given in Table I-1-6. The decimal integers in the sixteen squares for x correspond to the points of Q^4 with co-ordinates $x_1x_2x_3x_4$. The left boundary of the column of squares headed

TABLE I-1-6

x_1x_2 \ x \ x_3x_4	00	01	11	10
00	0	1	3	2
01	4	5	7	6
11	12	13	15	14
10	8	9	11	10

by 00 is to be identified with the right boundary of the column of squares headed by 10; therefore, the squares 0, 4, 12, 8 are adjacent to the squares 2, 6, 14, 10, respectively. On the other hand, the upper boundary of the row of squares headed by 00 is to be identified with the lower boundary of the row of squares headed by 10; therefore, the squares 0, 1, 3, 2 are adjacent to the squares 8, 9, 11, 10, respectively. Thus, the sixteen squares for x are on a torus. With this understanding, one can easily verify that any two points of Q^4 are adjacent iff they are located in adjacent squares.

Note that we have introduced a slight modification in the Karnaugh maps presented above by putting the row heading at the left of the column heading in forming the coordinates of the points x of Q^n. In more con-ventional Karnaugh map presentations, column headings precede row headings in the coordinates of the points x. There are two reasons for this modification. First, since the row headings are on the left side of the table, it is natural to read the row heading before the column heading. Second, it is an established rule in matrix theory that the row index comes before the column index.

2. Switching Functions

Let n denote an arbitrarily given positive integer. By a *switching function* of n variables, we mean a function

$$f : Q^n \to Q$$

from the n-cube Q^n to the set Q. In other words, a switching function

$$f(x_1, \cdots, x_n)$$

of n variables $x_1, \cdots, x_n$ is defined by assigning one of the two integers in Q to each of the 2^n points $(x_1, \cdots, x_n)$ of Q^n. Thus, there are

$$\phi(n) = 2^{2^n}$$

switching functions of n variables. For $n \leq 6$, we have

$$\phi(1) = 4,$$
$$\phi(2) = 16,$$
$$\phi(3) = 256,$$
$$\phi(4) = 65{,}536,$$
$$\phi(5) = 4{,}294{,}967{,}296,$$
$$\phi(6) = 18{,}446{,}744{,}073{,}709{,}551{,}616.$$

The table of correspondence of a switching function $f : Q^n \to Q$ is called the *truth table* of f. As an example, let us consider the case $n = 4$ and the switching function $f : Q^4 \to Q$ given by

$$f(x) = \begin{cases} 1 & \text{(if } x = 0, 3, 8, 11, 15), \\ 0 & \text{(otherwise)}. \end{cases}$$

Table I-2-1 is the truth table of this switching function f of four variables.

Because the set Q consists of the two integers 1 and 0, a switching function $f : Q^n \to Q$ is completely determined by either of its two inverse images

$$f^{-1}(1) = \{x \in Q^n \,|\, f(x) = 1\},$$
$$f^{-1}(0) = \{x \in Q^n \,|\, f(x) = 0\},$$

which will be called the *on-set* and the *off-set* of the switching function f. In other words, the on-set $f^{-1}(1)$ of a switching function $f : Q^n \to Q$ of n variables consists of those points x of Q^n at which f has the value 1, and the off-set $f^{-1}(0)$ of f consists of those points x of Q^n at which f has the value 0. When the coordinates of the points in $f^{-1}(1)$ are fully displayed in the form of an array, $f^{-1}(1)$ is usually called the *on-array*, or the *on-matrix*,

TABLE I-2-1

x	x_1	x_2	x_3	x_4	$f(x)$
0	0	0	0	0	1
1	0	0	0	1	0
2	0	0	1	0	0
3	0	0	1	1	1
4	0	1	0	0	0
5	0	1	0	1	0
6	0	1	1	0	0
7	0	1	1	1	0
8	1	0	0	0	1
9	1	0	0	1	0
10	1	0	1	0	0
11	1	0	1	1	1
12	1	1	0	0	0
13	1	1	0	1	0
14	1	1	1	0	0
15	1	1	1	1	1

of the switching function f. In a similar situation, $f^{-1}(0)$ is usually called the *off-array*, or the *off-matrix*, of f.

In the preceding example, $n = 4$ and the switching function

$$f: Q^4 \to Q$$

is defined by its truth table (Table I-2-1). Thus we obtain

$$f^{-1}(1) = \{0, 3, 8, 11, 15\},$$

$$f^{-1}(0) = \{1, 2, 4, 5, 6, 7, 9, 10, 12, 13, 14\}.$$

In fully displayed form, the on-array $f^{-1}(1)$ and the off-array $f^{-1}(0)$ of f are as shown in Table I-2-2.

When $n \leq 4$, a switching function $f: Q^n \to Q$ can be defined by circling the integers in the Karnaugh map of Q^n which correspond to the points of the on-set $f^{-1}(1)$. For example, the switching function

$$f: Q^4 \to Q,$$

defined by its truth table (Table I-2-1), may be indicated by Table I-2-3.

By a *blank Karnaugh map* of Q^n, we mean a Karnaugh map in which the squares for the points x of Q^n are left blank. If a blank Karnaugh map of Q^n is used, it is customary to define a switching function

$$f: Q^n \to Q$$

TABLE I-2-2

On-array $f^{-1}(1)$	Off-array $f^{-1}(0)$
0 0 0 0	0 0 0 1
0 0 1 1	0 0 1 0
1 0 0 0	0 1 0 0
1 0 1 1	0 1 0 1
1 1 1 1	0 1 1 0
	0 1 1 1
	1 0 0 1
	1 0 1 0
	1 1 0 0
	1 1 0 1
	1 1 1 0

TABLE I-2-3

x_1x_2 \\ x_3x_4	00	01	11	10
00	⓪	1	③	2
01	4	5	7	6
11	12	13	⑮	14
10	⑧	9	⑪	10

TABLE I-2-4

x_1x_2 \\ x_3x_4	00	01	11	10
00	1		1	
01				
11			1	
10	1		1	

by writing the integer 1 in each of the squares corresponding to the points
of the on-set $f^{-1}(1)$. In this case, the switching function

$$f : Q^4 \to X,$$

defined by its truth table (Table I-2-1), will be indicated by Table I-2-4.
   Both Table I-2-3 and Table I-2-4 will be referred to as the Karnaugh map
of the switching function $f : Q^4 \to Q$ with truth table I-2-1.
   When $n \leq 3$, a switching function $f : Q^n \to Q$ may be defined by circling
the vertices of the geometric n-cube which correspond to the points of the
on-set $f^{-1}(1)$. For example, the switching function

$$f : Q^3 \to Q$$

with on-set

$$f^{-1}(1) = \{0, 3, 5, 7\}$$

can be indicated by Figure I-2-5.

FIGURE I-2-5

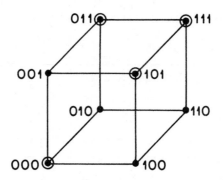

3. Some Special Functions

Since Q consists of two members 1 and 0, there are exactly two *constant
functions* of n variables: the switching function

$$f : Q^n \to Q$$

with $f(x) = 1$ for all $x \in Q^n$ is called the *unit function*, and that with
$f(x) = 0$ for all $x \in Q^n$ is called the *zero function*. These constant functions
of n variables are denoted by 1 and 0, respectively, when there is no danger
of ambiguity.

Now let i denote any integer satisfying $0 \le i \le n$. By the i-th *elementary function* of n variables, we mean the switching function

$$e_i : Q^n \to Q$$

defined by $e_i(x) = x_i$ for every point

$$x = x_1 x_2 \cdots x_n$$

of the n-cube Q^n. Thus the value of the function e_i at an arbitrary point x of Q^n is exactly the i-th coordinate x_i of the point x. For this reason, we will denote the i-th elementary function of n variables by the symbol x_i so long as there is no danger of ambiguity.

By the i-th *complementary function* of n variables, we mean the switching function

$$c_i : Q^n \to Q$$

defined by $c_i(x) = 1 - x_i$ for every point $x = x_1 x_2 \cdots x_n$ of the n-cube Q^n. So long as there is no danger of ambiguity, we will denote the i-th complementary function by the symbol x_i'.

For the case $n = 1$, there is only one elementary function. This lone elementary function of one variable is the *identity function*

$$e : Q \to Q$$

on the set Q; that is, $e(x) = x$ for every $x \in Q$. On the other hand, there is only one complementary function. This lone complementary function

$$c : Q \to Q$$

is defined by $c(x) = 1 - x$ for every $x \in Q$ and will be referred to as the *complementation function*. The

$$\phi(1) = 4$$

switching functions of one variables are

$$1, 0, e, c.$$

If $n = 2$, we have two constant functions 1 and 0, two elementary functions x_1 and x_2, and two complementary functions x_1' and x_2'. Since

$$\phi(2) = 16,$$

there are ten switching functions of two variables other than these six functions.

Three of these switching functions of two variables are frequently referred to in this book, namely, the *conjunction function* $\wedge$, the *disjunction*

TABLE I-3-1

x	$x_1\ x_2$	$\wedge(x)$	$\vee(x)$	$\varotimes(x)$
0	0 0	0	0	0
1	0 1	0	1	1
2	1 0	0	1	1
3	1 1	1	1	0

function $\vee$, and the *exclusive disjunction function* $\varotimes$, defined by their truth tables shown in Table I-3-1.

In the literature of switching theory, the conjunction function $\wedge$ is often called the *AND function*, denoted by &, the disjunction function $\vee$ is often called the *OR function*, and the exclusive disjunction function $\varotimes$ is often called the *exclusive OR* function.

Another three of these switching functions of two variables are the compositions

$$\wedge' = c \circ \wedge, \qquad \vee' = c \circ \vee, \qquad \varotimes' = c \circ \varotimes$$

of the switching functions $\wedge$, $\vee$, $\varotimes$ with the complementation function

$$c : Q \to Q.$$

In other words, the switching functions $\wedge'$, $\vee'$, $\varotimes'$ of two variables are defined by

$$\wedge'(x) = c[\wedge(x)] = 1 - \wedge(x),$$
$$\vee'(x) = c[\vee(x)] = 1 - \vee(x),$$
$$\varotimes'(x) = c[\varotimes(x)] = 1 - \varotimes(x)$$

for every point x of Q^2. Their truth tables are given in Table I-3-2.

In the literature of switching theory, the switching function $\wedge'$ is called the *NAND function* or the *AND-NOT function*, the switching function $\vee'$ is called the *NOR function* or the *OR-NOT function*, and the switching

TABLE I-3-2

x	$x_1\ x_2$	$\wedge'(x)$	$\vee'(x)$	$\varotimes'(x)$
0	0 0	1	1	1
1	0 1	1	0	0
2	1 0	1	0	0
3	1 1	0	0	1

function $\bigcirc'$ is called the *exclusive NOR function* or the *exclusive OR-NOT function*.

The four remaining switching functions of two variables are the two functions

$$d_1 : Q^2 \to Q, \qquad d_2 : Q^2 \to Q$$

defined by

$$d_1(x) = \begin{cases} 1 & \text{(if } x_1 = 1 \text{ and } x_2 = 0), \\ 0 & \text{(otherwise)}, \end{cases}$$

$$d_2(x) = \begin{cases} 1 & \text{(if } x_1 = 0 \text{ and } x_2 = 1), \\ 0 & \text{(otherwise)}, \end{cases}$$

for every point $x = x_1 x_2$ of Q^2, and their compositions

$$d_1' = c \circ d_1, \qquad d_2' = c \circ d_2$$

with the complementation function

$$c : Q \to Q.$$

Their truth tables are given in Table I-3-3.

TABLE I-3-3

x	$x_1 \ x_2$	$d_1(x)$	$d_1'(x)$	$d_2(x)$	$d_2'(x)$
0	0 0	0	1	0	1
1	0 1	0	1	1	0
2	1 0	1	0	0	1
3	1 1	0	1	0	1

Thus we have determined all of the sixteen switching functions of two variables:

$$1, 0, x_1, x_1', x_2, x_2', d_1, d_1', d_2, d_2', \wedge, \wedge', \vee, \vee', \bigcirc, \bigcirc'.$$

These switching functions of two variables can be generalized to n variables. In fact, the first six of these have their obvious meaning as switching functions of n variables.

Let n denote an arbitrarily given positive integer. To generalize the last six functions $\wedge, \wedge', \vee, \vee', \bigcirc, \bigcirc'$ to n variables, let us first define a function

$$\sigma : Q^n \to R$$

from the n-cube Q^n to the set R of all real numbers by taking

$$\sigma(x) = \sum_{i=1}^{n} x_i$$

for every point $x = x_1 x_2 \cdots x_n$ of Q^n. In words, $\sigma(x)$ is the sum of the integers $x_1, x_2, \cdots, x_n$.

By the *conjunction function*, or the *AND function*, of n variables, we mean the switching function

$$\wedge : Q^n \to Q$$

defined by

$$\wedge(x) = \begin{cases} 1 & \text{(if } \sigma(x) \geq n), \\ 0 & \text{(otherwise)}, \end{cases}$$

for every point x of Q^n. Since $\sigma(x) \geq n$ holds for $x = x_1 x_2 \cdots x_n$ iff $x_k = 1$ is true for every $k = 1, 2, \cdots, n$, it follows that the functional value $\wedge(x)$ is 1 iff all of the coordinates of the point x are 1.

By the *disjunction function*, or the *OR function*, of n variables, we mean the switching function

$$\vee : Q^n \to Q$$

defined by

$$\vee(x) = \begin{cases} 1 & \text{(if } \sigma(x) \geq 1), \\ 0 & \text{(otherwise)}, \end{cases}$$

for every point x of Q^n. Since $\sigma(x) \geq 1$ holds for $x = x_1 x_2 \cdots x_n$ iff $x_k = 1$ is true for some k, it follows that the functional value $\vee(x)$ is 1 iff at least one of the coordinates of the point x is 1.

By the *exclusive disjunction function*, or the *exclusive OR function*, of n variables, we mean the switching function

$$\text{\textcircled{V}} : Q^n \to Q$$

defined by

$$\text{\textcircled{V}}(x) = \begin{cases} 1 & \text{(if } \sigma(x) = 1), \\ 0 & \text{(otherwise)}, \end{cases}$$

for every point x of Q^n. Hence the functional value $\text{\textcircled{V}}(x)$ is 1 iff exactly one of the coordinates of the point x is 1.

By the *NAND function* of n variables, we mean the composition

$$\wedge' = c \circ \wedge : Q^n \to Q$$

of the *AND* function $\wedge : Q^n \to Q$ and the complementation function $c : Q \to Q$. Hence this switching function $\wedge'$ of n variables is defined by

$$\wedge'(x) = c[\wedge(x)] = \begin{cases} 0 & \text{(if } \sigma(x) \geq n), \\ 1 & \text{(otherwise)}, \end{cases}$$

for every point x of Q^n. Therefore, the fuctional value $\wedge'(x)$ is 0 iff all the coordinates of the point x are 1.

By the *NOR function* of n variables, we mean the composition

$$\vee' = c \circ \vee : Q^n \to Q$$

of the *OR* function $\vee : Q^n \to Q$ and the complementation function $c : Q \to Q$. Hence this switching function $\vee'$ of n variables is defined by

$$\vee'(x) = c[\vee(x)] = \begin{cases} 0 & (\text{if } \sigma(x) \geq 1), \\ 1 & (\text{otherwise}), \end{cases}$$

for every point x of Q^n. Therefore, the functional value $\vee'(x)$ is 0 iff at least one of the coordinates of the point x is 1.

By the *exclusive NOR function* of n variables, we mean the composition

$$\otimes' = c \circ \otimes : Q^n \to Q$$

of the exclusive *OR* function $\otimes : Q^n \to Q$ and the complementation function $c : Q \to Q$. Hence this switching function $\otimes'$ of n variables is defined by

$$\otimes'(x) = c[\otimes(x)] = \begin{cases} 0 & (\text{if } \sigma(x) = 1), \\ 1 & (\text{otherwise}), \end{cases}$$

for every point x of Q^n. Therefore, the functional value $\otimes'(x)$ is 0 iff exactly one of the coordinates of the point x is 1.

The generalizations of the remaining four switching functions of two variables are not interesting at this moment and hence are omitted.

4. Boolean Operations

For an arbitrarily given positive integer n, let us consider the set

$$\Phi$$

of all switching functions of n variables. In the present section, we shall turn Φ into a *Boolean algebra* by introducing two binary operations, the *conjunction* $\wedge$ and the *disjunction* $\vee$, together with a unary operation, the *complementation*.

Let f and g denote any two switching functions of n variables. By the *conjunction* of f and g, we mean the switching function

$$h = f \wedge g : Q^n \to Q$$

of n variables defined by

$$h(x) = \wedge[f(x), g(x)]$$

for every point x of the n-cube Q^n. Here, $\wedge$ on the right-hand side of the equations stands for the conjunction function

$$\wedge : Q^2 \to Q$$

of two variables with its truth table given in Table I-3-1.

Since, for an arbitrarily given point x of Q^n, $(f \wedge g)(x) = 1$ iff $f(x) = 1$ and $g(x) = 1$, the symbol $f \wedge g$ ordinarily reads "f and g."

On the other hand, one can easily verify that

$$(f \wedge g)(x) = f(x)g(x)$$

holds for every $x \in Q^n$. Here, $f(x)g(x)$ stands for the ordinary product of the integers $f(x)$ and $g(x)$; therefore, the conjunction $f \wedge g$ will be called the *product* of the switching functions f and g and will be denoted simply by fg.

Let f and g denote any two switching functions of n variables. By the *disjunction* of f and g, we mean the switching function

$$h = f \vee g : Q^n \to Q$$

of n variables defined by

$$h(x) = \vee[f(x), g(x)]$$

for every point x of the n-cube Q^n. Here, $\vee$ on the right-hand side of the equation stands for the disjunction function

$$\vee : Q^2 \to Q$$

of two variables with its truth table given in Table I-3-1.

Since, for an arbitrarily given point x of Q^n, $(f \vee g)(x) = 1$ iff $f(x) = 1$ or $g(x) = 1$, the symbol $f \vee g$ ordinarily reads "f or g."

Traditionally, $f \vee g$ is called the *sum* or the *logical sum* of f and g; however, one must observe that, in general,

$$(f \vee g)(x) = f(x) + g(x), \qquad (x \in Q^n),$$

fails to be true even in the sense of modulo 2. For this reason, the disjunction $f \vee g$ will simply be called the *join* of the switching functions f and g throughout this book, so as to avoid possible ambiguity.

By the definitions of the products and the joins of switching functions of n variables, one can easily verify statements (4.1)–(4.5) which follow.

(4.1) THE COMMUTATIVE LAWS: *For any two switching functions f and g of n variables, we have*

$$fg = gf, \qquad\qquad\qquad\qquad (4.1a)$$

$$f \vee g = g \vee f. \qquad\qquad\qquad\qquad (4.1b)$$

(4.2) THE ASSOCIATIVE LAWS: *For any three switching functions f, g, and h of n variables, we have*

$$(fg)h = f(gh), \tag{4.2a}$$

$$(f \vee g) \vee h = f \vee (g \vee h). \tag{4.2b}$$

(4.3) THE DISTRIBUTIVE LAWS: *For any three switching functions f, g, and h of n variables, we have*

$$f(g \vee h) = fg \vee fh, \tag{4.3a}$$

$$f \vee gh = (f \vee g)(f \vee h). \tag{4.3b}$$

(4.4) THE IDEMPOTENT LAWS: *For any switching function f of n variables, we have*

$$ff = f, \tag{4.4a}$$

$$f \vee f = f. \tag{4.4b}$$

(4.5) THE LAWS OF OPERATION WITH THE CONSTANT FUNCTIONS 0 AND 1: *For any switching function f of n variables, we have*

$$0 \vee f = f, \tag{4.5a}$$

$$1f = f, \tag{4.5b}$$

$$0f = 0, \tag{4.5c}$$

$$1 \vee f = 1. \tag{4.5d}$$

Next, we shall introduce the unary operation in Φ. Let f denote an arbitrarily given switching function of n variables. By the *complement* of f, we mean the composition

$$f' = c \circ f : Q^n \to Q$$

of f and the complementation function

$$c : Q \to Q$$

defined in the previous section. Hence, the complement f' of f is a switching function of n variables defined by

$$f'(x) = c[f(x)] = 1 - f(x)$$

for every point x of the n-cube Q^n.

EXAMPLES OF COMPLEMENTS:

(1) For every integer $i = 1, 2, \cdots, n$, the complementary function $x_i' : Q^n \to Q$ defined in the preceding section is the complement of the elementary function $x_i : Q^n \to Q$.

(2) The *NAND* function $\wedge' : Q^n \to Q$ defined in the preceding section is the complement of the *AND* function $\wedge : Q^n \to Q$.

(3) The *NOR* function $\vee' : Q^n \to Q$ defined in the preceding section is the complement of the *OR* function $\vee : Q^n \to Q$.

(4) The exclusive *NOR* function $\oslash' : Q^n \to Q$ defined in the preceding section is the complement of the exclusive *OR* function $\oslash : Q^n \to Q$.

Thus we have justified the notations used in the previous section for these switching functions.

By the definitions of the products, the joins, and the complements of switching functions, one can easily verify statements (4.6)–(4.8) which follow.

(4.6) THE LAWS OF COMPLEMENTARITY: *For any switching function f of n variables, we have*

$$ff' = 0, \tag{4.6a}$$

$$f \vee f' = 1. \tag{4.6b}$$

(4.7) DE MORGAN'S LAWS: *For any two switching functions f and g of n variables, we have*

$$(fg)' = f' \vee g', \tag{4.7a}$$

$$(f \vee g)' = f'g'. \tag{4.7b}$$

(4.8) THE LAW OF INVOLUTION: *For any switching function f of n variables, we have*

$$(f')' = f.$$

To make the set Φ of all switching functions of n variables a Boolean algebra as defined in [Ho, p. xii], it remains to introduce an equivalence relation and a partial order into the set Φ. For this purpose, let f and g be any two switching functions of n variables. We define f and g to be *equal*, in symbol,

$$f = g,$$

iff f and g are precisely the same switching function of n variables, that is,

$$f(x) = g(x)$$

holds for every point x of the n-cube Q^n. On the other hand, we say that f *implies* g, in symbol,

$$f \leq g,$$

iff $f(x) \leq g(x)$ holds for every point x of the n-cube Q^n. Here, since $f(x)$ and $g(x)$ are integers, the inequality

$$f(x) \leq g(x)$$

means as usual that the integer $f(x)$ is either less than or equal to the integer $g(x)$. For example, the three switching functions

$$\wedge, \vee, \oslash : Q^n \to Q,$$

defined in the preceding section, have the following relations:

$$\wedge \le \vee, \qquad \oslash \le \vee.$$

Obviously, "$=$" is an equivalence relation in the set Φ as defined in [H2, p. 30]. One can also easily verify statements (4.9)–(4.13) concerning the relation "$\le$" in Φ.

(4.9) THE UNIVERSAL BOUNDS PROPERTY: *For any switching function f of n variables, we have*

$$0 \le f \le 1.$$

(4.10) THE REFLEXIVE LAW: *For any switching function f of n variables, we have*

$$f \le f.$$

(4.11) THE ANTISYMMETRIC LAW: *Let f and g denote any two switching functions of n variables. If $f \le g$ and $g \le f$, then $f = g$.*

(4.12) THE TRANSITIVE LAW: *Let f, g, and h denote any three switching functions of n variables. If $f \le g$ and $g \le h$, then $f \le h$.*

(4.13) THE CONSISTENCY PRINCIPLE: *For any two switching functions f and g of n variables, we have*

$$f \le g \quad \text{iff} \quad fg = f, \tag{4.13a}$$

$$f \le g \quad \text{iff} \quad f \vee g = g. \tag{4.13b}$$

Thus, in accordance with the usual definition [Ho, pp. xii–xv], the set Φ of all switching functions of n variables becomes a Boolean algebra.

Finally, two switching functions f and g of n variables are said to be *comparable* iff $f \le g$ or $g \le f$. For example, consider the three switching functions

$$\wedge, \vee, \oslash : Q^n \to Q$$

of n variables. Because of the relations

$$\wedge \le \vee, \qquad \oslash \le \vee,$$

it follows that $\wedge$, $\vee$ are comparable and so are $\oslash$, $\vee$. However, if $n \ge 2$, $\wedge$ and $\oslash$ are obviously not comparable.

5. Set-Theoretic Operations

For an arbitrarily given positive integer n, let us consider the set

$$\Psi$$

of all possible subsets of the n-cube Q^n. In the present section, we shall recall the usual set-theoretic operations that turn the set Ψ into a Boolean algebra. It will also be shown that Φ and Ψ are naturally isomorphic and hence can be identified.

Let F and G denote any two subsets of the n-cube Q^n. By the *intersection* of F and G, we mean the subset

$$F \cap G$$

of the n-cube Q^n consisting of those points of Q^n which belong to both F and G. By the *union* of F and G, we mean the subset

$$F \cup G$$

of the n-cube Q^n consisting of those points of Q^n which belong to at least one of the sets F and G. Finally, the *difference*

$$G \backslash F$$

is defined to be the subset of the n-cube Q^n consisting of those points of Q^n which belong to G but not to F. In particular, if $G = Q^n$, the difference $G \backslash F$ is called the *complement* of F and will be denoted by F'. Thus, we have

$$F' = Q^n \backslash F.$$

We shall also use the symbol $\square$ to denote the empty subset of Q^n. Hence we have

$$\square' = Q^n.$$

For general definitions and intuitive illustrations of these set-theoretic notions, see [H2, pp. 3–14].

By means of the definitions given above, one can easily verify the statements (5.1)–(5.8) which follow.

(5.1) THE COMMUTATIVE LAWS: *For any two subsets F and G of the n-cube Q^n, we have*

$$F \cap G = G \cap F, \tag{5.1a}$$

$$F \cup G = G \cup F. \tag{5.1b}$$

(5.2) THE ASSOCIATIVE LAWS: *For any three subsets F, G, and H of the n-cube Q^n, we have*

$$(F \cap G) \cap H = F \cap (G \cap H), \tag{5.2a}$$

$$(F \cup G) \cup H = F \cup (G \cup H). \tag{5.2b}$$

(5.3) THE DISTRIBUTIVE LAWS: *For any three subsets F, G, and H of the n-cube Q^n, we have*

$$F \cap (G \cap H) = (F \cap G) \cup (F \cap H), \tag{5.3a}$$

$$F \cup (G \cap H) = (F \cup G) \cap (F \cup H). \tag{5.3b}$$

(5.4) THE IDEMPOTENT LAWS: *For any subset F of the n-cube Q^n, we have*

$$F \cap F = F, \tag{5.4a}$$

$$F \cup F = F. \tag{5.4b}$$

(5.5) THE LAWS OF OPERATION WITH $\square$ AND Q^n: *For any subset F of the n-cube Q^n, we have*

$$\square \cup F = F, \tag{5.5a}$$

$$Q^n \cap F = F, \tag{5.5b}$$

$$\square \cap F = \square, \tag{5.5c}$$

$$Q^n \cup F = Q^n. \tag{5.5d}$$

(5.6) THE LAWS OF COMPLEMENTARITY: *For any subset F of the n-cube Q^n, we have*

$$F \cap F' = \square, \tag{5.6a}$$

$$F \cup F' = Q^n. \tag{5.6b}$$

(5.7) DE MORGAN'S LAWS: *For any two subsets F and G of the n-cube Q^n, we have*

$$(F \cap G)' = F' \cup G', \tag{5.7a}$$

$$(F \cup G)' = F' \cap G'. \tag{5.7b}$$

(5.8) THE LAW OF INVOLUTION: *For any subset F of the n-cube Q^n, we have*

$$(F')' = F.$$

To make the set Ψ of all possible subsets of Q^n a Boolean algebra, it remains to define an equivalence relation and a partial order in Ψ. For this purpose, let F and G denote any two subsets of the *n*-cube Q^n. We define F and G to be *equal*, in symbol,

$$F = G,$$

iff F and G are precisely the same subset of Q^n. On the other hand, we say that F *is contained in* G, in symbol,

$$F \subset G,$$

iff every point x in F is also in G. Obviously, "$=$" is an equivalence relation in the set Ψ as defined in [H2, p. 30]. One can also easily verify statements (5.9)–(5.13) concerning the relation "$\subset$" in the set Ψ

(5.9) THE UNIVERSAL BOUNDS PROPERTY: *For any subset F of the n-cube* Q^n, *we have*

$$\square \subset F \subset Q^n.$$

(5.10) THE REFLEXIVE LAW: *For any subset F of the n-cube* Q^n, *we have*

$$F \subset F.$$

(5.11) THE ANTISYMMETRIC LAW: *Let F and G denote any two subsets of the n-cube* Q^n. *If* $F \subset G$ *and* $G \subset F$, *then* $F = G$.

(5.12) THE TRANSITIVE LAWS: *Let F, G, and H denote any three subsets of the n-cube* Q^n. *If* $F \subset G$ *and* $G \subset H$, *then* $F \subset H$.

(5.13) THE CONSISTING PRINCIPLE: *For any two subsets F and G of the n-cube* Q^n, *we have*

$$F \subset G \quad \text{iff} \quad F \cap G = F, \tag{5.13a}$$

$$F \subset G \quad \text{iff} \quad F \cup G = G. \tag{5.13b}$$

Thus, the set Ψ of all subsets of the n-cube Q^n becomes a Boolean algebra. Obviously, in the construction given above, the n-cube Q^n can be replaced by any given set X.

This Boolean algebra Ψ of all subsets of the n-cube Q^n is essentially the same as the Boolean algebra Φ of all switching functions of n variables constructed in the preceding section. To show that this statement is so, we first construct two transformations

$$\rho : \Phi \to \Psi, \qquad \theta : \Psi \to \Phi.$$

To define ρ, let us consider any switching function $f : Q^n \to Q$ of n variables. The on-set $f^{-1}(1)$ of f is a subset of the n-cube Q^n and hence is a member of the set Ψ. We define ρ by setting

$$\rho(f) = f^{-1}(1)$$

for every $f \in \Phi$. To define θ, let us consider an arbitrarily given subset F of the n-cube Q^n. As in the theory of sets, F determines a so-called *characteristic function* $\chi_F : Q^n \to Q$ defined by

$$\chi_F(x) = \begin{cases} 1 & \text{(if } x \in F\text{)}, \\ 0 & \text{(if } x \in F'\text{)}. \end{cases}$$

This characteristic function χ_F is a switching function of n variables and hence is a member of the set Φ. We define θ by taking

$$\theta(F) = \chi_F$$

for every $F \in \Psi$.

By the definitions of ρ and θ, one can easily see that the compositions

$$\theta \circ \rho : \Phi \to \Phi, \qquad \rho \circ \theta : \Psi \to \Psi$$

are the identity transformations on Φ and Ψ, respectively, that is,

$$\theta[\rho(f)] = f, \qquad \rho[\theta(F)] = F$$

for each $f \in \Phi$ and each $F \in \Psi$. Hence, both ρ and θ are *bijective* (i.e., 1-1 and onto), and each is the inverse of the other.

Furthermore, ρ and θ are *isomorphisms* of the Boolean algebras Φ and Ψ. In fact, we have the following statement (5.14) which can be easily verified by means of the definitions.

(5.14) *For any two switching functions f and g of n variables, we have*

$$\rho(fg) = \rho(f) \cap \rho(g), \qquad (5.14a)$$

$$\rho(f \vee g) = \rho(f) \cup \rho(g), \qquad (5.14b)$$

$$\rho(f') = [\rho(f)]', \qquad (5.14c)$$

$$\rho(f) \subset \rho(g) \quad \text{iff} \quad f \leq g. \qquad (5.14d)$$

This completes the demonstration that Φ and Ψ are naturally isomorphic and hence can be identified by means of the natural isomorphisms ρ and θ.

6. Boolean Expressions

Let n denote an arbitrarily given positive integer. Consider the n elementary functions

$$x_i : Q^n \to Q, \qquad (i = 1, 2, \cdots, n),$$

of n variables defined in §3. By a *Boolean expression* of n variables, we mean an expression

$$E(x_1, x_2, \cdots, x_n)$$

built up from these elementary functions $x_1, x_2, \cdots, x_n$ and the constant functions 0, 1 by a finite number of applications of the Boolean operations, namely, the product, the join, and the complementation. For example

$$(x_1 \vee x_2)[(x_1x_2)' \vee (x_1'x_3)] \vee x_3'$$

is a Boolean expression of n variables for every $n \geq 3$.

Since the elementary functions $x_1, x_2, \cdots, x_n$ are switching functions, it follows from the definitions of the Boolean operations that any Boolean expression $E(x_1, x_2, \cdots, x_n)$ represents a unique switching function of n variables. If a Boolean expression $E(x_1, x_2, \cdots, x_n)$ represents the switching function

$$f : Q^n \to Q,$$

then we say that $E(x_1, x_2, \cdots, x_n)$ is a *Boolean expression of the switching function f* and we denote

$$f = E(x_1, x_2, \cdots, x_n).$$

Some special Boolean expressions are of fundamental importance. By a *minterm* or a *fundamental product* of n variables, we mean a Boolean product of the n elementary functions where each elementary function is present as a factor precisely once, either complemented or not. Since each of the n elementary functions is chosen in either complemented or uncomplemented form, there are 2^n minterms of n variables. When $n = 2$, the 4 minterms of two variables are

$$x_1x_2, \quad x_1x_2', \quad x_1'x_2, \quad x_1'x_2'.$$

Comparing with the functions of two variables in §3, we obtain

$$x_1x_2 = \wedge, \qquad x_1x_2' = d_1, \qquad x_1'x_2 = d_2, \qquad x_1'x_2' = \vee'.$$

If we define $x_i^1 = x_i$ and $x_i^0 = x_i'$ for every $i = 1, 2, \cdots, n$, then a minterm of n variables may be represented in the form

$$x_1^{a_1} x_2^{a_2} \cdots x_n^{a_n}$$

where $a_i \in Q$ for every $i = 1, 2, \cdots, n$. Thus, we obtain a point

$$a = a_1 a_2 \cdots a_n$$

of the n-cube Q^n which is uniquely determined by the minterm. Let

$$p_a : Q^n \to Q$$

denote the switching function represented by the minterm, in symbol,

$$p_a = x_1^{a_1} x_2^{a_2} \cdots x_n^{a_n}.$$

Then, for an arbitrary point x of Q^n, we obviously have

$$p_a(x) = \begin{cases} 1 & \text{(if } x = a\text{)}, \\ 0 & \text{(if } x \neq a\text{)}. \end{cases}$$

In other words, the on-set $p^{-1}(1)$ consists of a single point a of the n-cube Q^n.

Now let us consider an arbitrarily given switching function

$$f : Q^n \to Q$$

of n variables and let

$$F = f^{-1}(1)$$

denote its on-set. Then it follows from the isomorphism ρ of the preceding section that f is the join of the switching functions p_a for all points $a \in F$; in symbols,

$$f = \mathbf{V}_{a\in F}\, p_a.$$

Hence we obtain the following theorem.

THEOREM 6.1. *Any given switching function $f : Q^n \to Q$ of n variables has a Boolean expression*

$$f = \mathbf{V}_{a\in F}\, x_1^{a_1} x_2^{a_2} \cdots x_n^{a_n}$$

where $a_1, a_2, \cdots, a_n$ denote the coordinates of the point $a \in F$, and $x_i^1 = x_i$, $x_i^0 = x_i'$ for every $i = 1, 2, \cdots, n$.

This theorem answers affirmatively the question whether or not every switching function of n variables has a Boolean expression. On the other hand, it is obvious from (4.4) that every switching function of n variables has an infinite number of Boolean expressions.

The Boolean expression of the switching function $f : Q^n \to Q$ in (6.1) is a join of distinct minterms completely determined by f and referred to as the *(disjunctive) standard expressions* of f. It is clear by the definition that knowing the standard expression of a switching function $f : Q^n \to Q$ is exactly the same as knowing the on-set $F = f^{-1}(1)$. If one of these is given, the other can be obtained immediately.

The standard expression of a switching function f of n variables in (6.1) is a special case of the Boolean polynomials. By a *Boolean monomial* of n variables we mean a Boolean product of some of the n elementary functions, either complemented or not. Because of (4.4) and (4.6), we may assume that each elementary function appears, at most, once in the monomial. Hence, the minterms defined above are special cases of Boolean monomials. For completeness, the constant functions 0 and 1 are also considered as

Boolean monomials. By a *Boolean polynomial* of n variables, we mean a join of Boolean monomials of n variables. In particular, the standard expression of any given switching function f of n variables is a Boolean polynomial of n variables. By (6.1), every switching function f of n variables can be expressed by a Boolean polynomial.

Frequently, a switching function f of n variables is given by a Boolean expression $E(x_1, \cdots, x_n)$. By means of the laws in §4, we can develop $E(x_1, \cdots, x_n)$ into a Boolean polynomial $P(x_1, \cdots, x_n)$ which represents f. For example, let us consider the switching function

$$f = (x_1 \vee x_2)[(x_1 x_2)' \vee (x_1' x_3)] \vee x_3'$$

of $n \geq 3$ variables. Applying the laws in §4, we obtain

$$
\begin{aligned}
(x_1 \vee x_2)&[(x_1 x_2)' \vee (x_1' x_3)] \vee x_3' \\
&= (x_1 \vee x_2)[(x_1' \vee x_2') \vee (x_1' x_3)] \vee x_3' \\
&= [(x_1 \vee x_2)x_1' \vee (x_1 \vee x_2)x_2' \vee (x_1 \vee x_2)x_1' x_3] \vee x_3' \\
&= (x_1 x_1' \vee x_1' x_2 \vee x_1 x_2' \vee x_2 x_2' \vee x_1 x_1' x_3 \vee x_1' x_2 x_3) \vee x_3' \\
&= x_1' x_2 \vee x_1 x_2' \vee x_1' x_2 x_3 \vee x_3'.
\end{aligned}
$$

Thus, we obtain a polynomial expression

$$f = x_1' x_2 \vee x_1 x_2' \vee x_1' x_2 x_3 \vee x_3'$$

for the given switching function f.

If a switching function f of n variables is given by a Boolean polynomial $P(x_1, \cdots, x_n)$, we can easily construct the standard expression of f by the following process. Consider an arbitrary term T in the Boolean polynomial $P(x_1, \cdots, x_n)$. Then T is a Boolean monomial. Let s denote the *degree* of the monomial T, that is, the number of factors in T; and let $t = n - s$. Then there are 2^t minterms of n variables each of which implies T.

One can easily see that the standard expression of f is the join of all distinct minterms of n variables obtained in this way for all terms in $P(x_1, \cdots, x_n)$. For example, let $n = 3$ and consider the switching function

$$f = x_1' x_2 \vee x_1 x_2' \vee x_1' x_2 x_3 \vee x_3'$$

of 3 variables. For the first term $T_1 = x_1' x_2$, we get 2 minterms, $x_1' x_2 x_3$ and $x_1' x_2 x_3'$. For the second term $T_2 = x_1 x_2'$, we get 2 minterms, $x_1 x_2' x_3$ and $x_1 x_2' x_3'$. The third term $T_3 = x_1' x_2 x_3$ is a minterm itself. For the last term $T_4 = x_3'$, we get 4 minterms $x_1 x_2 x_3'$, $x_1 x_2' x_3'$, $x_1' x_2 x_3'$, and $x_1' x_2' x_3'$. Thus, we obtain 6 distinct minterms and the standard expression of f:

$$f = x_1' x_2' x_3' \vee x_1' x_2 x_3' \vee x_1' x_2 x_3 \vee x_1 x_2' x_3' \vee x_1 x_2' x_3 \vee x_1 x_2 x_3'.$$

From this standard expression of f, we immediately find the on-set of f:

$$f^{-1}(1) = \{0, 2, 3, 4, 5, 6\}.$$

Let $P(x_1, \cdots, x_n)$ denote an arbitrarily given Boolean polynomial of n variables. For each term T in $P(x_1, \cdots, x_n)$, let us denote by $\deg(T)$ its *degree*, that is, the number of factors in T. The sum of these degrees for all terms in the given Boolean polynomial $P(x_1, \cdots, x_n)$ will be called the *size* of $P(x_1, \cdots, x_n)$. In other words, the size of a Boolean polynomial $P(x_1, \cdots, x_n)$ is the total number of occurrences of the letters that represent the elementary functions. The size of $P(x_1, \cdots, x_n)$ indicates the number of switches needed in the contact network mechanizing $P(x_1, \cdots, x_n)$. See [Ca. pp. 87–88].

In the preceding example, the size of the original Boolean polynomial

$$x_1'x_2 \vee x_1x_2' \vee x_1'x_2x_3 \vee x_3'$$

is 8, while the standard expression

$$x_1'x_2'x_3' \vee x_1'x_2x_3' \vee x_1'x_2x_3 \vee x_1x_2'x_3' \vee x_1x_2'x_3 \vee x_1x_2x_3'$$

is of size 18. Thus, the original Boolean polynomial is much *simpler* than the standard expression. However, it is not the *simplest* polynomial expression for the switching function f that it represents. In fact, we have

$$x_1'x_2 \vee x_1x_2' \vee x_1'x_2x_3 \vee x_3' = x_1'x_2 \vee x_1x_2' \vee x_3'$$

since $x_1'x_2x_3 \leq x_1'x_2$, and the Boolean polynomial $x_1'x_2 \vee x_1x_2' \vee x_3'$ is of size 5.

One of the major problems facing logical designers is to find the simplest Boolean polynomial that represents a given switching function. In a later chapter, a broader problem is discussed.

7. Functional Completeness

The problem of functional completeness arises when one is trying to select a primitive set of components for the design of a computer or other switching system. The fundamental criterion is that one must be able to realize every switching function by a finite network of these components. This requirement leads to the following definition of functional completeness.

Let B denote an arbitrarily given set of switching functions of various numbers of variables. The members of this set B will be called the *basic switching functions*. The set B is said to be *functionally complete* iff every switching function of any finite number of variables can be expressed as a composite function of the basic switching functions.

THEOREM 7.1. *The conjunction functions $\wedge$ and the disjunction functions $\vee$ of all finite numbers of variables, together with the complementation function $c : Q \to Q$, constitute a functionally complete set of switching functions.*

Proof.   Let n denote any given positive integer and consider an arbitrary switching function

$$f : Q^n \to Q$$

of n variables. If the on-set $F = f^{-1}(1)$ is empty, then we have $f = 0$. Hence we obtain

$$f(x) = \wedge\{\vee(x), c[\vee(x)]\}$$

for every point x of Q^n, and f can be expressed as a composite function of the basic switching functions. On the other hand, if $F \neq \square$, then we obtain

$$f = \bigvee_{a \in F} x_1^{a_1} x_2^{a_2} \cdots x_n^{a_n}$$

according to (6.1), where $a_1, a_2, \cdots, a_n$ denote the coordinates of the point $a \in F$, and $x_i^1 = x_i$, $x_i^0 = x_i'$ for every $i = 1, 2, \cdots, n$. Hence f can be expressed as a composite function of the basic switching functions. ‖

COROLLARY 7.2. *The three switching functions*

$$\wedge : Q^2 \to Q, \qquad \vee : Q^2 \to Q, \qquad c : Q \to Q$$

constitute a functionally complete set of switching functions.

Proof.   In view of (7.1), it suffices to show that, for every $n \geq 2$, the two switching functions

$$\wedge : Q^n \to Q, \qquad \vee : Q^n \to Q$$

of n variables can be expressed as a composite function of the three basic switching functions. This assertion is trivial when $n = 2$. Next, let $n > 2$ and assume the assertion for $n - 1$. Since

$$\wedge(x_1, \cdots, x_n) = \wedge[\wedge(x_1, \cdots, x_{n-1}), x_n],$$
$$\vee(x_1, \cdots, x_n) = \vee[\vee(x_1, \cdots, x_{n-1}), x_n]$$

are true for every point $(x_1, \cdots, x_n)$ of the n-cube Q^n, it follows that the assertion holds for n. According to the principle of mathematical induction, this proof is complete. ‖

COROLLARY 7.3. *The two switching functions*

$$\wedge : Q^2 \to Q, \qquad c : Q \to Q$$

constitute a functionally complete set of switching functions.

Proof. In view of (7.2), it suffices to show that the disjunction function $\vee : Q^2 \to Q$ can be expressed as a composite function of the conjunction function $\wedge : Q \to Q$ and the complementation junction $c = Q \to Q$. It can be so expressed because

$$\vee(x_1 x_2) = c\{\wedge[c(x_1), c(x_2)]\}$$

holds for every point (x_1, x_2) of Q^2. ‖

Similarly, one can establish the following corollary (7.4). In fact, (7.4) can be proved by the proof of (7.3) after interchanging $\vee$ and $\wedge$.

COROLLARY 7.4. *The two switching functions*

$$\vee : Q^2 \to Q, \qquad c : Q \to Q$$

constitute a functionally complete set of switching functions.

Because of (7.2)–(7.4), it is natural to ask whether the two switching functions

$$\wedge : Q^2 \to Q, \qquad \vee : Q^2 \to Q$$

constitute a functionally complete set of switching functions; but it can be shown that they do not. A switching function $f : Q^n \to Q$ of n variables is said to be *positive* iff it has a Boolean polynomial expression

$$P(x_1, x_2, \cdots, x_n)$$

in which no term contains a complemented factor.

PROPOSITION 7.5. *A switching function* $f : Q^n \to Q$ *of n variables can be expressed as a composite function of*

$$\wedge : Q^2 \to Q, \qquad \vee : Q^2 \to Q,$$

iff f is positive.

Proof. In view of the proof of (7.2), the sufficiency, that is, the "if" part, of (7.5) is obvious. Only the necessity, that is, the "only if" part, of (7.5) remains to be established. For the purpose of establishing this necessity, assume that f can be expressed as a composite function of $\wedge : Q^2 \to Q$ and $\vee : Q^2 \to Q$. Such a function gives a Boolean expression

$$E(x_1, x_2, \cdots, x_n)$$

containing no complementation sign $'$. By a finite number of applications of (4.3a), one can develop $E(x_1, x_2, \cdots, x_n)$ into a Boolean polynomial

$$P(x_1, x_2, \cdots, x_n)$$

whose terms clearly contain no complemented factor. Thus f is proven to be positive. ‖

Next, let us establish an important property of positive switching functions as given by the following lemma.

LEMMA 7.6.   *If $f : Q^n \to Q$ is a positive switching function of n variables, then, for every integer i satisfying $1 \le i \le n$ and every point*

$$a = a_1 a_2 \cdots a_n$$

of the on-set $F = f^{-1}(1)$ with $a_i = 0$, the point

$$b = b_1 b_2 \cdots b_n$$

of the n-cube Q^n with

$$
b_j = \begin{cases} 1 & (\text{if } j = i), \\ a_j & (\text{if } j \ne i), \end{cases}
$$

is also in the on-set F of f.

Proof.   According to the definition of positive switching functions, f has a Boolean polynomial expression

$$P(x_1, x_2, \cdots, x_n)$$

in which no term contains a complemented factor. Since $a = a_1 a_2 \cdots a_n$ is a point of the on-set $F = f^{-1}(1)$, it follows from (6.1) that

$$p_a = x_1^{a_1} x_2^{a_2} \cdots x_n^{a_n}$$

is a minterm of f and hence implies a certain term T of $P(x_1, x_2, \cdots, x_n)$. Because $a_i = 0$, we have

$$x_i^{a_i} = x_i'.$$

Since T contains no complemented factor, it follows that T does not contain x_i as a factor. Hence

$$p_b = x_1^{b_1} x_2^{b_2} \cdots x_n^{b_n}$$

implies T and, consequently, is also in the on-set $F = f^{-1}(1)$. ‖

By means of the property in (7.6), one can prove that many switching functions are not positive. In particular, we have the following lemma.

LEMMA 7.7.   *The complementation function $c : Q \to Q$ is not positive.*

Proof.   The on-set $c^{-1}(1)$ consists of a single point $a = 0$. Since the point $b = 1$ is not in $c^{-1}(1)$, it follows from (7.6) that c is not positive. ‖

The following theorem is a direct consequence of (7.5)–(7.7).

THEOREM 7.8.   *The two switching functions*

$$\vee : Q^2 \to X, \qquad \wedge : Q^2 \to Q$$

do not constitute a functionally complete set of switching functions.

Since a switching function of two or more variables obviously cannot be expressed as a composite function of switching functions of one variable, we have the following proposition.

PROPOSITION 7.9. *The complementation function*

$$c : Q \to Q$$

does not constitute a functionally complete set.

PROPOSITION 7.10. *The NAND function*

$$\wedge' : Q^2 \to Q$$

forms a functionally complete set by itself.

Proof. In view of (7.3), it suffices to prove that the two switching functions

$$\wedge : Q^2 \to Q, \qquad c : Q \to Q$$

can be expressed in terms of $\wedge'$. For this purpose, we have

$$c(x) = \wedge'(x, x)$$

for every $x \in Q$ and

$$\wedge(y) = c[\wedge'(y)]$$

for every $y \in Q^2$. $\|$

Similarly, one can establish the following proposition.

PROPOSITION 7.11. *The NOR function*

$$\vee' : Q^2 \to Q$$

forms a functionally complete set by itself.

8. Don't Care Points

The variables $x_1, x_2, \cdots, x_n$ of a switching function

$$f : Q^n \to Q$$

are frequently fed by the outputs of other switching circuits, and hence certain points of the n-cube Q^n may never occur in normal operation. These points of Q^n are called the *don't care points* of Q^n.

Since a don't care point x of Q^n can never occur in normal operation, the functional value $f(x)$ of the switching function f at x is immaterial and can be left undetermined. At such a point x, the logical designer is free to assign the unspecified functional value $f(x)$ as he pleases. This freedom is very helpful in simplifying the function f or in achieving other desirable purposes. Much use will be made of this freedom in the sequel.

As an example of don't care points, consider the case $n = 4$ and the switching function

$$f : Q^4 \to Q$$

with truth table I-2-1. Assume that the first two variables x_1 and x_2 are fed by the output of the same circuit. Then a point

$$x = x_1 x_2 x_3 x_4$$

of Q^4 can never occur if $x_1 \neq x_2$. If we leave the functional values of f at these don't care points of Q^4 undetermined and denote them by $*$, then the truth table I-2-1 of f can be replaced by Table I-8-1. On the other hand, the Karnaugh map I-2-4 of f can be replaced by Table I-8-2. The $*$ in Tables I-8-1 and I-8-2 will be referred to as the *don't care sign*.

Let D denote any given set of don't care points of the n-cube Q^n. In view of the isomorphism

$$\theta : \Psi \to \Phi$$

constructed in §5, this subset D of the n-cube Q^n determines a switching function

$$d = \theta(D) : Q^n \to Q$$

of n variables defined by

$$d(x) = \begin{cases} 1 & (\text{if } x \in D), \\ 0 & (\text{if } x \in D'). \end{cases}$$

This switching function d completely determines the given don't care points of Q^n and will be referred to as the *don't care function* of the n-cube Q^n.

Frequently, the set D of don't care points of the n-cube Q^n is defined by one or more conditions on the coordinates of the points of Q^n. Such conditions will be referred to as the *don't care conditions* of the n-cube Q^n. For example, the don't care points of Q^4 indicated by the don't care sign $*$ in the Tables I-8-1 and I-8-2 are defined by the condition

$$x_1 \neq x_2.$$

Since the values of the coordinates x_1 and x_2 are either 0 or 1, this inequality $x_1 \neq x_2$ holds iff the equation

$$x_1 + x_2 = 1$$

is satisfied. Therefore, this equation gives the don't care condition of Q^4

Table I-8-1

x	x_1	x_2	x_3	x_4	$f(x)$
0	0	0	0	0	1
1	0	0	0	1	0
2	0	0	1	0	0
3	0	0	1	1	1
4	0	1	0	0	*
5	0	1	0	1	*
6	0	1	1	0	*
7	0	1	1	1	*
8	1	0	0	0	*
9	1	0	0	1	*
10	1	0	1	0	*
11	1	0	1	1	*
12	1	1	0	0	0
13	1	1	0	1	0
14	1	1	1	0	0
15	1	1	1	1	1

Table I-8-2

x_1x_2 \ x_3x_4	00	01	11	10
00	1		1	
01	*	*	*	*
11			1	
10	*	*	*	*

in this instance. On the other hand, the don't care function of Q^4 for this case is the switching function

$$x_1 \ominus x_2$$

of four variables, where x_1 and x_2 denote the elementary functions.

Throughout the remainder of this section, we are concerned with an arbitrarily given set D of don't care points in the n-cube Q^n.

Any two switching functions

$$f, g : Q^n \rightarrow Q$$

of n variables are said to be *congruent modulo D*, in symbols,

$$f \equiv g \bmod(D),$$

iff $f(x) = g(x)$ holds for every point x in the complement

$$D' = Q^n \backslash D$$

of the set D of don't care points. In particular, if a switching function

$$f : Q^n \rightarrow Q$$

and a Boolean expression

$$E(x_1, x_2, \cdots, x_n)$$

of n variables are congruent modulo D, then we say that $E(x_1, x_2, \cdots, x_n)$
is a *Boolean expression* of f modulo D. For example, let D denote the set
of don't care points of Q^4 defined by the condition

$$x_1 + x_2 = 1.$$

Then two switching functions

$$f, g : Q^4 \rightarrow Q,$$

defined by their on-sets

$$f^{-1}(1) = \{0, 3, 8, 11, 15\},$$
$$g^{-1}(1) = \{0, 3, 15\},$$

are congruent modulo D. Furthermore,

$$x_3 x_4 \vee x_1' x_3' x_4'$$

is a Boolean polynomial for f modulo D and is also a Boolean polynomial
for g modulo D.

The *congruence modulo D* defined above is obviously an equivalence
relation in the set Φ of all switching functions of n variables. On the other
hand, we shall define a new partial order in Φ, namely, the *implication
modulo D*. For any two switching functions

$$f, g : Q^n \rightarrow Q$$

of n variables, we say that *f implies g modulo D*, in symbols,

$$f \leq g \bmod(D),$$

iff $f(x) \leq g(x)$ holds for every point x in the complement D' of the set D
of don't care points. For example, let D denote the set of don't care
points of Q^4 defined by the condition

$$x_1 + x_2 = 1$$

and let $f, h : Q^4 \to Q$ denote switching functions defined by their on-sets

$$f^{-1}(1) = \{0, 3, 8, 11, 15\},$$
$$h^{-1}(1) = \{0, 2, 3, 15\}.$$

Then we have

$$f \leq h \bmod(D).$$

One can easily verify that the usual product, join, and complementation in the set Φ of all switching functions of n variables together with the congruence modulo D and the implication modulo D turn the set Φ into a new Boolean algebra. From a more modern point of view, however, we consider the set

$$\Phi_D$$

of all *congruence classes modulo D* in Φ, that is, all equivalence classes in Φ defined by the congruence modulo D which is an equivalence relation in Φ. The members of this set Φ_D will be referred to as the *switching functions of n variables modulo D*.

To make Φ_D a Boolean algebra, we have to define product, join, complementation, an equivalence relation, and a partial order in this set Φ_D. For this purpose, let ξ and η denote any two members of Φ_D. Select switching functions $f \in \xi$ and $g \in \eta$ from these congruence classes ξ and η modulo D. Then one can easily verify that the congruence classes

$$[fg], \quad [f \vee g], \quad [f'],$$

containing the switching functions $fg, f \vee g, f'$, respectively, depend only on the given congruence classes ξ and η. Hence we may define the *product* $\xi\eta$, the *join* $\xi \vee \eta$, and the *complement* ξ' by setting

$$\xi\eta = [fg], \qquad \xi \vee \eta = [f \vee g], \qquad \xi' = [f'].$$

Furthermore, we define an equivalence relation "$=$" and a partial order "$\leq$" in Φ_D as follows:

$$\xi = \eta \quad \text{iff} \quad f \equiv g \bmod(D),$$
$$\xi \leq \eta \quad \text{iff} \quad f \leq g \bmod(D).$$

Then it is straightforward to verify that these turn the set Φ_D into a Boolean algebra. Also it is clear that this Boolean algebra Φ_D can be considered as the functions

$$\xi : D' \to Q$$

defined on the complement D' of D with product, join, complementation, $=$, and $\leq$ defined in the obvious way.

9. Classification

By a *linear transformation* of the n-dimensional Euclidean space R^n, we mean a mapping

$$\lambda : R^n \to R^n$$

given by $\lambda(x) = y = (y_1, \cdots, y_n)$ for each point $x = (x_1, \cdots, x_n)$ of R^n with

$$y_i = a_i + \sum_{j=1}^{n} a_{ij}x_j, \qquad (i = 1, 2, \cdots, n),$$

where a_i and a_{ij} are real numbers. The linear transformation λ of R^n is said to be *nonsingular* iff the determinant $|a_{ij}|$ of λ is different from zero. Clearly a linear transformation λ of R^n is nonsingular iff λ sends R^n *onto* itself, that is, iff

$$\lambda(R^n) = R^n.$$

By an *admissible transformation* of the n-cube Q^n, we mean a bijective (i.e., one-to-one and onto) mapping

$$\alpha : Q^n \to Q^n$$

which can be extended to a linear transformation of R^n. In other words, α is admissible iff there exists a linear transformation λ of R^n such that

$$\alpha(x) = \lambda(x)$$

holds for every point x of $Q^n \subset R^n$. The linear transformation λ is unique as a consequence of the following lemma.

LEMMA 9.1. *If two linear transformations*

$$\lambda, \mu : R^n \to R^n$$

agree on Q^n, then $\lambda = \mu$.

Proof. For an arbitrary point $x = (x_1, \cdots, x_n)$, let

$$\lambda(x) = y = (y_1, \cdots, y_n), \qquad \mu(x) = z = (z_1, \cdots, z^n).$$

Then we have

$$y_i = a_i + \sum_{j=1}^{n} a_{ij}x_i, \qquad z_i = b_i + \sum_{j=1}^{n} b_{ij}x_i$$

for every $i = 1, \cdots, n$. It suffices to prove

$$a_i = b_i, \qquad a_{ij} = b_{ij}$$

for every $i = 1, \cdots, n$ and every $j = 1, \cdots, n$. For this purpose, let us first take x to be the origin

$$v_0 = (0, \cdots, 0).$$

Since λ and μ agree on Q^n and since $v_0 \in Q^n$, we have

$$\lambda(v_0) = \mu(v_0).$$

Thus, $a_i = b_i$ for every $i = 1, \cdots, n$.

Next, take x to be the unit point v_j on the j-th coordinate axis, that is to say,

$$x_i = \begin{cases} 1 & (\text{if } i = j), \\ 0 & (\text{if } i \neq j). \end{cases}$$

Since v_j is in Q^n, we have

$$\lambda(v_j) = \mu(v_j).$$

Thus

$$a_i + a_{ij} = b_i + b_{ij}$$

for every $i = 1, \cdots, n$ and every $j = 1, \cdots, n$. Since $a_i = b_i$, we deduce $a_{ij} = b_{ij}$. ‖

On the other hand, the unique linear extension

$$\bar{\alpha} : R^n \to R^n$$

of an arbitrarily given admissible transformation

$$\alpha : Q^n \to Q^n$$

must be nonsingular as a consequence of the following lemma.

LEMMA 9.2.   *If a linear transformation*

$$\lambda : R^n \to R^n$$

carries Q^n onto itself, it must be nonsingular.

Proof. If λ were singular, then the image $\lambda(R^n)$ would be a linear variety of dimension less than n. This contradicts the hypothesis that

$$Q^n = \lambda(Q^n) \subset \lambda(R^n)$$

and hence proves the lemma. ‖

The following two propositions are obvious.

PROPOSITION 9.3.   *If $\alpha : Q^n \to Q^n$ is an admissible transformation, so is its inverse $\alpha^{-1} : Q^n \to Q^n$.*

PROPOSITION 9.4.   *If α and β are admissible transformations of Q^n, then the composition $\beta \circ \alpha$ is also an admissible transformation of Q^n.*

Consequently, the set of all admissible transformations of Q^n forms a group with composition as the group operation. For the definition of groups, see [H2, p. 104]. This group is called the *hyper-octahedral group* and denoted by O_n. See [Todd 1].

Now let us consider the set Φ_n of all switching functions of n variables. Every admissible transformation $\alpha \in O_n$ induces a bijective transformation

$$\alpha^{\#} : \Phi_n \to \Phi_n$$

of the set Φ_n defined by

$$\alpha^{\#}(f) = f \circ \alpha$$

for each $f \in \Phi_n$, where $f \circ \alpha$ stands for the composition of α and f. Hence for each point $x \in Q^n$, we have

$$[\alpha^{\#}(f)](x) = f[\alpha(x)].$$

The *functorial properties* of the operation $\#$ given in the following two propositions are obvious.

PROPOSITION 9.5.   *If α is the identity transformation of $Q:$, then $\alpha^{\#}$ is the identity transformation of Φ_n.*

PROPOSITION 9.6.   *For any two admissible transformations $\alpha, \beta : Q^n \to Q^n$, we have*

$$(\beta \circ \alpha)^{\#} = \alpha^{\#} \circ \beta^{\#}.$$

Consequently, the hyper-octahedral group O_n acts on Φ_n as a *transformation group* of Φ_n.

Two switching functions

$$f, g : Q^n \to Q$$

of n variables are said to be *equivalent* iff there exists an admissible transformation $\alpha \in O_n$ such that

$$\alpha^{\#}(f) = f \circ \alpha = g;$$

in this case, we use the notation

$$f \sim g.$$

It follows easily from (9.5) and (9.6) that $\sim$ is an *equivalence relation* in the set Φ_n as defined in [H2, p. 30]. Hence, the 2^{2^n} switching functions of n variables are divided into disjoint equivalence classes called the *classes* of switching functions of n variables. In the terminology of transformation groups, these are called the *orbits* of the group O_n in Φ_n. In [Slepian 1], these are called the *symmetry types*.

To facilitate the study of the admissible transformations of the n-cube Q^n, we shall investigate two important special cases, namely, the *complementations* and the *permutations* of the variables, and establish a *unique decomposition theorem* for admissible transformations of Q^n.

Let j denote an arbitrary integer satisfying $1 \leq j \leq n$. The admissible transformation

$$\gamma_j : Q^n \to Q^n$$

defined for every point $x = x_1 \cdots x_n$ of Q^n by $\gamma_j(x) = y = y_1 \cdots y_n$ with

$$y_i = \begin{cases} 1 - x_j, & \text{(if } i = j\text{),} \\ x_i, & \text{(if } i \neq j\text{),} \end{cases}$$

is called the *complementation of the j-th variable*.

As an element of the hyper-octahedral group O_n, γ_j is clearly of order 2, that is, the composition $\gamma_j \circ \gamma_j$ is the identity transformation of the n-cube Q^n. On the other hand, γ_j commutes with γ_k for every $k \in N = \{1, \cdots, n\}$; in symbols,

$$\gamma_j \circ \gamma_k = \gamma_k \circ \gamma_j.$$

For any given $f \in \Phi_n$, the switching function

$$g = \gamma_j^\#(f) : Q^n \to Q$$

is said to be *obtained from f by complementing the j-th variable*.

Let $u = u_1 \cdots u_n$ denote an arbitrary point of the n-cube Q^n and consider the admissible transformation

$$\gamma_u : Q^n \to Q^n$$

defined for each point $x = x_1 \cdots x_n$ of Q^n by $\gamma_u(x) = y = y_1 \cdots y_n$ with

$$y_i = \begin{cases} x_i, & \text{(if } u_i = 0\text{),} \\ 1 - x_i, & \text{(if } u_i = 1\text{).} \end{cases}$$

Since γ_u carries the origin v_0 to the given point u, it will be called the *admissible transformation obtained by moving the origin to the point u*.

Let K denote the set of all integers $j \in N$ such that $u_j = 1$. Then γ_u is clearly the composition of the complementations γ_j for all $j \in K$, and the admissible transformation γ_u may also be called the *complementation of the variables K*.

Next, let j and k denote any two integers satisfying $1 \leq j < k \leq n$. The admissible transformation

$$\delta_{jk} : Q^n \to Q^n$$

defined for every point $x = x_1 \cdots x_n$ of Q^n by $\delta_{jk}(x) = y = y_1 \cdots y_n$ with

$$y_i = \begin{cases} x_k, & \text{(if } i = j\text{),} \\ x_j, & \text{(if } i = k\text{),} \\ x_i, & \text{(otherwise),} \end{cases}$$

is called the *interchange of the j-th variable and the k-th variable*.

As an element of the hyper-octahedral group O_n, δ_{jk} is obviously of order 2, that is, the composition $\delta_{jk} \circ \delta_{jk}$ is the identity transformation of the n-cube Q^n.

For any given $f \in \Phi_n$, the switching function

$$g = \delta_{jk}^{\#}(f) : Q^n \to Q^n$$

is said to be *obtained from f by interchanging the j-th variable and the k-th variable*.

By a *permutation* of the integers $N = \{1, \cdots, n\}$ we mean a bijective function

$$p : N \to N.$$

For any given permutation p of the integers N, consider the admissible transformation

$$\delta_p : Q^n \to Q^n$$

defined for each point $x = x_1 \cdots x_n$ of Q^n by $\delta_p(x) = y = y_1 \cdots y_n$ with

$$y_i = x_{p(i)}, \qquad (i \in N).$$

This admissible transformation δ_p of Q^n will be called a *permutation of the variables*. In particular, the interchange δ_{jk} studied above is a permutation of the variables.

According to the elementary theory of permutations, every permutation p of the integers N can be decomposed into a product of a finite number of interchanges of two integers in N. It follows that δ_p is the composition of a finite number of admissible transformations obtained by interchanging pairs of integers in N.

THEOREM 9.7. *Every admissible transformation $\alpha : Q^n \to Q^n$ of the n-cube Q^n has a unique decomposition*

$$\alpha = \gamma_u \circ \delta_p$$

where u denotes a point of Q^n, and p, a permutation of the integers N.

Proof: Uniqueness. Assume $\alpha = \gamma_u \circ \delta_p$. Then we have

$$\alpha(v_0) = \gamma_u[\delta_p(v_0)] = \gamma_u(v_0) = u,$$
$$\delta_p = \gamma_u^{-1} \circ \alpha = \gamma_u \circ \alpha,$$

where v_0 denotes the origin of Q^n. Hence, u and p are uniquely determined by α.

Existence. Let $u = \alpha(v_0)$. The composition

$$\beta = \gamma_u \circ \alpha : Q^n \to Q^n$$

is an admissible transformation of Q^n which leaves the origin v_0 fixed. Since the linear extension

$$\bar{\beta} : R^n \to R^n$$

of β carries the real n-cube I^n onto itself, β preserves adjacent points. Consider the unit point v_j on the j-th coordinate axis for each $j = 1, \cdots, n$. Since $\beta(v_0) = v_0$ and $v_1, \cdots, v_n$ are the only points adjacent to v_0, it follows that β permutes the n points $v_1, \cdots, v_n$. In other words, there exists a permutation p of the integers N such that

$$\beta(v_i) = v_{p(i)}$$

for every $i = 1, \cdots, n$. Hence the composition

$$\theta = \delta_p^{-1} \circ \beta : Q^n \to Q^n$$

is an admissible transformation of Q^n which leaves each of the points $v_0, v_1, \cdots, v_n$ fixed. As a linear transformation of R^n which leaves each of the points $v_0, v_1, \cdots, v_n$ fixed, the unique linear extension

$$\bar{\theta} : R^n \to R^n$$

of θ must be the identity transformation of R^n. In particular, θ must be the identity transformation of Q^n and hence

$$\beta = \delta_p.$$

Since $\beta = \gamma_u \circ \alpha$, we obtain

$$\alpha = \gamma_u^{-1} \circ \beta = \gamma_u \circ \delta_p.$$

This completes the proof of (9.7). ∥

COROLLARY 9.8. *An admissible transformation* $\alpha : Q^n \to Q^n$ *is a permutation of variables iff* α *leaves the origin* v_0 *fixed.*

If we apply (9.7) to the inverse α^{-1} of any given admissible transformation α of X^n and make use of (9.8), we can deduce the following corollary.

COROLLARY 9.9. *Every admissible transformation* $\alpha : Q^n \to Q^n$ *of the n-cube* Q^n *has a unique decomposition*

$$\alpha = \delta_p \circ \gamma_u$$

where u denotes a point of Q^n, *and p, a permutation of the integers* N.

Here, we have

$$u = \alpha^{-1}(v_0), \qquad \delta_p = \alpha \circ \gamma_u.$$

Since there are $n!$ permutations of the integers $N = \{1, \cdots, n\}$ and 2^n

choices of the point $u \in Q^n$, we obtain the following classical corollary of (9.7), [Todd 1, Young 1].

COROLLARY 9.10. *The hyper-octahedral group O_n is of order $(n!)2^n$.*

By an application of the theory of group characters, a formula for computing the number of all classes of switching functions of n variables was given in [Slepian 1] and the computations for $n \leq 6$ were carried out. These can also be computed by Pólya's counting technique [Pólya 1]. See also [Ha, pp. 123–153].

10. Nondegenerate Functions

Let n denote an arbitrarily given positive integer. A switching function

$$f : Q^n \to Q$$

of n variables is said to be *independent of the j-th variable*, $1 \leq j \leq n$, iff we have

$$f = \gamma_j^{\#}(f) = f \circ \gamma_j,$$

where γ_j stands for the complementation

$$\gamma_j : Q^n \to Q^n$$

of the j-th variable defined in the preceding section. In other words, the switching function f is independent of the j-th variable iff

$$f(x_1, \cdots, x_n) = f(x_1, \cdots, x_{j-1}, 1 - x_j, x_{j+1}, \cdots, x_n)$$

holds for every point $(x_1, \cdots, x_n)$ of Q^n. If f is not independent of the j-th variable, we say that f *depends on the j-th variable*.

A switching function

$$f : Q^n \to Q$$

of n variables is said to be *nondegenerate* iff it depends on each of the n variables; otherwise, f is said to be *degenerate*. For example, among the sixteen switching functions of two variables exhibited in §3, the six functions

$$1, 0, x_1, x_1', x_2, x_2'$$

are degenerate while the remaining ten functions are nondegenerate.

In §2, we used the symbol $\phi(n)$ to denote the number of all switching functions of n variables. Now, let us use the symbol $\psi(n)$ to denote the number of all nondegenerate switching functions of n variables and use

$$\delta(n) = \phi(n) - \psi(n)$$

to denote the number of all degenerate switching functions of n variables. To determine $\psi(n)$ and $\delta(n)$, let k denote an integer satisfying $0 \leq k \leq n$ and consider an arbitrary subset

$$K = \{i_1, i_2, \cdots, i_k\}$$

of the set $N = \{1, 2, \cdots, n\}$ containing k distinct integers

$$i_1 < i_2 < \cdots < i_k$$

of the set N. Let us use the symbol

$$\Phi_n(K)$$

to denote the set of all switching functions of n variables which depend on the j-th variable iff j is in K.

LEMMA 10.1. *The set* $\Phi_n(K)$ *consists of* $\psi(k)$ *switching functions.*

Proof. Let Ψ_k denote the set of all nondegenerate switching functions of k variables. Define a function

$$\mu : \Psi_k \to \Phi_n$$

from Ψ_k to the set Φ_n of all switching functions of n variables as follows: For each nondegenerate switching function

$$f : Q^k \to Q$$

in Ψ_k, its image is the switching function

$$g = \mu(f) : Q^n \to Q$$

defined for every point $x = (x_1, \cdots, x_n)$ of the n-cube Q^n by

$$g(x) = f(x_{i_1}, x_{i_2}, \cdots, x_{i_k}).$$

Obviously, the function μ is injective (i.e., one-to-one). On the other hand, since Ψ_k is the set of all nondegenerate switching functions of k variables, it follows that

$$\mu(\Psi_k) = \Phi_n(K).$$

It also follows that $\Phi_n(K)$ has the same number of switching functions as Ψ_k, thus proving the lemma. ‖

LEMMA 10.2. *For every nonnegative integer n, we have*

$$\sum_{k=0}^{n} \binom{n}{k} \psi(k) = \phi(n),$$

where $\binom{n}{0}, \binom{n}{1}, \cdots, \binom{n}{n}$ *stand for the binomial coefficients.*

Proof. For each integer $k = 0, 1, \cdots, n$, let

$$\Phi_{n,k}$$

denote the set of all switching functions of n variables each of which depends on precisely k of the n variables. Then $\Phi_{n,k}$ is the disjoint union of the sets $\Phi_n(K)$ for all of the $\binom{n}{k}$ possible choices of the subset

$$K = \{i_1, i_2, \cdots, i_k\}$$

of N. It follows from (10.1) that $\Phi_{n,k}$ consists of

$$\binom{n}{k}\psi(k)$$

switching functions. The fact that the set Φ_n of all switching functions of n variables is clearly the disjoint union of the sets $\Phi_{n,k}$ for all $k = 0, 1, \cdots, n$ implies that

$$\sum_{k=0}^{n}\binom{n}{k}\psi(k) = \phi(n)$$

holds for every positive integer n. ‖

Now let us establish the following theorem which determines the number $\psi(n)$.

THEOREM 10.3.   *For every nonnegative integer n, we have*

$$\psi(n) = \sum_{k=0}^{n}(-1)^{n-k}\binom{n}{k}\phi(k).$$

Proof. We shall prove the theorem by induction on the integer n. For $n = 0$, we have

$$\psi(0) = \phi(0) = 2$$

because there are precisely two switching functions of zero variables— namely, the constant functions 1 and 0—and these are nondegenerate. Hence the theorem holds for $n = 0$.

Next, let m denote an arbitrary positive integer and assume that the theorem has been proved for every nonnegative integer $n < m$. It remains to prove that the theorem holds for $n = m$. According to (10.2), we have

$$\sum_{j=0}^{m}\binom{m}{j}\psi(j) = \phi(m).$$

Solving this equation for $\psi(m)$, we obtain

$$\psi(m) = -\sum_{j=0}^{m-1} \binom{m}{j} \psi(j) + \phi(m).$$

Because of our inductive assumption, we have

$$\psi(j) = \sum_{k=0}^{j} (-1)^{j-k} \binom{j}{k} \phi(k)$$

for every $j = 0, 1, \cdots, m - 1$. Consequently, we obtain

$$\psi(m) = -\sum_{j=0}^{m-1} \binom{m}{j} \left[\sum_{k=0}^{j} (-1)^{j-k} \binom{j}{k} \phi(k) \right] + \phi(m)$$

$$= \sum_{j=0}^{m-1} \sum_{k=0}^{j} (-1)^{j-k+1} \binom{m}{j} \binom{j}{k} \phi(k) + \phi(m).$$

Changing the order of the summations, we obtain

$$\psi(m) = \sum_{k=0}^{m-1} \sum_{j=k}^{m-1} (-1)^{j-k+1} \binom{m}{j} \binom{j}{k} \phi(k) + \phi(m)$$

$$= \sum_{k=0}^{m-1} (-1)^{m-k} \left[\sum_{j=k}^{m-1} (-1)^{m-j+1} \binom{m}{j} \binom{j}{k} \right] \phi(k) + \phi(m).$$

Therefore, it remains to establish the equality

$$\sum_{j=k}^{m-1} (-1)^{m-j+1} \binom{m}{j} \binom{j}{k} = \binom{m}{k}.$$

For this purpose, we first observe that

$$\binom{m}{j} \binom{j}{k} = \frac{m!}{j!(m-j)!} \cdot \frac{j!}{k!(j-k)!}$$

$$= \frac{m!}{k!(m-k)!} \cdot \frac{(m-k)!}{(j-k)!(m-j)!}$$

$$= \binom{m}{k} \binom{m-k}{j-k}$$

holds whenever $k \le j < m$. Hence we get

$$\sum_{j=k}^{m-1} (-1)^{m-j+1} \binom{m}{j} \binom{j}{k} = \binom{m}{k} \left[\sum_{j=k}^{m-1} (-1)^{m-j+1} \binom{m-k}{j-k} \right].$$

Let $i = j - k$. Then we obtain

$$\sum_{j=k}^{m-1} (-1)^{m-j+1} \binom{m}{j} \binom{j}{k} = \binom{m}{k} \left[\sum_{i=0}^{m-k-1} (-1)^{m-k-i+1} \binom{m-k}{i} \right].$$

Next, in the binomial expansion

$$(1 - x)^{m-k} = \sum_{i=0}^{m-k} (-1)^{m-k-i} \binom{m-k}{i} x^i,$$

set $x = 1$. Thus we obtain

$$\sum_{i=0}^{m-k} (-1)^{m-k-i} \binom{m-k}{i} = 0,$$

which implies

$$\sum_{i=0}^{m-k-1} (-1)^{m-k-i+1} \binom{m-k}{i} = \binom{m-k}{m-k} = 1$$

and hence

$$\sum_{j=k}^{m-1} (-1)^{m-j+1} \binom{m}{j} \binom{j}{k} = \binom{m}{k},$$

completing the proof of (10.3). ‖

According to §2, we have

$$\phi(k) = 2^{2^k}$$

for every integer $k \geq 0$. The following corollary of (10.3) is obvious.

COROLLARY 10.4.   *For every nonnegative integer n, we have*

$$\psi(n) = \sum_{k=0}^{n} (-1)^{n-k} \binom{n}{k} 2^{2^k},$$

$$\delta(n) = \sum_{k=0}^{n-1} (-1)^{n-k+1} \binom{n}{k} 2^{2^k}.$$

For $n \leq 6$, we have:

$\psi(1) = 2,$	$\delta(1) = 2,$
$\psi(2) = 10,$	$\delta(2) = 6,$
$\psi(3) = 218,$	$\delta(3) = 38,$
$\psi(4) = 64, 594,$	$\delta(4) = 942,$
$\psi(5) = 4, 294, 642, 034,$	$\delta(5) = 325, 262,$
$\psi(6) = 18, 446, 744, 047, 940, 725, 978,$	$\delta(6) = 25, 768, 825, 638.$

These values suggest the following theorem.

THEOREM 10.5. $\psi(n)$ *and* $\delta(n)$ *have the following properties:*

$$\lim_{n \to \infty} \frac{\psi(n)}{\phi(n)} = 1,$$

$$\lim_{n \to \infty} \frac{\delta(n)}{\phi(n)} = 0.$$

Proof. Since $\psi(n) = \phi(n) - \delta(n)$, it suffices to prove

$$\lim_{n \to \infty} \frac{\delta(n)}{\phi(n)} = 0.$$

For this purpose, we observe

$$\delta(n) = \sum_{k=0}^{n-1} (-1)^{n-k+1} \binom{n}{k} 2^{2^k} \leq \sum_{k=0}^{n-1} \binom{n}{k} 2^{2^k}.$$

The last sum contains n terms. To show that these terms are strictly increasing, let k denote an integer with $0 \leq k < n - 1$ and compare the $(k + 1)$-st term with the k-th term. Doing so yields the following ratio:

$$\binom{n}{k + 1} 2^{2^{k+1}} \Big/ \binom{n}{k} 2^{2^k} = (n - k) 2^{2^k} (k + 1).$$

Because of the inequalities

$$n - k > 1, \qquad 2^{2^k} > k + 1,$$

this ratio implies

$$\binom{n}{k} 2^{2^k} < \binom{n}{k + 1} 2^{2^{k+1}}$$

and hence the n terms in the last sum are strictly increasing. Therefore, the last term

$$\binom{n}{n - 1} 2^{2^{n+1}} = n 2^{2^{n+1}}$$

in the sum is the largest. Consequently, we obtain

$$\delta(n) \leq \sum_{k=0}^{n-1} \binom{n}{k} 2^{2^k} < n \cdot n 2^{2^{k+1}},$$

which implies

$$\lim_{n \to \infty} \frac{\delta(n)}{\phi(n)} \leq \lim_{n \to \infty} [n^2 2^{2^{n-1}} / 2^{2^n}] = \lim_{n \to \infty} [n^2 / 2^{2^{n-1}}] = 0$$

and completes the proof of (10.5). ‖

COROLLARY 10.6. $\psi(n)$ *is asymptotic to* 2^{2^n}.

11. Symmetric Functions

Let n denote an arbitrarily given positive integer. A switching function

$$f : Q^n \to Q$$

of n variables is said to be *symmetric* iff it is preserved by every permutation of the n variables, that is, iff

$$f = \delta_p^{\#}(f) = f \circ \delta_p$$

holds for every permutation

$$\delta_p : Q^n \to Q^n$$

of the n variables defined in §9. In other words, the switching function f is symmetric iff

$$f(x_1, x_2, \cdots, x_n) = f(x_{p(1)}, x_{p(2)}, \cdots, x_{p(n)})$$

holds for every point $x = (x_1, x_2, \cdots, x_n)$ of the n-cube X^n and every permutation

$$p : N \to N$$

of the set $N = \{1, 2, \cdots, n\}$. For example, among the sixteen switching functions of two variables exhibited in §3, the eight functions

$$1, 0, \wedge, \wedge', \vee, \vee', \bigotimes, \bigotimes'$$

are symmetric while the remaining eight functions are not symmetric.

For convenience in studying the symmetric switching functions of n variables, let us define a function

$$\rho : Q^n \to N^*$$

from Q^n to the set $N^* = \{0, 1, \cdots, n\}$ by taking

$$\rho(x) = \sum_{i=1}^{n} x_i$$

for every point $x = (x_1, \cdots, x_n)$ of the n-cube Q^n. This function ρ will be referred to as the *rank function* of Q^n; and, for every point $x \in Q^n$, the integer $\rho(x)$ will be called the *rank* of the point x. Hence the rank $\rho(x)$ of an arbitrary point $x = (x_1, \cdots, x_n)$ is the number of coordinates of x which are 1.

Now let us establish the following *fundamental theorem* of symmetric switching functions.

THEOREM 11.1. *A switching function*

$$f : Q^n \to Q$$

of n variables is symmetric iff there exists a subset A of the set

$$N^* = \{0, 1, 2, \cdots, n\}$$

satisfying the condition

$$f^{-1}(1) = \rho^{-1}(A);$$

in words, this condition means that, for an arbitrary point x of the n-cube Q^n, $f(x) = 1$ holds iff $\rho(x) \in A$.

Proof. *Necessity.* Assume that f is symmetric and consider the on-set

$$F = f^{-1}(1)$$

of f. To establish the condition, let

$$A = \rho(F) \subset N^*.$$

Then it follows immediately that the inclusion

$$F \subset \rho^{-1}(A)$$

is valid. Conversely, let x denote an arbitrary point in $\rho^{-1}(A)$. Then we have

$$a = \rho(x) \in A.$$

Since $A = \rho(F)$, there exists a point $y \in F$ with $\rho(y) = a$. Since $\rho(x) = \rho(y)$, one can clearly see that there exists a permutation of variables

$$\delta_p : Q^n \to Q^n$$

satisfying $\delta_p(y) = x$. Since f is symmetric and y is in F, we have

$$f(x) = f[\delta_p(y)] = (f \circ \delta_p)(y) = f(y) = 1.$$

This implies $x \in F$ and hence we have the inclusion

$$\rho^{-1}(A) \subset F.$$

Consequently, we have established the equality

$$f^{-1}(1) = \rho^{-1}(A).$$

Sufficiency. Let A denote a subset of N^* satisfying the equality

$$f^{-1}(1) = \rho^{-1}(A).$$

To prove that f is symmetric, let

$$\delta_p : Q^n \to Q^n$$

denote an arbitrary permutation of variables. For every point $x \in Q^n$, the point $y = \delta_p(x)$ clearly has the same rank as x, that is,

$$\rho(x) = \rho(y).$$

Because of $f^{-1}(1) = \rho^{-1}(A)$, this equation implies

$$(f \circ \delta_p)(x) = f[\delta_p(x)] = f(y) = f(x).$$

Since x is an arbitrary point of Q^n, we obtain

$$f \circ \delta_p = f.$$

Since δ_p is an arbitrary permutation of variables, this result proves that f is symmetric. ‖

For an arbitrarily given symmetric function

$$f : Q^n \to Q$$

of n variables, the subset A of the set N^* is uniquely determined by f; in fact, we have

$$A = \rho[f^{-1}(1)].$$

This subset A of N^* will be referred to as the *index* of the symmetric switching function f. Conversely, because of

$$f^{-1}(1) = \rho^{-1}(A),$$

the symmetric switching function f is uniquely determined by its index A. The symmetric switching function of n variables with index A will be denoted by

$$s_A : Q^n \to Q.$$

Now the following corollary of (11.1) is obvious.

COROLLARY 11.2.   *The assignment $A \to s_A$ defines a bijective* (i.e., 1–1 *and onto*) *function*

$$S : 2^{N^*} \to \Sigma_n$$

from the set 2^{N^*} of all subsets of the set $N^* = \{0, 1, \cdots, n\}$ to the set Σ_n of all symmetric switching functions of n variables.

Since N^* consists of $n + 1$ elements, it follows that the set 2^{N^*} has 2^{n+1} elements.   Hence we obtain the following corollary.

COROLLARY 11.3.   *There are 2^{n+1} symmetric switching functions of n variables.*

The following three lemmas are immediate consequences of (11.1).

LEMMA 11.4.   *The join of any two symmetric switching functions of n variables is a symmetric switching function, and its index is the union of the indices of the given functions; in symbols,*

$$s_A \vee s_B = s_{A \cup B}.$$

LEMMA 11.5.   *The product of any two symmetric switching functions of n variables is a symmetric switching function, and its index is the intersection of the indices of the given functions; in symbols,*

$$s_A s_B = s_{A \cap B}.$$

LEMMA 11.6. *The complement of any symmetric switching function of n variables is a symmetric switching function, and its index is the complement of the index of the given function; in symbols,*

$$(s_A)' = s_{N^* \setminus A}.$$

Because of these three lemmas, we have the following theorem.

THEOREM 11.7. *The set Σ_n of all symmetric switching functions of n variables forms a Boolean subalgebra of the Boolean algebra Φ_n of all switching functions of n variables, and the function*

$$S : 2^{N^*} \to \Sigma_n$$

is an isomorphism of the Boolean algebra 2^{N^*} of all subsets of $N^* = \{0, 1, \cdots, n\}$ onto the Boolean algebra Σ_n.

Since the switching functions

$$\wedge : Q^2 \to Q, \qquad \vee : Q^2 \to Q, \qquad c : Q \to Q$$

are symmetric, the following theorem is a direct consequence of (7.2).

THEOREM 11.8. *The symmetric switching functions constitute a functionally complete set of switching functions.*

By an *elementary symmetric switching function* of n variables, we mean a symmetric switching function

$$s_A : Q^n \to Q$$

such that its index A is a *singleton*, that is, A consists of a single integer in the set $N^* = \{0, 1, \cdots, n\}$.

Since N^* contains $n + 1$ integers, there are $n + 1$ elementary symmetric switching functions of n variables, namely,

$$s_{\{0\}}, s_{\{1\}}, \cdots, s_{\{n\}} : Q^n \to Q.$$

The following theorem is a direct consequence of (11.4).

THEOREM 11.9. *The $n + 1$ elementary symmetric switching functions of n variables generate the Boolean algebra Σ_n of all symmetric switching functions of n variables; in fact, we have*

$$s_A = \bigvee_{a \in A} s_{\{a\}}.$$

The elementary symmetric switching functions of n variables should not be mistaken for the elementary symmetric Boolean polynomials in the variables $x_1, x_2, \cdots, x_n$. The latter represent symmetric switching functions of n variables but not primarily the elementary ones. To illustrate the difference, let us take $n = 3$. In this case, we have three elementary symmetric polynomials in the variables x_1, x_2, x_3, namely,

$$p_1 = x_1 \vee x_2 \vee x_3,$$
$$p_2 = x_2 x_3 \vee x_3 x_1 \vee x_1 x_2,$$
$$p_3 = x_1 x_2 x_3.$$

These Boolean polynomials represent the symmetric switching functions

$$p_1 = s_{\{1,2,3\}}, \qquad p_2 = s_{\{2,3\}}, \qquad p_3 = s_{\{3\}}$$

of three variables. On the other hand, the four elementary symmetric switching functions of three variables have Boolean polynomial expressions as follows:

$$s_{\{0\}} = x_1' x_2' x_3',$$
$$s_{\{1\}} = x_1 x_2' x_3' \vee x_1' x_2 x_3' \vee x_1' x_2' x_3,$$
$$s_{\{2\}} = x_1' x_2 x_3 \vee x_1 x_2' x_3 \vee x_1 x_2 x_3',$$
$$s_{\{3\}} = x_1 x_2 x_3.$$

The remainder of this section gives a few propositions for detecting symmetric switching functions.

PROPOSITION 11.10.   *A switching function* $f : Q^n \to Q$ *of n variables is symmetric iff*

$$f \circ \delta_{ij} = f$$

holds for every interchange of variables

$$\delta_{ij} : Q^n \to Q^n, \qquad (i \neq j).$$

This proposition is an immediate consequence of the classical result in the elementary theory of permutations that every permutation of the integers $N = \{1, \cdots, n\}$ can be decomposed into a product of a finite number of interchanges of two integers in N.

PROPOSITION 11.11.   *A switching function* $f : Q^n \to Q$ *of n variables is symmetric iff*

$$f \circ \delta_{1i} = f$$

holds for every integer i satisfying $1 < i \leq n$.

Proof.   Let i and j denote any two integers satisfying $1 < i < j \leq n$. As in the elementary theory of permutations, one can easily verify

$$(ij) = (1i) \circ (1j) \circ (1i).$$

Consequently, if f satisfies the condition in (11.11), we have

$$f \circ \delta_{ij} = f \circ \delta_{1i} \circ \delta_{1j} \circ \delta_{1i} = f \circ \delta_{1j} \circ \delta_{1i} = f \circ \delta_{1i} = f,$$

thus establishing the sufficiency. The necessity is obvious. ‖

PROPOSITION 11.12. *A switching function* $f : Q^n \to Q$ *of* n *variables is symmetric iff the following two conditions are satisfied:*

$$f \circ \delta_{12} = f, \qquad f \circ \delta_{(23 \cdots n)} = f.$$

Here, $(23 \cdots n)$ denotes the cyclic permutation of the integers as usual.

Proof. In view of (11.11), it suffices to show that these conditions imply that

$$f \circ \delta_{1i} = f$$

holds for every integer i satisfying $1 < i \leq n$. We shall establish this by induction on i. Since this holds obviously for $i = 2$, we assume that $i > 2$ and

$$f \circ \delta_{1h} = f, \qquad (h = i - 1).$$

One can easily verify the relation

$$(23 \cdots n)^{-1} \circ (1h) \circ (23 \cdots n) = (n \cdots 32) \circ (1h) \circ (23 \cdots n) = (1i).$$

Here, as compositions of functions, the products begin from the right. Hence we obtain

$$\begin{aligned}
f \circ \delta_{1i} &= f \circ \delta_{(23 \cdots n)}^{-1} \circ \delta_{1h} \circ \delta_{(23 \cdots n)} \\
&= f \circ \delta_{(23 \cdots n)} \circ \delta_{(23 \cdots n)}^{-1} \circ \delta_{1h} \circ \delta_{(23 \cdots n)} \\
&= f \circ \delta_{1h} \circ \delta_{(23 \cdots n)} \\
&= f \circ \delta_{(23 \cdots n)} = f,
\end{aligned}$$

thus completing the inductive proof. ‖

PROPOSITION 11.13. *A switching function* $f : Q^n \to Q$ *of* n *variables is symmetric iff the following two conditions are satisfied:*

$$f \circ \delta_{12} = f, \qquad f \circ \delta_{(12 \cdots n)} = f.$$

Proof. One can easily verify the relation

$$(12) \circ (12 \cdots n) = (23 \cdots n).$$

As a composition of functions, the product begins from the right end. Hence we obtain

$$f \circ \delta_{(23 \cdots n)} = f \circ \delta_{12} \circ \delta_{(12 \cdots n)} = f \circ \delta_{(12 \cdots n)} = f.$$

In view of (11.12), this proves (11.13). ‖

By an appropriate rearrangement of the integers $N = \{1, 2, \cdots, n\}$, the integers 1 and 2 in (11.11)–(11.13) can be replaced by any two distinct integers in N.

12. Threshold Functions

Let n denote an arbitrarily given positive integer. A switching function

$$f : Q^n \to Q$$

of n variables is said to be *linearly separable* iff there exists a hyperplane [i.e., an $(n-1)$-dimensional linear variety] π in the Euclidean n-space R^n which strictly separates $f^{-1}(1)$ from $f^{-1}(0)$; that is to say, the on-set $f^{-1}(1)$ of f lies on one side of π, the off-set $f^{-1}(0)$ of f lies on the other side of π, and the intersection $\pi \cap Q^n$ is empty. The hyperplane π will be called a *strict separating hyperplane* of the given linearly separable switching function f.

For example, among the sixteen switching functions of two variables exhibited in §3, the two functions $\ominus$, $\ominus'$ are not linearly separable, while the remaining fourteen functions are linearly separable.

Let π denote any strict separating hyperplane of a given linearly separable switching function $f : Q^n \to Q$ and let

$$w_1 x_1 + \cdots + w_n x_n = T$$

denote an equation of the hyperplane π in the n variables $x_1, \cdots, x_n$. Multiplying both sides of the equation by -1 if necessary, we may always assume that, for an arbitrary point

$$x = x_1 \cdots x_n$$

of the n-cube Q^n, we have

$$w_1 x_1 + \cdots + w_n x_n > T, \qquad \text{if} \quad f(x) = 1,$$
$$w_1 x_1 + \cdots + w_n x_n < T, \qquad \text{if} \quad f(x) = 0.$$

In this case, the system

$$(w_1, \cdots, w_n; T)$$

of $n+1$ real numbers is called a *strict separating system* for the linearly separable switching function f. The first n real numbers $w_1, \cdots, w_n$ in this system are called the *weights*, and the last real number T is referred to as the *threshold*.

The definition of linear separability given above can be changed into other equivalent forms which might be convenient on various occasions. In fact, we have the following theorem.

THEOREM 12.1.   *For an arbitrarily given switching function $f : Q^n \to Q$ of n variables, the following five conditions are equivalent:*

(i) *f is linearly separable.*
(ii) *There exist real numbers $a_1, \cdots, a_n$ and A such that, for an arbitrary point $x = x_1 \cdots, x_n$ of Q^n, we have*

$$a_1 x_1 + \cdots + a_n x_n \geq A, \quad \text{if} \;\; f(x) = 1,$$
$$a_1 x_1 + \cdots + a_n x_n < A, \quad \text{if} \;\; f(x) = 0.$$

(ii′) *There exist real numbers $b_1, \cdots, b_n$ and B such that, for an arbitrary point $x = x_1 \cdots x_n$ of Q^n, we have*

$$b_1 x_1 + \cdots + b_n x_n \leq B, \quad \text{if} \;\; f(x) = 1,$$
$$b_1 x_1 + \cdots + b_n x_n > B, \quad \text{if} \;\; f(x) = 0.$$

(iv) *There exist real numbers $c_1, \cdots, c_n$ and C such that, for an arbitrary point $x = x_1 \cdots x_n$ of Q^n, we have*

$$c_1 x_1 + \cdots + c_n x_n < C, \quad \text{if} \;\; f(x) = 1,$$
$$c_1 x_1 + \cdots + c_n x_n \geq C, \quad \text{if} \;\; f(x) = 0.$$

(v) *There exist real numbers $d_1, \cdots, d_n$ and D such that, for an arbitrary point $x = x_1 \cdots x_n$ of Q^n, we have*

$$d_1 x_1 + \cdots + d_n x_n > D, \quad \text{if} \;\; f(x) = 1,$$
$$d_1 x_1 + \cdots + d_n x_n \leq D, \quad \text{if} \;\; f(x) = 0.$$

Proof.   (i) $\Rightarrow$ (ii). Assume that f is linearly separable. Then, by definition, f admits a strict separating system

$$(w_1, \cdots, w_n; T).$$

Take $A = T$ and $a_i = w_i$ for every $i = 1, \cdots, n$. Then the condition (ii) holds.

(ii) $\Rightarrow$ (iii). Assume that f satisfies the condition (ii). Take $B = -A$ and $b_i = -a_i$ for every $i = 1, \cdots, n$. Then we obtain (iii) by multiplying the inequalities in (ii) by -1.

(iii) $\Rightarrow$ (iv). Assume that f satisfies the condition (iii). Consider the offset $F' = f^{-1}(0)$ of f. Then, for each point $x = x_1 \cdots x_n$ in F', we have

$$p(x) = b_1 x_1 + \cdots + b_n x_n - B > 0$$

Define a positive real number r as follows: If F' is empty, we set $r = 1$; otherwise, we set r to be the smallest of the real numbers $p(x)$ for all $x \in F'$. Then we obtain (iv) by taking $C = B + r$ and $c_i = b_i$ for every $i = 1, \cdots, n$.

(iv) $\Rightarrow$ (v). Assume that f satisfies the condition (iv). Take $D = -C$

and $d_i = -c_i$ for every $i = 1, \cdots, n$. Then we obtain (v) by multiplying the inequalities in (iv) by -1.

(v) $\Rightarrow$ (i). Assume that f satisfies the condition (v). Consider the on-set $F = f^{-1}(1)$ of f. Then, for each point $x = x_1 \cdots x_n$ in F, we have

$$q(x) = d_1 x_1 + \cdots + d_n x_n - D > 0.$$

Define a positive real number s as follows: If F is empty, we set $s = 1$; otherwise, we set s to be the smallest of the real numbers $q(x)$ for all $x \in F$. Let $T = D + \frac{1}{2}s$ and $w_i = d_i$ for every $i = 1, \cdots, n$. Then

$$(w_i, \cdots, w_n; T)$$

is clearly a strict separating system of f. Hence (i) holds. $\parallel$

For the sake of definiteness, the system

$$(a_1, \cdots, a_n; A)$$

of $n + 1$ real numbers in the condition (ii) will be called a *separating system* for the linearly separable switching function

$$f : Q^n \rightarrow Q,$$

with $a_1, \cdots, a_n$ as *weights* and A as *threshold*. Hence, every strict separating system for f is always a separating system for f but the converse is not always true.

COROLLARY 12.2.   *If a switching function $f : Q^n \rightarrow Q$ is linearly separable, so is its complement $f' : Q^n \rightarrow Q$.*

Proof.   Since f is linearly separable, it admits a separating system $(w_1, \cdots, w_n; T)$. Then the condition (iv) in (12.1) holds for its complement f' with $C = T$ and $c_i = w_i$ for every $i = 1, \cdots, n$. Hence f' is linearly separable. $\parallel$

One of the most important properties of linear separability of the switching of n variables is that it is a *class invariant*, that is to say, it is preserved by every admissible transformation of the n-cube Q^n as defined in §9. In fact, we have the following *invariance theorem*.

THEOREM 12.3.   *If a switching function $f : Q^n \rightarrow Q$ of n variables is linearly separable, so is the switching function*

$$\alpha^{\#}(f) = f \circ \alpha : Q^n \rightarrow Q$$

for every admissible transformation α of the n-cube Q^n.

Proof. Let $\alpha : Q^n \to Q^n$ denote any admissible transformation of the n-cube Q^n. According to §9, α extends to a unique nonsingular linear transformation

$$\lambda : R^n \to R^n$$

of the Euclidean n-space R^n which contains the n-cube Q^n. Since λ is nonsingular, it has a unique inverse

$$\mu = \lambda^{-1} : R^n \to R^n,$$

which is also a nonsingular linear transformation of R^n.

Assume that $f : Q^n \to Q$ is linearly separable. We have to prove that the switching function

$$g = f \circ \alpha : Q^n \to Q$$

is also linearly separable. According to the definition of the linear separability of f, there exists a hyperplane π of the Euclidean n-space R^n which strictly separates the on-set $F = f^{-1}(1)$ of f and the off-set $F' = f^{-1}(0)$ of f.

The on-set G and the off-set G' of the switching function $g = f \circ \alpha$ are as follows:

$$G = g^{-1}(1) = \alpha^{-1}[f^{-1}(1)] = \mu(F),$$
$$G' = g^{-1}(0) = \alpha^{-1}[f^{-1}(0)] = \mu(F').$$

Since μ is a nonsingular linear transformation of R^n, the image $\mu(\pi)$ of the hyperplane π of R^n is a hyperplane that strictly separates $\mu(F)$ from $\mu(F')$. This implies that g is linearly separable and completes the proof of (12.3). ‖

Linearly separable switching functions are simply called *threshold functions*. Since the three switching functions

$$\wedge : Q^2 \to Q, \qquad \vee : Q^2 \to Q, \qquad c : Q \to Q$$

are linearly separable, it follows from (7.2) that the set of all threshold functions is functionally complete. In fact, we have the following theorem.

THEOREM 12.4. *For every integer $t \geq 2$, the threshold functions of not more than t variables constitute a functionally complete set of switching functions.*

In the literature, numerous properties of threshold functions have been studied during the last seven years. Interested readers should refer to [H1].

Exercises

1. Prove that a finite set of m elements has 2^m subsets. Hence show that there are 2^{2^n} switching functions of n variables.

2. Establish the following generalized De Morgan's laws: For any finite number m of switching functions $f_1, f_2, \cdots, f_m$ of n variables, we have

$$(f_1 f_2 \cdots f_m)' = f_1' \vee f_2' \vee \cdots \vee f_m',$$
$$(f_1 \vee f_2 \vee \cdots \vee f_m)' = f_1' f_2' \cdots f_m'.$$

3. Find the Karnaugh maps of the switching functions of four variables represented by the following Boolean polynomials:

      (i) $x_1 x_3' \vee x_2 x_3 x_4 \vee x_1' x_2' x_3$,

      (ii) $x_1 x_2 \vee x_1 x_3 \vee x_1 x_4 \vee x_2 x_3 \vee x_2 x_4 \vee x_3 x_4$.

4. For any two switching functions f and g of n variables, let

$$f/g = (fg)'.$$

This operation is called the *Sheffer stroke* or the *product denial*. Prove the following relations:

(i) $fg = (f/g)/(f/g)$,

(ii) $f \vee g = (f/f)/(g/g)$,

(iii) $f' = f/f$.

5. For any two switching functions f and g of n variables, let

$$f \downarrow g = (f \vee g)'.$$

This operation is called the *Pierce arrow* or the *joint denial*. Prove the following relations:

(i) $fg = (f \downarrow f) \downarrow (g \downarrow g)$,

(ii) $f \vee g = (f \downarrow g) \downarrow (f \downarrow g)$,

(iii) $f' = f \downarrow f$.

6. For any two switching functions f and g of n variables, let

$$f \oslash g = (f'g) \vee (fg').$$

This operation is called the *exclusive disjunction*. Prove the following relations:

(i) $f \oslash g = (ab)'(a \vee b)$,

(ii) $f \vee g = (f \oslash g) \oslash (fg)$

7. For any three switching functions f, g, and h of n variables, prove the following relations:

(i) $f \oslash g = g \oslash f$,

(ii) $f \oslash (g \oslash h) = (f \oslash g) \oslash h$,

(iii) $f(g \oslash h) = fg \oslash fh$.

Because of (ii), $f \oslash g \oslash h$ is well defined.

8. Consider the switching function $f : Q^n \to Q$ of n variables defined by the expression

$$x_1 \ominus x_2 \ominus \cdots \ominus x_n,$$

where $x_1, x_2, \cdots, x_n$ denote the n elementary switching functions of n variables. Prove that, for every point $x = x_1 \cdots x_n$ of the n-cube Q^n, we have $f(x) = 1$ iff the rank

$$\rho(x) = \sum_{i=1}^{n} x_i$$

of the point x is odd. Hence, this switching function $f : Q^n \to Q$ is different from the switching function $\ominus : Q^n \to Q$ whenever $n > 2$.

9. By the *distance* between two points $x = x_1 \cdots x_n$ and $y = y_1 \cdots y_n$ of the n-cube Q^n, we mean the integer

$$d(x, y) = \sum_{i=1}^{n} |x_i - y_i|.$$

Hence, the distance $d(x, y)$ is simply the number of the integers i such that $x_i \neq y_i$. Verify that the distance function d has the following properties:

(i) $d(x, y) = 0$ if $x = y$;

(ii) $d(x, y) > 0$ if $x \neq y$;

(iii) $d(x, y) = d(y, x)$;

(iv) $d(x, y) + d(y, z) \geq d(x, z)$.

10. Compute all the pairwise distances for the points in the 4-cube Q^4. Arrange these in a square matrix whose rows and columns are labeled $0, 1, 2, \cdots, 15$ corresponding to the points of Q^4. The pairwise distances for Q^n with $n < 4$ are given by the submatrices of this matrix. Generalize to the n-cube Q^n.

11. Prove that every admissible transformation $\alpha : Q^n \to Q^n$ preserves the distance, that is, for any two points x and y of the n-cube Q^n, we have

$$d[\alpha(x), \alpha(y)] = d(x, y).$$

12. Prove that the number of equivalence classes of switching functions of n variables is given by

$$\chi(n) = \frac{1}{n! \, 2^n} \sum_{\alpha \varepsilon O_n} I(\alpha),$$

where O_n denotes the hyper-octahedral group in §9 and, for each $\alpha \in O_n$, $I(\alpha)$ stands for the number of switching functions $f : Q^n \to Q$ such that

$$\alpha^{\#}(f) = f \circ \alpha = f.$$

Also, for $\alpha, \beta \in O_n$, prove that we have

$$I(\alpha) = I(\beta)$$

if α and β are conjugates in O_n.

13. Consider the switching function $f : Q^3 \to Q$ defined by the Boolean polynomial

$$x_1' x_2' x_3 \vee x_1 x_2 x_3 \vee x_1 x_2' x_3'.$$

Let $u = 101 \in Q^3$. Prove that the switching function

$$\gamma_u^{\#}(f) = f \circ \gamma_u : Q^3 \to Q$$

is symmetric. In the literature, f is said to be *symmetric in the variables* $x_1', x_2,$ *and* x_3'.

14. Prove that the number of equivalence classes of switching functions of n variables which contain at least one symmetric function is

$$2^n + 2^{[n/2]} + 2[\tfrac{1}{2}(n + 1)] - n - 1,$$

where $[x]$ denotes the largest integer not exceeding x. See [Povarov 1].

15. Prove that the number of switching functions of n variables equivalent to some symmetric function is

$$2^{2n} - 2^{n+1} + 4.$$

See [Povarov 1].

Chapter II

MINIMIZATION METHODS

This chapter is devoted to the methods of finding minimal disjunctive normal forms for arbitrarily given switching functions. The terminology used follows the topological approach introduced by Mueller and Roth. The notions of cubical complexes and cubical covers of switching functions are introduced in the first two sections. Three different methods for finding prime implicants—the map method, the tabular method, and the consensus method—are carefully described and illustrated in §3, §4, and §5. In §6, the prime implicant table is defined and various reduction methods are described. In §7, three methods for attacking cyclic tables are described. It is shown in §8 that, by passing to the complement of a given switching function, the methods given in this chapter can also be used to find minimal conjunctive normal forms. Minimization of multiple-output circuits is studied in the final sections. The first four exercises at the end of the chapter provide the necessary routine practice of the various methods given in the chapter. The remaining exercises contain sketches of interesting related operations, refinements and generalizations of the methods given in the chapter, and examples indicating the complexity of the problem.

1. Cubical Complexes

Let n denote a given positive integer and consider the n-cube Q^n as defined in (I, §1). We shall define the notion of a *cube* in Q^n. For this purpose, let us consider the set

$$Q^* = \{1, 0, *\}$$

which consists of three elements, namely, the integers 1 and 0 together with the "don't care" sign $*$. Thus we have

$$Q \subset Q^*, \qquad Q^* = Q \cup \{*\}.$$

On the other hand, let

$$N = \{1, 2, \cdots, n\}$$

denote the set of the first n positive integers.

To define the notion of a cube in Q^n, let

$$\phi : N \to Q^*$$

denote an arbitrarily given function defined on the set N with values in Q^*. Then ϕ determines a subset C of the n-cube Q^n as follows: A point $x = x_1 \cdots x_n$ of Q^n is in the subset C iff

$$x_i = \phi(i)$$

for every integer $i \in N$ such that

$$\phi(i) \neq *.$$

This subset C of Q^n will be called the *cube* in Q^n defined by the function ϕ, which will be referred to as the *coordinate function* of the cube C. For each integer $i \in N$, the element

$$\phi(i) \in Q^*$$

will be called the i-th *coordinate* of the cube C. Since the cube C is completely determined by its coordinates $\phi(1), \phi(2), \cdots, \phi(n)$, we can denote by

$$(\phi(1), \phi(2), \cdots, \phi(n))$$

the cube C in Q^n defined by the given coordinate function ϕ. As in (I, §1), there is no danger of ambiguity if we delete the commas between the coordinates of C, as well as the parentheses at both ends. Thus we have

$$C = \phi(1)\phi(2) \cdots \phi(n).$$

Let C denote an arbitrarily given cube in Q^n defined by its coordinate function

$$\phi : N \to Q^*.$$

By the *dimension* of the cube C, we mean the cardinality of the subset $\phi^{-1}(*)$ of N; in other words, the dimension of C is the number of $*$'s in its coordinates

$$\phi(1)\phi(2) \cdots \phi(n).$$

The dimension of C is denoted by the symbol dim (C) and obviously satisfies the inequalities

$$0 \leq \dim(C) \leq n.$$

If $\dim(C) = r$, then C will be called an r-cube in Q^n. In this instance, C consists of the 2^r points of Q^n which can be obtained by replacing the r $*$'s in the coordinates of C by the integers 1 or 0. In particular, a 0-cube in Q^n consists of a single point of Q^n and hence is usually identified with the lone point of Q^n which it contains. On the other hand, there is only one n-cube in Q^n, namely, Q^n itself.

For convenience in the applications, we shall also introduce the notion of the codimension of a cube in Q^n. By the *codimension* of a cube C in Q^n, we mean the integer

$$\mathrm{cod}(C) = n - \dim(C).$$

Hence the codimension $\mathrm{cod}(C)$ of a cube C in Q^n with coordinate function $\phi : N \to Q^*$ is the cardinality of the subset $\phi^{-1}(Q)$ of N, that is, the total number of the integers 1 and 0 in its coordinates

$$\phi(1)\phi(2) \cdots \phi(n).$$

Clearly the following relations are satisfied:

$$0 \leq \mathrm{cod}(C) \leq n,$$
$$\dim(C) + \mathrm{cod}(C) = n.$$

Since the correspondence between the functions $\phi : N \to Q^*$ and the cubes

$$C = \phi(1)\phi(2) \cdots \phi(n)$$

is obviously one-to-one, there are 3^n cubes in the n-cube Q^n. By an easy combinatorial argument, one can also see that the number $\nu_n(r)$ of r-cubes in Q^n is given by

$$\nu_n(r) = \binom{n}{r} 2^{n-r} = \frac{n!\, 2^{n-r}}{r!\,(n-r)!}$$

for every integer r satisfying $0 \leq r \leq n$.

Now let us consider an arbitrarily given cube C in Q^n with coordinate function

$$\phi : N \to Q^*.$$

As a subset of the n-cube Q^n, C corresponds to a switching function

$$\theta(C) = \chi_C : Q^n \to Q$$

according to (I, §5). The on-set of this switching function χ_C is precisely the cube C; in symbols, we have

$$\chi_C^{-1}(1) = C.$$

Consequently, for an arbitrary point $x = x_1 \cdots x_n$ of the n-cube Q^n, we have

$$\chi_C(x) = 1$$

iff $x_i = \phi(i)$ holds for every $i \in N$ with $\phi(i) \neq *$.

This indicates that χ_C has a Boolean expression obtained as follows: Let us define

$$x_i^1 = x_i, \qquad x_i^0 = x_i', \qquad x_i^* = 1$$

for every $i = 1, 2, \cdots, n$. Then the switching function χ_C obviously has the following Boolean expression

$$\chi_C = x_1^{\phi(1)} x_2^{\phi(2)} \cdots x_n^{\phi(n)}.$$

Since x_i^* stands for the constant switching function 1, we can delete the factor

$$x_i^{\phi(i)}$$

from this Boolean expression when $\phi(i) = *$. By doing so we obtain a Boolean monomial

$$\chi_C = \mu(C)$$

of s irredundant factors x_i or x_i' according as $\phi(i) = 1$ or $\phi(i) = 0$, where

$$s = \text{cod}(C).$$

This Boolean monomial $\mu(C)$ will be referred to as the *Boolean monomial* of the cube C. It is of *degree* s; in symbols, we have

$$\deg[\mu(C)] = \text{cod}(C).$$

For example, the Boolean monomial of the 2-cube $C = *10*1$ in the 5-cube Q^5 is the following Boolean monomial of degree 3:

$$\mu(C) = x_2 x_3' x_5.$$

It is obvious that the assignment $C \rightarrow \mu(C)$ establishes a one-to-one correspondence between the cubes in Q^n and the irredundant Boolean monomials of n variables.

The following two propositions are obvious consequences of the definition and of (I, 5.14).

PROPOSITION 1.1. *For any two cubes C and D in Q^n, C is contained in D iff $\mu(C)$ implies $\mu(D)$; in symbols, we have*

$$C \subset D \quad \text{iff} \quad \mu(C) \le \mu(D).$$

PROPOSITION 1.2. *For any two cubes C and D in Q^n with coordinate functions $\phi : N \rightarrow Q^*$ and $\psi : N \rightarrow Q^*$, respectively, C is contained in D iff we have*

$$\psi^{-1}(1) \subset \phi^{-1}(1), \qquad \psi^{-1}(0) \subset \phi^{-1}(0)$$

and consequently

$$\phi^{-1}(*) \subset \psi^{-1}(*).$$

For example, in the 5-cube Q^5, the 2-cube $C = *10*1$ is contained in the 3-cube $D = *10**$.

Next let us introduce the notion of consecutive cubes in Q^n. Two cubes C and D in Q^n of the same dimension are said to be *consecutive* iff they differ in one and only one coordinate. Since C and D are of the same dimension, it is clear that the lone disagreeing coordinate of C or D can never be a *. For example, the 2-cubes $0**1$ and $0**0$ in Q^4 are consecutive.

The 0-cubes, the 1-cubes, and the 2-cubes in Q^n will be simply called the *vertices*, the *edges*, and the *squares* of Q^n.

An arbitrary edge e of Q^n consists of two consecutive vertices of Q^n called the *end points* of e. Conversely, any two consecutive vertices u and v of Q^n form an edge of Q^n obtained by replacing the disagreeing coordinate in u and v by the don't care sign *. For example, the edge of Q^4 formed by the vertices 0111 and 0101 is 01*1.

An arbitrary square s of Q^n consists of four points of Q^n called the *vertices* of s. If we replace one of the two *'s in the coordinates of the square s by the integers 1 or 0, respectively, we obtain two consecutive edges d and e of Q^n, called a pair of *opposite sides* of the square s. Besides, we have

$$s = d \cup e;$$

in words, the square s is the union of any pair of opposite sides. Conversely, any two consecutive edges d and e of Q^n form a square of Q^n obtained by replacing the disagreeing coordinate (which can never be a *) by *. For example, the square of Q^4 formed by the consecutive edges 01*1 and 00*1 is 0**1.

Now let $r \geq 3$ and consider any given r-cube C in Q^n. If we replace one of the r *'s in the coordinates of C by the integers 1 or 0, respectively, we obtain two consecutive $(r-1)$-cubes D and E, called a pair of *opposite faces* of the r-cube C. Besides, C is the union of any pair of opposite faces; in symbols,

$$C = D \cup E.$$

Conversely, any two consecutive $(r-1)$-cubes D and E in Q^n form a pair of opposite faces of an r-cube C whose coordinates are obtained by replacing the disagreeing coordinate in D or E by the don't care sign *. For example, the 3-cube in Q^4 formed by the consecutive squares 0**1 and 0**0 is 0***.

Now let us define the notion of a cubical complex in Q^n. For this purpose, let F denote an arbitrarily given subset of Q^n. By the *cubical complex* of the set F, we mean the collection

$$K(F)$$

of all cubes in Q^n contained in the set F. For each nonnegative integer $r \leq n$, let

$$K_r(F)$$

denote the collection of all r-cubes in Q^n contained in the set F. Then $K(F)$ is the union of these collections; in symbols,

$$K(F) = K_0(F) \cup K_1(F) \cup \cdots \cup K_n(F).$$

To construct the cubical complex $K(F)$ of a set F in Q^n, it suffices to construct the collections

$$K_0(F), K_1(F), \cdots, K_n(F)$$

by the following algorithm. By definition, $K_0(F)$ is the set of all points in F, that is

$$K_0(F) = F.$$

Let $r > 0$ and assume that $K_{r-1}(F)$ has already been constructed. Consider all possible pairs of consecutive $(r - 1)$-cubes in $K_{r-1}(F)$. If D and E are such a pair, then D and E form a pair of opposite faces of an r-cube

$$C(D, E)$$

whose coordinates are obtained by replacing the lone disagreeing co-ordinate in D or E by $*$. Since $D \subset F$ and $E \subset F$, we have

$$C(D, E) = D \cup E \subset F.$$

Then $K_r(F)$ is the collection of all r-cubes $C(D, E)$ for all possible pairs of consecutive $(r - 1)$-cubes D and E in $K_{r-1}(F)$. This completes the inductive description of the algorithm for constructing $K(F)$.

A cube C in the cubical complex $K(F)$ is said to be *maximal* iff $C \subset D$ implies $C = D$ for every cube D in $K(F)$. In other words, a maximal cube in $K(F)$ is a cube C in $K(F)$ which is not contained in any other cube in $K(F)$. These maximal cubes in cubical complexes will play extremely important roles in the following sections.

Now let us consider an arbitrarily given switching function

$$f : Q^n \to Q$$

of n variables. By the *cubical complex*

$$K(f)$$

of this switching function f, we mean the cubical complex $K(F)$ of the on-set

$$F = f^{-1}(1)$$

of f in Q^n. The Boolean monomials $\mu(C)$ of the maximal cubes C in the cubical complex

$$K(f) = K(F)$$

are called the *prime implicants* of the given switching function f.

As an illustrative example, let $n = 4$ and consider the switching function

$$f : Q^4 \rightarrow Q$$

defined by Table I-2-1. Then, by definition, $K_0(f) = F = f^{-1}(1)$ consists of the following five vertices:

$$0000, \quad 0011, \quad 1000, \quad 1011, \quad 1111.$$

Among these vertices, there are three pairs of consecutive vertices, namely,

$$(0000, 1000), \quad (0011, 1011), \quad (1011, 1111).$$

Hence $K_1(f)$ consists of three edges, namely,

$$*000, \quad *011, \quad 1*11.$$

Among these three edges, there is no pair of consecutive edges. Hence $K_r(f)$ is empty for $r = 2, 3$, and 4. The three edges in $K(f)$ are the maximal cubes; therefore, the Boolean monomials

$$x_2' x_3' x_4', \quad x_2' x_3 x_4, \quad x_1 x_3 x_4$$

are the prime implicants of f.

Finally, let us consider an arbitrarily given switching function

$$f : Q^n \rightarrow Q^*$$

of n variables with a given set

$$D = f^{-1}(*)$$

of don't care points. The subsets

$$F = f^{-1}(1), \qquad F^* = f^{-1}\{1, *\} = F \cup D$$

will be called the *restricted on-set* and the *extended on-set* of f, respectively. The cubical complex

$$K^*(f) = K(F^*)$$

will be referred to as the *cubical complex* of f. The Boolean monomials $\mu(C)$ of the maximal cubes C in $K^*(f)$ are called the *prime implicants* of f.

As an illustrative example, let $n = 4$ and consider the switching function

$$f : Q^4 \rightarrow Q^*$$

defined by Table I-8-1. Then, by definition, $K_0^*(f) = F^*$ consists of the following eleven vertices:

$$0000, \ 0011, \ 0100, \ 0101, \ 0110, \ 0111, \ 1000, \ 1001, \ 1010, \ 1011, \ 1111.$$

Among these vertices, there are fourteen pairs of consecutive vertices, namely,

$$(0000, 0100), \quad (0000, 1000),$$
$$(0100, 0101), \quad (0100, 0110),$$
$$(1000, 1001), \quad (1000, 1010),$$
$$(0011, 0111), \quad (0101, 0111),$$
$$(0110, 0111), \quad (0011, 1011),$$
$$(1001, 1011), \quad (1010, 1011),$$
$$(0111, 1111), \quad (1011, 1111).$$

Hence $K_1^*(f)$ consists of the following fourteen edges:

$$*000, \quad 0*00, \quad 01*0, \quad 010*,$$
$$*011, \quad 0*11, \quad 01*1, \quad 011*,$$
$$*111, \quad 1*11, \quad 10*0, \quad 100*,$$
$$10*1, \quad 101*.$$

Among these edges, there are six pairs of consecutive edges, namely,

$$(*011, *111), \quad (0*11, 1*11),$$
$$(01*0, 01*1), \quad (10*0, 10*1),$$
$$(010*, 011*), \quad (100*, 101*).$$

However, we obtain only three distinct squares, namely,

$$**11, \quad 01**, \quad 10**.$$

Hence $K_2^*(f)$ consists of these three squares. Among these squares, there is no pair of consecutive squares. Hence both $K_3^*(f)$ and $K_4^*(f)$ are empty. The maximal cubes of $K^*(f)$ are

$$*000, \quad 0*00, \quad **11, \quad 01**, \quad 10**;$$

therefore, the Boolean monomials

$$x_2'x_3'x_4', \quad x_1'x_3'x_4', \quad x_3x_4, \quad x_1'x_2, \quad x_1x_2'$$

are the prime implicants of f.

2. Cubical Covers

Let n denote a given positive integer and consider a switching function

$$f: Q^n \to Q^* = Q \cup \{*\}$$

of n variables possibly with don't care points

$$D = f^{-1}(*).$$

As in the preceding section, the subsets

$$F = f^{-1}(1), \qquad F^* = f^{-1}\{1, *\} = F \cup D$$

of the n-cube Q^n are called the *restricted on-set* and the *extended on-set* of f. The switching function f has no don't care point iff

$$F = F^*.$$

By a *cubical cover* of the switching function f, we mean a subcollection γ of the cubical complex

$$K^*(f) = K(F^*)$$

of f such that the restricted on-set F of f is contained in the union of all cubes in γ. Since every cube of the cubical complex $K^*(f)$ is contained in the extended on-set F^* of f, we obtain

$$F \subset \mathbf{U}_{C \in \gamma} \, C \subset F^*.$$

Consequently, if f has no don't care point, we must have

$$F = \mathbf{U}_{C \in \gamma} \, C.$$

For example, the switching function

$$f : Q^4 \to Q$$

defined by Table I-2-1 and studied in the preceding section has a cubical cover

$$\gamma = \{*000, *011, 1*11\}.$$

On the other hand, the switching function

$$f : Q^4 \to Q^*$$

defined by Table I-8-1 and studied in the preceding section has a cubical cover

$$\gamma = \{*000, 0*00, **11, 01**, 10**\}.$$

The cubical covers γ in the preceding examples consist of all maximal cubes of the cubical complexes. This statement suggests the following proposition which is an obvious consequence of the fact that every point of the restricted on-set F of f is contained in at least one maximal cube in the cubical complex $K^*(f)$ of f.

PROPOSITION 2.1. *The collection of all maximal cubes in the cubical complex $K^*(f)$ of an arbitrary switching function*

$$f : Q^n \to Q^*,$$

possibly with don't care points, forms a cubical cover of f.

This proposition establishes the existence of cubical covers of any switching function. These are clearly not unique. For example, the switching function

$$f : Q^4 \to Q^*$$

defined by the Table I-8-1 and studied above has a cubical cover

$$\delta = \{0{*}00, {**}11\}$$

which is different from the cubical cover γ given by (2.1).

Now let us investigate the usefulness of cubical covers. For this purpose, let γ denote an arbitrary cubical cover of any given switching function

$$f : Q^n \to Q^*,$$

possibly with don't care points. Consider an arbitrary cube C in the cubical cover γ of f. As described in the preceding section, C determines an irredundant Boolean monomial $\mu(C)$ called the Boolean monomial of the cube C. Taking the join of these Boolean monomials $\mu(C)$ for all cubes C in γ, we obtain a Boolean polynomial

$$\mu(\gamma) = \mathbf{V}_{C \in \gamma}\, \mu(C)$$

which will be referred as the *Boolean polynomial* of the cubical cover γ of the switching function f. For example, the Boolean polynomial of the cubical cover

$$\delta = \{0{*}00, {**}11\}$$

of the switching function $f : Q^4 \to Q^*$ defined by Table I-8-1 and studied above is

$$\mu(\delta) = x_1' x_3' x_4' \vee x_3 x_4.$$

According to (I, §6), the Boolean polynomial $\mu(\gamma)$ of the given cubical cover γ of f represents a switching function

$$g : Q^n \to Q$$

with no don't care point. According to (I, §5), the on-set

$$G = g^{-1}(1)$$

of this switching function g is the union

$$\mathbf{U}_{C \in \gamma}\, C$$

of all the cubes C in γ. Hence we obtain

$$F \subset G \subset F^* = Q^n \backslash f^{-1}(0).$$

This implies $f(x) = g(x)$ for every point $x \in Q^n$ with $f(x) \neq *$; in symbols,

$$f \equiv g \bmod(D)$$

as defined in (I, §8) with D standing for the set $f^{-1}(*)$ of all don't care points. Hence we obtain the following theorem.

THEOREM 2.2.   *For every cubical cover γ of an arbitrary switching function*

$$f : Q^n \to Q^*,$$

possibly with don't care points, the Boolean polynomial

$$\mu(\gamma) = \mathsf{V}_{C \in \gamma}\, \mu(C)$$

of the cubical cover γ is a Boolean expression of f modulo the set $D = f^{-1}(*)$ of don't care points, in symbols,

$$f \equiv \mu(\gamma) \bmod(D).$$

For example, consider the switching function $f : Q^n \to Q^*$ defined by Table I-8-1. The Boolean polynomial

$$\mu(\delta) = x_1' x_3' x_4' \vee x_3 x_4$$

given above is a Boolean expression of f modulo the set D of all don't care points. In particular, if the given switching function f has no don't care points, that is, if $D = \square$, then we have

$$f = \mu(\gamma).$$

Because of (2.2), the Boolean polynomial $\mu(\gamma)$ of any cubical cover γ of a switching function f suggests a precise mechanization of f using either branch-type or gate-type switching components.

If branch-type components are being used, the Boolean polynomial $\mu(\gamma)$ suggests a series-parallel relay-contact network for the given switching function f. For example, consider the switching function $f : Q^4 \to Q^*$ defined by Table I-8-1. The Boolean polynomial

$$\mu(\delta) = x_1' x_3' x_4' \vee x_3 x_4$$

of the cubical cover δ of f obtained above suggests the relay-contact network for f shown in Figure II-2-1. In general, if γ consists of k cubes,

FIGURE   II-2-1

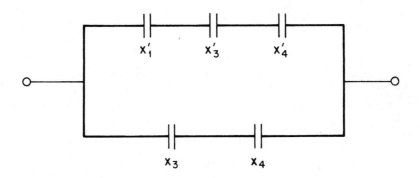

$$x_1' \qquad x_3' \qquad x_4'$$

$$x_3 \qquad x_4$$

the relay-contact network suggested by the Boolean polynomial $\mu(\gamma)$ consists of k parallel branches corresponding to the terms of $\mu(\gamma)$ and hence to the cubes in γ. The branch corresponding to the cube $C \in \gamma$ contains $\text{cod}(C)$ contacts corresponding to the literals in the term $\mu(C)$. Hence the total number of contacts in the relay-contact network suggested by $\mu(\gamma)$ is

$$c_1(\gamma) = \textstyle\sum_{C \in \gamma} \text{cod}(C).$$

If gate-type components are being used, the Boolean polynomial $\mu(\gamma)$ suggests a two-stage AND-OR network for the given switching function f. For example, consider the switching function $f : Q^4 \to Q^*$ defined by Table I-8-1. The Boolean polynomial

$$\mu(\delta) = x_1' x_3' x_4' \vee x_3 x_4$$

of the cubical cover δ of f obtained above suggested the gate-type network for f shown in Figure II-2-2. In general, if γ consists of k cubes of which

FIGURE II-2-2

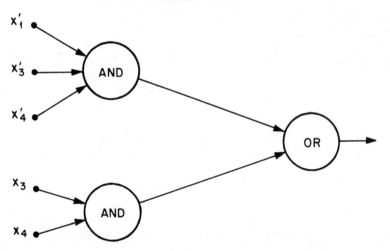

$b_1(\gamma)$ are of codimension greater than one, the gate-type network suggested by $\mu(\gamma)$ consists of $b_1(\gamma)$ AND-gates corresponding to the cubes in γ of codimension greater than one and a lone OR-gate. The AND-gate corresponding to the cube $C \in \gamma$ has $\text{cod}(C)$ inputs, and the OR-gate has k inputs. Hence the total number of gates in the network is

$$b_1(\gamma) + 1$$

and the total number of inputs to the gates is

$$c_2(\gamma) = b_1(\gamma) + c_1(\gamma) = b_1(\gamma) + \textstyle\sum_{C \in \gamma} \text{cod}(C).$$

Our main problem in the present chapter is to look for a cubical cover γ of an arbitrarily given switching function

$$f : Q^n \to Q^*,$$

possibly with don't care points, such that its Boolean polynomial $\mu(\gamma)$ suggests the cheapest network. For the precise formulation of this problem, we must investigate the cost of the network suggested by $\mu(\gamma)$ which will be simply called the *cost of the cubical cover* γ.

The cost of a branch-type network is usually measured by the number of contacts it contains. Hence, if branch-type components are being used, the cost of a cubical cover γ should be

$$c_1(\gamma) = \textstyle\sum_{C \in \gamma} \text{cod}(C).$$

Next, if a network is built directly from diodes, its cost is usually measured by the total number of diodes it contains. Since the number of diodes is equal to the number of inputs to the gates, the cost of a cubical cover γ should be

$$c_2(\gamma) = b_1(\gamma) + c_1(\gamma) = b_1(\gamma) + \textstyle\sum_{C \in \gamma} \text{cod}(C),$$

where $b_1(\gamma)$ stands for the number of cubes C in γ with $\text{cod}(C) > 1$.

Finally, if a network is built from ready-made AND-gates and OR-gates, its cost is usually measured by the total number of gates it contains together with a slight preference in favor of fewer total inputs. Hence the cost of a cubical cover γ should be

$$c_3(\gamma) = b_1(\gamma) + 1 + \varepsilon c_1(\gamma),$$

where ε stands for fixed real number satisfying

$$0 < \varepsilon < \frac{1}{n2^n}.$$

Since $c_1(\gamma) \le n2^n$, it follows that $b_1(\gamma)$ dominates the cost $c_3(\gamma)$.

In the preceding investigation about the cost of a cubical cover γ, we have deliberately neglected the trivial cases where the cubical cover γ might be empty or might consist of a single cube.

Motivated by the special costs $c_1(\gamma)$, $c_2(\gamma)$, and $c_3(\gamma)$ explained above, we shall introduce the general notion of a cost function for cubical covers.

By a *cost function* for cubical covers in Q^n, we mean a function c that assigns to each collection γ of cubes in Q^n a nonnegative real number $c(\gamma)$

satisfying the condition that, for any two collections γ and δ of cubes in Q^n,

$$c(\gamma) < c(\delta)$$

holds if $b_1(\gamma) \leq b_1(\delta)$ and $c_1(\gamma) < c_1(\delta)$ are both satisfied. Clearly this condition is satisfied by each of the functions c_1, c_2, and c_3; hence these are cost functions for cubical covers in Q^n.

Throughout the remainder of the present section, let c denote an arbitrarily given cost function for cubical covers in Q^n.

A cubical cover γ of a switching function

$$f : Q^n \to Q^*,$$

possibly with don't care points, is said to be *minimal* with respect to the cost function c iff

$$c(\gamma) \leq c(\delta)$$

holds for every cubical cover δ of f. Hence a minimal cubical cover of f gives a cheapest network for f.

To conclude the present section, let us establish the following crucial theorem.

THEOREM 2.3.   *If a cubical cover γ of a switching function $f : Q^n \to Q^*$, possibly with don't care points, is minimal with respect to a cost function c, then every cube in γ must be maximal in the cubical complex $K^*(f)$.*

Proof.   Assume that γ is a cubical cover of f containing a cube C which is not maximal in $K^*(f)$. It suffices to prove that γ is not minimal with respect to the cost function c.

Since the cube C is not maximal in $K^*(f)$, there exists a cube D in $K^*(f)$ satisfying $C \subset D$ and $C \neq D$. Replacing the cube C in γ by the cube D, we obtain a cubical cover δ of f. Because of $C \subset D$ and $C \neq D$, we have

$$\mathrm{cod}(D) < \mathrm{cod}(C),$$

which implies both $b_1(\delta) \leq b_1(\gamma)$ and $c_1(\delta) < c_1(\gamma)$. According to the definition of a cost function c, these two inequalities imply

$$c(\delta) < c(\gamma).$$

Hence γ is not minimal with respect to the cost function c. $\|$

This theorem tells us that, in looking for a minimal cover of a switching function f with respect to a cost function c, we may consider only the maximal cubes in $K^*(f)$. Therefore, the first step to solving the minimization problem is the systematic construction of all maximal cubes in $K^*(f)$. Three methods for constructing these cubes are explained in the sections that follow.

3. Map Method

If $n \leq 4$, the maximal cubes of a switching function

$$f : Q^n \to Q^*,$$

possibly with don't care points, can be very conveniently obtained on its Karnaugh map defined in (I, §2 and §8) by means of visual recognition of certain patterns. Generalizations to $n = 5$ and $n = 6$ will be given in the exercises at the end of the chapter. Since the similarities for the simpler cases where $n \leq 3$ will become obvious, we shall study only the case where $n = 4$.

For this purpose, let us consider the Karnaugh map of Q^4 given in Table II-3-1. The decimal integers in the sixteen cells for x correspond to the points of Q^4 with coordinates $x_1 x_2 x_3 x_4$.

TABLE II-3-1

$x_1 x_2$ \ x \ $x_3 x_4$	00	01	11	10
00	0	1	3	2
01	4	5	7	6
11	12	13	15	14
10	8	9	11	10

Two distinct cells in the Karnaugh map of Q^4 are said to be *adjacent* iff they have a side in common. Since the left boundary of the column of cells headed by 00 is identified with the right boundary of the column of cells headed by 10, the cells 0, 4, 12, 8 are adjacent to the cells 2, 6, 14, 10, respectively. Similarly, since the upper boundary of the row of cells headed by 00 is identified with the lower boundary of the row of cells headed by 10, the cells 0, 1, 3, 2 are adjacent to the cells 8, 9, 11, 10, respectively. With this understanding, it is clear that any two vertices of Q^4 are consecutive iff they are located in adjacent cells of the Karnaugh map of Q^4. Hence the

$$\nu_4(1) = \binom{4}{1} 2^{4-1} = 4.2^3 = 32$$

TABLE II-3-2

edges of Q^4 are located at the 32 pairs of adjacent cells in the Karnaugh map.

According to §1, there are

$$\nu_4(2) = \binom{4}{2} 2^{4-2} = 24$$

squares in Q^4. In its Karnaugh map, these are the four rows—the four columns—together with sixteen actual squares. In fact, there are four squares that can be formed from each of the four pairs of adjacent rows. Because of the identifications of boundary lines, these sixteen squares may look like those in Table II-3-2.

According to §1, there are

$$\nu_4(3) = \binom{4}{3} 2^{4-3} = 8$$

3-cubes in Q^4. In its Karnaugh map, these are the four pairs of adjacent rows and the four pairs of adjacent columns. Because of the identifications of boundary lines, the pairs of adjacent rows may look like those in Table II-3-3. Similar situations may exist for the adjacent columns.

Having learned the various patterns of subcubes of Q^4 in its Karnaugh map, one can easily find the maximal cubes of a switching function

$$f : Q^4 \rightarrow Q^*,$$

possibly with don't care points, by means of visual recognition from the Karnaugh map of f. For example, let us consider the switching function $f : Q^4 \rightarrow Q^*$ defined by Table I-8-1. Its Karnaugh map is given in Table

TABLE II-3-3

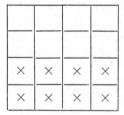 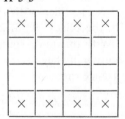

TABLE II-3-4

x_1x_2 \ x \ x_3x_4	00	01	11	10
00	1		1	
01	*	*	*	*
11			1	
10	*	*	*	*

I-8-2. Remembering the patterns of the subcubes of Q^4, we find the maximal cubes of f by means of visual recognition and mark these maximal cubes with broken-lined rectangles as shown in Table II-3-4. Thus the set $M(f)$ of all maximal cubes of f is

$$M(f) = \{*000, 0*00, **11, 01**, 10**\},$$

which agrees with the last example in §1.

Two additional examples will further illustrate this method. First, consider the switching function $f : Q^4 \rightarrow Q^*$ defined by

$$f(x) = \begin{cases} 1, & (\text{if } x = 3, 4, 7, 11, 13), \\ 0, & (\text{if } x = 0, 1, 6, 9, 10, 12, 14), \\ *, & (\text{if } x = 2, 5, 8, 15). \end{cases}$$

Then its Karnaugh map with its maximal cubes is as shown in Table II-3-5.

TABLE II-3-5

x_1x_2 \ x \ x_3x_4	00	01	11	10
00			1	*
01	1	*	1	
11		1	*	
10	*		1	

Thus the set $M(f)$ of all maximal cubes of this function f is as follows:

$$M(f) = \{1000, 001*, 010*, **11, *1*1\}.$$

Next, consider the switching function $f: Q^4 \to Q^*$ defined by

$$f(x) = \begin{cases} 1, & \text{(if } x = 0, 1, 2, 4, 6, 7, 8, 9, 15), \\ 0, & \text{(if } x = 5, 10, 12, 13, 14) \\ *, & \text{(if } x = 3, 11). \end{cases}$$

Then its Karnaugh map with its maximal cubes is as shown in Table II-3-6.

TABLE II-3-6

x_1x_2 \ x_3x_4 (x)	00	01	11	10
00	1	1	*	1
01	1		1	1
11			1	
10	1	1	*	

Thus the set $M(f)$ of all maximal cubes of this function f is as follows:

$$M(f) = \{00**, 0**0, 0*1*, *00*, *0*1, **11\}.$$

4. Tabular Method

The map method described in the preceding section is very satisfactory for switching functions of not more than four variables. To handle switching functions of more than four variables, the tabular method, devised by Quine and McCluskey, gives a relatively straightforward procedure for constructing the cubical complex of any switching function

$$f: Q^n \to Q^*,$$

possibly with don't care points, as well as its maximal cubes, without relying on any geometric intuition. Not only can it be used for hand calculation, but it can be programmed on a digital computer as well.

For convenience, let us first define the *addition* mod 2, denoted by $\oplus$, in the set Q^* by means of Table II-4-1. Therefore, for any two elements x and y of Q^*, we have

$$x \oplus y = \begin{cases} 0, & \text{(if } x = y), \\ 1, & \text{(if } x \neq y). \end{cases}$$

Next, let us define the addition mod 2 of any two cubes in Q^n. For this purpose, let C and D denote any two cubes in Q^n with coordinate functions

TABLE II-4-1

$\oplus$	1	0	*
1	0	1	1
0	1	0	1
*	1	1	0

$\phi : N \to Q^*$ and $\psi : N \to Q^*$, respectively. Then the mod 2 *sum*

$$C \oplus D$$

of the cubes C and D is the point $x = x_1 \cdots x_n$ of Q^n with

$$x_i = \phi(i) \oplus \psi(i)$$

for every $i = 1, 2, \cdots, n$. In other words, $C \oplus D$ is obtained by *coordinate-wise addition* mod 2 of the coordinates of C and D.

Finally, by the *rank* $\rho(C)$ of a cube C in Q^n, we mean the number of coordinates of C which are 1. If $\dim(C) = 0$, C reduces to a point of Q^n, and rank $\rho(C)$ of C agrees with the rank of the point C defined in (I, §11). Hence, two cubes C and D of Q^n, with coordinate functions ϕ and ψ, respectively, differ in one and only one coordinate iff

$$\rho(C \oplus D) = \sum_{i=1}^{n} \phi(i) \oplus \psi(i) = 1.$$

The tabular method can be most conveniently described by means of an illustrative example. For this purpose, consider the switching function

$$f : Q^5 \to Q^*$$

defined for every point $x \varepsilon Q^5$ by

$$f(x) = \begin{cases} 1, & \text{(if } x = 0, 2, 4, 6, 12, 16, 18, 19, 30), \\ *, & \text{(if } x = 7, 8, 10, 11, 13, 14, 29), \\ 0, & \text{(otherwise).} \end{cases}$$

Then we have

$$F^* = f^{-1}\{1, *\} = \{0, 2, 4, 6, 7, 8, 10, 11, 12, 13, 14, 16, 18, 19, 29, 30\}.$$

By definition, the cubical complex $K^*(f)$ of f is the cubical complex $K(F^*)$ of this subset F^* of Q^5. To construct the cubical complex $K^*(f)$, we shall determine

$$K_0^*(f), K_1^*(f), K_2^*(f), K_3^*(f), K_4^*(f), K_5^*(f)$$

in the order exhibited. Finally, we shall also obtain the collection $M(f)$ of all maximal cubes of f.

By definition, we have

$$K(_0^* f) = F^*.$$

To construct $K_1^*(f)$, we must find all of the pairs of consecutive points in $K_0^*(f)$. For this purpose, we arrange the sixteen points of $K_0^*(f)$ in groups of increasing rank as shown in Table II-4-2. Here, the x column gives the decimal symbol of the point, the middle column gives the coordinates of the same point, and the CHECK column will be explained later.

TABLE II-4-2

x	x_1	x_2	x_3	x_4	x_5	CHECK
0	0	0	0	0	0	√
2	0	0	0	1	0	√
4	0	0	1	0	0	√
8	0	1	0	0	0	√
16	1	0	0	0	0	√
6	0	0	1	1	0	√
10	0	1	0	1	0	√
12	0	1	1	0	0	√
18	1	0	0	1	0	√
7	0	0	1	1	1	√
11	0	1	0	1	1	√
13	0	1	1	0	1	√
14	0	1	1	1	0	√
19	1	0	0	1	1	√
29	1	1	1	0	1	√
30	1	1	1	1	0	√

Since two points of Q^5 are consecutive iff they differ in one and only one coordinate, the difference between the ranks of any two consecutive points of Q^5 must be equal to 1. Consequently, any two consecutive points in $K_0^*(f)$ must belong to two adjacent groups. Hence, to construct $K_1^*(f)$, it suffices to consider only pairs of points in $K_0^*(f)$ belonging to adjacent groups. For this purpose, let

$$y = y_1 y_2 y_3 y_4 y_5 \qquad z = z_1 z_2 z_3 z_4 z_5$$

denote any two points in $K_0^*(f)$ belonging to adjacent groups. Without loss of generality, we may assume

$$\rho(z) = \rho(y) + 1.$$

Applying addition mod 2 to the points y and z, we obtain a point

$$y \oplus z = w = w_1 w_2 w_3 w_4 w_5$$

of Q^5. Since y and z are of different ranks, we must have

$$\rho(w) \geq 1.$$

If $\rho(w) > 1$, y and z differ in more than one coordinate and hence are not consecutive. On the other hand, if $\rho(w) = 1$, y and z differ in one coordinate and hence are consecutive. In the latter case, if w_i is the lone coordinate of w which is equal to 1, we obtain the coordinates of the edge $\{y, z\}$ of $K_1^*(f)$ from those of the point y by changing y_i into $*$. Then we enter this edge $\{y, z\}$ of $K_1^*(f)$ into Table II-4-3 and check the points y and z in the CHECK column of Table II-4-2. By doing so for all pairs of points in adjacent groups of Table II-4-2, we obtain all edges in $K_1^*(f)$ as shown in Table II-4-3. The C column gives the decimal symbols of the two points on the edge in $K_1^*(f)$, the middle column gives the coordinates of the same edge, and the CHECK column will be explained later. The rows are grouped according to rank in increasing order.

To construct the squares of $K_2^*(f)$, we must find the pairs of consecutive edges in $K_1^*(f)$. Since two edges of Q^5 are consecutive iff they differ in one and only one coordinate and since there is one and only one $*$ in the coordinates of every edge, it follows that the lone disagreeing coordinate can never be a $*$ and hence the difference between the ranks of any two consecutive edges of Q^5 must be equal to 1. Consequently, any two consecutive edges in $K_1^*(f)$ must belong to two adjacent groups in Table II-4-3. Hence, to construct $K_2^*(f)$, it suffices to consider only pairs of edges in $K_1^*(f)$ belonging to adjacent groups.

For this purpose, let

$$C = \phi(1)\phi(2)\phi(3)\phi(4)\phi(5) \qquad D = \psi(1)\psi(2)\psi(3)\psi(4)\psi(5)$$

TABLE II-4-3

C	x_1	x_2	x_3	x_4	x_5	CHECK
{ 0, 2}	0	0	0	*	0	√
{ 0, 4}	0	0	*	0	0	√
{ 0, 8}	0	*	0	0	0	√
{ 0, 16}	*	0	0	0	0	√
{ 2, 6}	0	0	*	1	0	√
{ 2, 10}	0	*	0	1	0	√
{ 2, 18}	*	0	0	1	0	√
{ 4, 6}	0	0	1	*	0	√
{ 4, 12}	0	*	1	0	0	√
{ 8, 10}	0	1	0	*	0	√
{ 8, 12}	0	1	*	0	0	√
{16, 18}	1	0	0	*	0	√
{ 6, 7}	0	0	1	1	*	
{ 6, 14}	0	*	1	1	0	√
{10, 11}	0	1	0	1	*	
{10, 14}	0	1	*	1	0	√
{12, 13}	0	1	1	0	*	
{12, 14}	0	1	1	*	0	√
{18, 19}	1	0	0	1	*	
{13, 29}	*	1	1	0	1	
{14, 30}	*	1	1	1	0	

denote any two edges in $K_1^*(f)$ belonging to adjacent groups. Without loss of generality, we may assume

$$\rho(D) = \rho(C) + 1.$$

Applying addition mod 2 to the edges C and D, we obtain a point

$$C \oplus D = w = w_1 w_2 w_3 w_4 w_5$$

of Q^5. Since C and D are of different ranks, we must have

$$\rho(w) \geq 1.$$

If $\rho(w) > 1$, C and D differ in more than one coordinate and hence are not consecutive. On the other hand, if $\rho(w) = 1$, C and D differ in one coordinate and hence are consecutive. In the latter case, if w_i is the lone

TABLE II-4-4

C	x_1	x_2	x_3	x_4	x_5	CHECK
{0, 2, 4, 6}	0	0	*	*	0	✓
{0, 2, 8, 10}	0	*	0	*	0	✓
{0, 2, 16, 18}	*	0	0	*	0	
{0, 4, 8, 12}	0	*	*	0	0	✓
{2, 6, 10, 14}	0	*	*	1	0	✓
{4, 6, 12, 14}	0	*	1	*	0	✓
{8, 10, 12, 14}	0	1	*	*	0	✓

coordinate of w which is equal to 1, we can derive the coordinates of the square $C \cup D$ of $K_2^*(f)$ from those of the edge C by changing $\phi(i)$ into *. Then we enter this square $C \cup D$ into Table II-4-4 and check the edges C and D in the CHECK column of Table II-4-3. By doing so for all pairs of edges in adjacent groups of Table II-4-3, we obtain all squares in $K_2^*(f)$ as listed in Table II-4-4. The C column gives the decimal symbols of the four points in the square in $K_2^*(f)$, the middle column gives the coordinates of the same square, and the CHECK column will be explained later. The rows are grouped according to rank in increasing order.

To construct the 3-cubes of $K_3^*(f)$, we must find the pairs of consecutive squares in $K_2^*(f)$. Since two squares of Q^5 are consecutive iff they differ in one and only one coordinate and since there are two and only two *'s in the coordinates of every square, it follows that the lone disagreeing coordinate can never be a * and hence the difference between the ranks of any two consecutive squares of Q^5 must be equal to 1. Consequently, any two consecutive squares in $K_2^*(f)$ must belong to two adjacent groups in Table II-4-4. Hence, to construct $K_3^*(f)$, it suffices to consider only pairs of squares in $K_2^*(f)$ belonging to adjacent groups.

For this purpose, let

$$C = \phi(1)\phi(2)\phi(3)\phi(4)\phi(5) \qquad D = \psi(1)\psi(2)\psi(3)\psi(4)\psi(5)$$

denote any two squares in $K_2^*(f)$ belonging to adjacent groups. Without loss of generality, we may assume

$$\rho(D) = \rho(C) + 1.$$

Applying addition mod 2 to the squares C and D, we obtain a point

$$C \oplus D = w = w_1 w_2 w_3 w_4 w_5$$

of Q^5. Since C and D are of different ranks, we must have
$$\rho(w) \geq 1.$$
If $\rho(w) > 1$, C and D differ in more than one coordinate and hence are
not consecutive. On the other hand, if $\rho(w) = 1$, C and D differ in one
coordinate and hence are consecutive. In the latter case, if w_i is the lone
coordinate of w which is equal to 1, we can derive the coordinates of the
3-cube $C \cup D$ of $K_3^*(f)$ from those of the square C by changing $\phi(i)$ into
$*$. Then we enter this 3-cube $C \cup D$ into Table II-4-5 and check the

TABLE II-4-5

C	x_1	x_2	x_3	x_4	x_5	CHECK
$\{0, 2, 4, 6, 8, 10, 12, 14\}$	0	*	*	*	0	

squares C and D in the CHECK column of Table II-4-4. By doing so for
all pairs of squares in adjacent groups of Table II-4-4, we obtain all 3-cubes
in $K_3^*(f)$ as listed in Table II-4-5. The C column gives the decimal
symbols of the eight points in the 3-cube in $K_3^*(f)$, the middle column
gives the coordinates of the same 3-cube, and the CHECK column should
be handled exactly as above. The rows sould be grouped according to
rank in increasing order as above.

Since $K_3^*(f)$ consists of only one 3-cube, it is obvious that both $K_4^*(f)$
and $K_5^*(f)$ are empty. This completes the construction of the cubical
complex $K^*(f)$ of the given switching function f.

The set $M(f)$ of all maximal cubes in $K^*(f)$ remains to be found and
can be easily obtained from the CHECK columns in Tables II-4-2 through
II-4-5. According to our rule, a row in any of these tables is "checked"
iff the cube of $K^*(f)$ in this row is contained in a higher dimensional cube
of $K^*(f)$. Hence the maximal cubes of the given switching function f are
precisely the unchecked rows in these tables. Thus we obtain

$$M(f) = \{0011*, 0101*, 0110*, 1001*, *1101, *1110, *00*0, 0***0\}.$$

The tabular method illustrated by the preceding example can clearly be
applied to any switching function of any number of variables.

5. Consensus Method

The tabular method described in the preceding section for constructing
the set $M(f)$ of a switching function
$$f : Q^n \to Q^*,$$

possibly with don't care points, requires one to start with the collection

$$K_0^*(f) = F^*.$$

To simplify the construction, a possible knowledge of the existence of higher dimensional cubes in $K^*(f)$ is not utilized.

Frequently, however, the switching function f is given by a Boolean polynomial together with the don't care points, if any, thus supplying us with a cubical cover γ of the set

$$F^* = f^{-1}\{1, *\}.$$

If we try to apply the tabular method of the preceding section, not only can we not utilize the higher dimensional cubes in the cubical cover γ, but also we must spend time in finding the points of the set F^* from these cubes. For these reasons, we will present the consensus method devised by Quine and Roth. In this method, the number of steps required to effect the computation of the set $M(f)$ of all maximal cubes in $K^*(f)$ will usually be reduced; and when the function f is initially given by the sets F and F', this new method reduces essentially to the method in the preceding section.

Before presenting the consensus method, let us first generalize the notion of consecutive cubes. For this purpose, let us define the *cap products* of elements in the set Q^* by means of Table II-5-1.

TABLE II-5-1

$\cap$	1	0	$*$
1	1	$\square$	1
0	$\square$	0	0
$*$	1	$\jmath$	$*$

Now let C and D denote any two cubes in Q^n with coordinate functions $\phi : N \to Q^*$ and $\psi : N \to Q^*$, respectively. The two cubes C and D are said to be *consensual* iff there exists one and only one integer $k \in N$ satisfying

$$\phi(k) \cap \psi(k) = \square.$$

Hence, consensual cubes are disjoint, and consecutive cubes are consensual. The converses of these statements are clearly false.

Assume that C and D are consensual and let k denote the unique integer in N satisfying

$$\phi(k) \cap \psi(k) = \square.$$

Define a function $\chi : N \to Q^*$ by setting

$$\chi(i) = \begin{cases} \phi(i) \cap \psi(i), & \text{(if } i \neq k), \\ *, & \text{(if } i = k), \end{cases}$$

for every integer i in N. Then the cube

$$E = C \,\natural\, D$$

in Q^n with $\chi : N \to Q^*$ as coordinate function is called the *consensus* of the cubes C and D. If C and D are consecutive, then the consensus $C \,\natural\, D$ obviously reduces to the union $C \cup D$.

If we replace the k-th coordinate $\chi(k) = *$ of the cube E by $\phi(k)$ and $\psi(k)$, respectively, we obtain two consecutive faces E_C and E_D of E satisfying

$$E_C \subset C, \qquad E_D \subset D,$$
$$E = E_C \cup E_D \subset C \cup D.$$

Since C and D are disjoint, we also have

$$E \,\natural\, C, \qquad E \,\natural\, D.$$

In fact, E is the largest cube of Q^n satisfying the last three conditions. Precisely, we have the following theorem.

THEOREM 5.1.   *Let C and D denote two consensual cubes in Q^n. If X is a cube in Q^n satisfying*

$$X \,\natural\, C, \qquad X \,\natural\, D, \qquad X \subset C \cup D,$$

then we must have

$$X \subset E = C \,\natural\, D.$$

Proof.   Let $\phi : N \to Q^*$ and $\psi : N \to Q^*$ denote the coordinate functions of the cubes C and D, respectively. Then the coordinate function of their consensus E is the function $\chi : N \to Q^*$ defined above.

Let $\xi : N \to Q^*$ denote the coordinate function of the cube X. To establish the inclusion $X \subset E$, we must prove that

$$\xi(i) = \chi(i)$$

holds for every $i \in N$ satisfying $\chi(i) \neq *$. For this purpose, let i denote an arbitrary integer in N satisfying $\chi(i) \neq *$. According to the definition of χ, this implies $i \neq k$ and hence

$$\chi(i) = \phi(i) \cap \psi(i).$$

In view of Table II-5-1, we must have $\chi(i) = \phi(i)$ or $\chi(i) = \psi(i)$. Without loss of generality, we may assume

$$\phi(i) = \chi(i) \neq *.$$

Since $X \subset C \cup D$ and $X \not\subset D$, there exists a point $x = x_1 \cdots x_n$ of X which belongs to C. Hence $x_i = \phi(i)$. This implies that $\xi(i)$ is either $\phi(i)$ or $*$. That $\xi(i) \neq *$ remains to be proved. To prove this by contradiction, let us assume $\xi(i) = *$. Then the cube X also contains the point $y = y_1 \cdots y_n$ defined for every $j \in N$ by

$$y_j = \begin{cases} x_j, & (\text{if } j \neq i), \\ 1 - x_i, & (\text{if } j = i). \end{cases}$$

Since $y_i = 1 - x_i = 1 - \phi(i)$, it follows that the point y is not in C. On the other hand, since

$$y_k = x_k = \phi(k) = 1 - \psi(k),$$

it follows that the point y is also not in D. This contradicts our assumption

$$X \subset C \cup D$$

and completes the proof of (5.1). ∥

Next, let us consider an arbitrarily given switching function

$$f : Q^n \to Q^*,$$

possibly with don't care points. We recall that a cubical cover of the set

$$F^* = f^{-1}\{1, *\}$$

is a collection γ of cubes in Q^n satisfying

$$\bigcup_{C \in \gamma} C = F^*.$$

Our problem in the present section is to construct the set $M(f)$ of all maximal cubes in the cubical complex

$$K^*(f) = K(F^*)$$

from an arbitrarily given cubical cover γ. Before describing an algorithm to solve this problem, let us establish the following crucial theorem due to Quine.

THEOREM 5.2. *A cubical cover γ of the set F^* in Q^n is the set $M(f)$ of all maximal cubes in $K^*(f)$ iff the following conditions are satisfied:*

(M1) *For any two different cubes C and D in γ, $C \subset D$ is always false.*

(M2) *For any two consensual cubes C and D in γ, there exists a cube H in γ which contains the consensus $C \notdiv D$.*

Proof. As usual, the proof of a necessary and sufficient condition breaks into two parts, namely, necessity and sufficiency.

Necessity.   Assume $\gamma = M(f)$. To establish (M1), let C and D denote any two different cubes in γ. Then C is a maximal cube in $K^*(f)$; and, therefore, $C \subset D$ is false. To establish (M2), let C and D denote any two consensual cubes in γ. Then their consensus $E = C \notcent D$ is a cube in $K^*(f)$. Let H denote a maximal cube in $K^*(f)$ which contains E. Since $\gamma = M(f)$, H is in γ. This completes the necessity proof.

Sufficiency.   Assume $\gamma \neq M(f)$. We must prove that (M1) and (M2) cannot both be satisfied. For this purpose, we branch out into two cases.

First case: $M(f) \not\subset \gamma$.   There exists a maximal cube H of $K^*(f)$ which is not in γ. Since H is maximal and is not in γ, it follows that H is not contained in any of the cubes in γ. Let X be a subcube of H of lowest possible dimension such that X is not contained in any of the cubes in γ. Since γ covers the set F^* and since X is contained in F^*, we must have

$$\dim(X) > 0.$$

Let $\xi : N \rightarrow Q^*$ denote the coordinate function of the cube X. Since $\dim(X) > 0$, there exists an integer $k \in N$ with $\xi(k) = *$. In the co-ordinates of X, if we replace $\xi(k) = *$ by the integers 1 and 0, respectively, we obtain two consecutive subcubes Y and Z of X with

$$Y \cup Z = X.$$

By the choice of X, there exist two cubes C and D in γ satisfying $Y \subset C$ and $Z \subset D$. This implies

$$X \subset C \cup D.$$

Since $X \not\subset C$ and $X \not\subset D$, it follows from (5.1) that

$$X \subset C \notcent D.$$

The fact that X is not contained in any of the cubes in γ proves that condition (M2) is not satisfied.

Second case: $M(f) \subset \gamma$.   Since $\gamma \neq M(f)$, there exists a cube C in γ which is not a maximal cube in $K^*(f)$. Let D denote a maximal cube in $K^*(f)$ which contains C. Since $M(f) \subset \gamma$, the cube D is in γ. Hence C and D are two different cubes in γ satisfying $C \subset D$, which proves that condition (M1) is not satisfied. ‖

Now let us define the *coordinatewise cap product* of cubes in Q^n. For this purpose, let us consider any two cubes C and D in Q^n with co-ordinates $c_1 c_2 \cdots c_n$ and $d_1 d_2 \cdots d_n$, respectively. By the *coordinatewise cap product* of the cubes C and D, we mean the n-tuple

$$(c_1 \cap d_1, c_2 \cap d_2, \cdots, c_n \cap d_n)$$

of symbols 1, 0, *, or □ given by Table II-5-1. This n-tuple contains no □ iff the intersection $C \cap D$ is not empty; in this case, this n-tuple gives the coordinates of the intersection $C \cap D$. Hence there is no danger of ambiguity to denote the coordinatewise cap product of C and D by $C \cap D$, that is,

$$C \cap D = (c_1 \cap d_1, c_2 \cap d_2, \cdots, c_n \cap d_n).$$

Thus $C \cap D$ will denote the intersection of C and D in case the intersection is not empty, otherwise $C \cap D$ stands for the coordinatewise cap product of C and D.

The following theorem is now obvious.

THEOREM 5.3. *For any two cubes C and D in Q^n, the following two statements are true:*

(i) $C \subset D$ iff $C \cap D = C$.

(ii) *C and D are consensual iff $C \cap D$ contains one and only one* □.

Now we are in a position to describe the *consensus algorithm* of finding $M(f)$ from an arbitrarily given cubical cover γ of the set F^*. This algorithm can be most conveniently described by means of an illustrative example. For this purpose, let us consider the switching function

$$f : Q^5 \to Q^*$$

represented by the Boolean polynomial

$$x_1'x_5' \vee x_2'x_3'x_5' \vee x_1x_2'x_3'x_4 \vee x_1x_2x_3x_4x_5'$$

with the points of the following cubes as don't care points:

$$00111, \quad 010*0, \quad 0101*, \quad 01*10, \quad *1101.$$

Each term of the Boolean polynomial which defines f represents a cube in $K^*(f)$. Thus we obtain four cubes:

$$0***0, \quad *00*0, \quad 1001*, \quad 11110.$$

These four cubes form a cubical cover β of f in $K^*(f)$. Hence, together with the five cubes of don't care points, we obtain a cubical cover γ of the set F^* in $K^*(f)$.

To construct the set $M(f)$ of all maximal cubes in $K^*(f)$, we list these nine cubes as the first nine rows in Table II-5-2. Starting from the left, the first column gives the numbers of the rows, the second column gives the cubes in coordinates, and the last two columns are explained later. Starting from the top, we compare every row with each of the preceding

TABLE II-5-2

Row	x_1	x_2	x_3	x_4	x_5	CHECK	REFERENCE
1	0	*	*	*	0		
2	*	0	0	*	0		
3	1	0	0	1	*		
4	1	1	1	1	0	√	10
5	0	0	1	1	1	√	11
6	0	1	0	*	0	√	1
7	0	1	0	1	*		
8	0	1	*	1	0	√	1
9	*	1	1	0	1		
10	*	1	1	1	0		(1, 4)
11	0	0	1	1	*		(1, 5)
12	0	1	1	0	*		(1, 9)

rows. Letting C and D denote the cubes of two rows in question, we form the coordinatewise cap product $C \cap D$ of C and D. If

$$C \cap D = C,$$

then we have $C \subset D$ according to (5.3). In this case, we check the row where C is in the CHECK column and write the number of the row where D is behind the check sign in the REFERENCE column. We follow the same procedure for

$$C \cap D = D.$$

A checked row is to be considered as removed from the table and hence will not be compared with any other row hereafter. If $C \cap D$ contains one and only one $\square$, then C and D are consensual according to (5.3). In this case, we obtain a cube

$$E = C \notcent D.$$

If this cube E is contained in some existing cube of the table, we do nothing; otherwise, we add this cube E to the bottom of the table as a new row and write the numbers of the rows where the cubes C and D are with parentheses in the REFERENCE column. It is possible that a new row be checked afterwards. In all other cases, we do nothing. This last operation completes the comparison of the cubes C and D, and we proceed to compare the next pair of cubes in the table. The algorithm ends when all cubes in the rows of the table, new as well as original, have been compared.

From the operations of this algorithm, it is clear that the cubes in the unchecked rows of the final Table II-5-2 constitute a cubical cover of F^* satisfying the two conditions (M1) and (M2) of (5.2). According to (5.2), this cubical cover of F^* is the set $M(f)$ of all maximal cubes in $K^*(f)$. Hence we obtain

$$M(f) = \{0***0, *00*0, 1001*, 0101*, *1101, *1110, 0011*, 0110*\}.$$

Note that $M(f)$ is precisely the same as in the example of the preceding section. In fact, we have deliberately used the same switching function and the same don't care points.

6. Tables of Maximal Cubes

Our problem in the present section is to find a cubical cover γ of any given switching function

$$f : Q^n \to Q^*,$$

possibly with don't care points, which is minimal with respect to a given cost function c in the sense of §2. According to (2.3), such a minimal cover γ of f must consist of maximal cubes of the cubical complex $K^*(f)$ of f. Hence we have devoted three preceding sections to various methods of finding the maximal cubes of $K^*(f)$. After we have found the set $M(f)$ of all maximal cubes of $K^*(f)$, we will form a rectangular table, with the rows corresponding to cubes in $M(f)$ and the columns corresponding to the points in the restricted on-set F of f, which will be referred to as the *table of maximal cubes* for the given switching function f. In the literature, it is frequently called the *prime implicant table* of f. For example, let $n = 5$ and consider the switching function $f : Q^5 \to Q^*$ defined by

$$f(x) = \begin{cases} 1, & \text{(if } x = 0, 2, 4, 6, 12, 16, 18, 19, 30), \\ *, & \text{(if } x = 7, 8, 10, 11, 13, 14, 29), \\ 0, & \text{(otherwise).} \end{cases}$$

In §4, we found the set $M(f)$ of all maximal cubes of $K^*(f)$, namely,

$$M(f) = \{0011*, 0101*, 0110*, 1001*, *1101, *1110, *00*0, 0***0\}.$$

On the other hand, the restricted on-set F of f is

$$F = f^{-1}(1) = \{0, 2, 4, 6, 12, 16, 18, 19, 30\}.$$

The table of maximal cubes is given in Table II-6-1. The left column gives the cubes of $M(f)$ in their coordinates, and the top row gives the

TABLE II-6-1

F M(f)	0	2	4	6	12	16	18	19	30	CHECK
0011∗	0	0	0	1	0	0	0	0	0	
0101∗	0	0	0	0	0	0	0	0	0	
0110∗	0	0	0	0	1	0	0	0	0	
1001∗	0	0	0	0	0	0	1	1	0	√
∗1101	0	0	0	0	0	0	0	0	0	
∗1110	0	0	0	0	0	0	0	0	1	√
∗00∗0	1	1	0	0	0	1	1	0	0	√
0∗∗∗0	1	1	1	1	1	0	0	0	0	√
CHECK	√	√	√	√	√	√	√	√	√	

decimal symbols of the points in F. The CHECK column and the CHECK row are explained later.

The interior rectangle of the table is a matrix of integers 1 and 0, which will be called the *incidence matrix* of maximal cubes for f. It is defined as follows. Let C denote an arbitrary cube in $M(f)$ and let P denote an arbitrary point in F. It suffices to define the integer α_{CP} at the intersection of the row headed by C and the column headed by P. This integer α_{CP} is defined by

$$\alpha_{CP} = \begin{cases} 1, & (\text{if } P \in C), \\ 0, & (\text{if } P \notin C). \end{cases}$$

For computer programming, the following method of defining α_{CP} might be more convenient. Form the coordinatewise cap product $C \cap P$ of the cube C and the point P, as a 0-cube and in binary coordinates. Then α_{CP} can be defined by

$$\alpha_{CP} = \begin{cases} 1, & (\text{if } C \cap P = P), \\ 0, & (\text{otherwise}). \end{cases}$$

A point $P \in F$ is said to be *distinguished* iff it is contained in only one maximal cube. According to the definition of the incidence matrix, a point $P \in F$ is distinguished iff its column contains only one 1 or, equivalently,

$$\sum_{C \in M(f)} \alpha_{CP} = 1.$$

In Table II-6-1, the points 4, 16, 19, and 30 are distinguished. To mark a distinguished point of F, we surround the lone 1 in its column by a broken-lined square.

A maximal cube C in $K^*(f)$ is said to be *essential* iff it contains a distinguished point, say P, of F. Since C is the only maximal cube that contains P, C must belong to every minimal cubical cover of f. A maximal cube C in $K^*(f)$ is said to be *inessential* iff it is not essential. In the table of maximal cubes, a cube $C \in M(f)$ is essential iff its row contains a broken-lined square. In Table II-6-1, four maximal cubes 1001∗, ∗1110, ∗00∗0, and 0∗∗∗0 are essential. We check these rows in the CHECK column.

The set $E(f)$ of all essential maximal cubes in $K^*(f)$ is called the *core* of $M(f)$. For our example, the core of $M(f)$ is

$$E(f) = \{1001∗, ∗1110, ∗00∗0, 0∗∗∗0\}.$$

Since every essential maximal cube of $K^*(f)$ belongs to every minimal cubical cover of f, we have the following theorem.

THEOREM 6.1.   *Every minimal cubical cover of a switching function*

$$f : Q^n \to Q^*$$

with respect to a cost function c contains the core $E(f)$ of the set $M(f)$ of all maximal cubes.

By a *basic point* of F, we mean a point $P \in F$ that is contained in some essential maximal cube of $K^*(f)$. The set B of all basic points of F will be called the *base* of F. Hence, B is the intersection of F with the union of all essential maximal cubes in $K^*(f)$. In symbols, we have

$$B = F \cap [\textstyle\bigcup_{C \in E(f)} C].$$

In the table of maximal cubes, the basic points of F can be determined as follows: A point $P \in F$ is basic iff

$$\textstyle\sum_{C \in E(f)} \alpha_{CP} \geq 1.$$

After finding the basic points of F, we check the columns of the basic points in the CHECK row. Having applied this procedure to Table II-6-1, we find that all columns are checked. Hence the core $E(f)$ of $M(f)$ covers the restricted on-set F of f, implying that the core $E(f)$ of $M(f)$ is the only minimal cubical cover of the given function f. In fact, this is an example of the following corollary which is a direct consequence of (6.1).

COROLLARY 6.2.   *If $B = F$, then the core $E(f)$ of $M(f)$ is the unique minimal cubical cover of f with respect to any cost function c.*

Therefore, for a switching function f such that every point of its restricted on-set F is basic, the minimization problem formulated at the beginning of the present section is completely solved by the core $E(f)$ of $M(f)$.

Usually, however, we have

$$B \neq F.$$

For example, let us consider the switching function $f : Q^5 \to Q^*$ defined by

$$f(x) = \begin{cases} 1, & (\text{if } x = 1, 3, 10, 11, 12, 15, 18, 19, 21, 23, 26), \\ *, & (\text{if } x = 4, 5, 6, 7, 13, 14, 20, 22, 25, 27), \\ 0, & (\text{if } x = 0, 2, 8, 9, 16, 17, 24, 28, 29, 30, 31). \end{cases}$$

Applying the tabular method of §4 to this switching function f, we obtain its set $M(f)$ of all maximal cubes of $K^*(f)$, namely, the following eleven maximal cubes:

$$0*1**, \quad *01**, \quad 00**1, \quad 0**11, \quad *0*11, \quad **011,$$
$$01*1*, \quad *101*, \quad 10*1*, \quad 1*01*, \quad 110*1.$$

On the other hand, the restricted on-set F of f is

$$F = f^{-1}(1) = \{1, 3, 10, 11, 12, 15, 18, 19, 21, 23, 26\}.$$

Hence we obtain its table of maximal cubes as in Table II-6-2. Thus we obtain the core $E(f)$ of $M(f)$ and the base B of F exhibited as follows:

$$E(f) = \{0*1**, *01**, 00**1\},$$
$$B = \{1, 3, 12, 15, 21, 23\}.$$

Since $B \neq F$, we must choose certain inessential maximal cubes to cover the nonbasic points of F so that, together with $E(f)$, they will form a

TABLE II-6-2

$M(f)$ \ F	1	3	10	11	12	15	18	19	21	23	26	CHECK
0*1**	0	0	0	0	1	1	0	0	0	0	0	√
*01**	0	0	0	0	0	0	0	0	1	1	0	√
00**1	1	1	0	0	0	0	0	0	0	0	0	√
0**11	0	1	0	1	0	1	0	0	0	0	0	
*0*11	0	1	0	0	0	0	0	1	0	1	0	
**011	0	1	0	1	0	0	0	1	0	0	0	
01*1*	0	0	1	1	0	1	0	0	0	0	0	
101	0	0	1	1	0	0	0	0	0	0	1	
10*1*	0	0	0	0	0	0	1	1	0	1	0	
1*01*	0	0	0	0	0	0	1	1	0	0	1	
110*1	0	0	0	0	0	0	0	0	0	0	0	√
CHECK	√	√			√	√			√	√		

TABLE II-6-3

E_1 / $M_1(f)$	10	11	18	19	26	CHECK
0**11	0	1	0	0	0	$\checkmark$
*0*11	0	0	0	1	0	$\checkmark$
**011	0	1	0	1	0	
01*1*	1	1	0	0	0	$\checkmark$
101	1	1	0	0	1	
10*1*	0	0	1	1	0	$\checkmark$
1*01*	0	0	1	1	1	
CHECK		$\checkmark$		$\checkmark$		

minimal cubical cover of f. For this purpose, we may remove the columns of the basic points and the rows of the essential maximal cubes from Table II-6-2 because these have been taken care of. Furthermore, we should also remove the rows of the useless cubes in $M(f)$. A maximal cube C in $K^*(f)$ is said to be *useless* iff it contains no point of F; in other words, C is useless iff it consists of exclusively don't care points. According to the definition of the incidence matrix, a maximal cube $C \in M(f)$ is useless iff its row in the incidence matrix consists of exclusively 0's, that is,

$$\alpha_{CP} = 0$$

holds for every $P \in F$. In Table II-6-2, the maximal cube 110*1 is useless; therefore, we check this row in the CHECK column.

Let F_1 denote the set $F \backslash B$ of all nonbasic points of F and let $M_1(f)$ denote the set of all inessential maximal cubes in $M(f)$ which are not useless. After having removed the checked rows and the checked columns from Table II-6-2, we obtain the *first reduced table of maximal cubes* for f as given in Table II-6-3. The matrix in the interior rectangle is called the *first reduced incidence matrix* of maximal cubes for f. The CHECK column and the CHECK row are explained later.

We shall perform further reduction of Table II-6-3 by means of *column dominance* and *row dominance*. Let S and T denote any two distinct points in F_1. We shall say that S is *dominated* by T or, equivalently, T *dominates* S, iff, for every cube $C \in M_1(f)$, $S \in C$ implies $T \in C$. In the first reduced incidence matrix, S is dominated by T iff the column headed by S is coordinatewisely less than or equal to the column headed by T, that is,

$$\alpha_{CS} \leq \alpha_{CT}$$

holds for every $C \in M_1(f)$. The points S and T are said to be of *equal dominance* iff S is dominated by T and T is dominated by S. If S and T are of equal dominance, then their columns in the first reduced incidence matrix must be identical, that is,

$$\alpha_{CS} = \alpha_{CT}$$

holds for $C \in M_1(f)$.

Assume that S is dominated by T. If S is covered by a cube $C \in M_1(f)$, then it follows from the definition that so is T; therefore, in searching for a minimal collection of cubes from $M_1(f)$ to cover the points of F_1, T would be taken care of whenever S is. For this reason, the column of T may be removed from the first reduced table of maximal cubes; however, if two or more points of F_1 are of equal dominance, we will leave one of the corresponding columns in the table and remove the others. In Table II-6-3, the point 10 is dominated by the point 11, and the point 18 is dominated by the point 19. Hence we check the columns 11 and 19 in the CHECK row at the bottom of the table.

Let C and D denote any two distinct cubes in $M_1(f)$. We shall say that C is *dominated* by D or, equivalently, D *dominates* C, iff the following conditions are satisfied:

(i) For every point $P \in F_1$, $P \in C$ implies $P \in D$.

(ii) $\dim(C) \leq \dim(D)$.

In the first reduced incidence matrix, the condition (i) means that the row headed by C is coordinatewisely less than or equal to the row head by D, that is,

$$\alpha_{CP} \leq \alpha_{DP}$$

holds for every point P in F_1.

The cubes C and D are said to be of *equal dominance* iff C is dominated by D and D is dominated by C. If C and D are of equal dominance, then they must be of the same dimension and their rows in the first reduced incidence matrix must be identical, that is,

$$\alpha_{CP} = \alpha_{DP}$$

holds for every point P in F_1.

Let γ denote an arbitrary collection of cubes in Q^n. If we replace a certain cube $C \in \gamma$ by another cube D in Q^n satisfying

$$\dim(C) \leq \dim(D),$$

we obtain a collection δ of cubes in Q^n with

$$b_1(\gamma) \geq b_1(\delta),$$

where $b_1(\gamma)$ and $b_1(\delta)$ are integers defined in §2. If

$$\dim(C) < \dim(D),$$

we also have

$$c_1(\gamma) > c_1(\delta);$$

and hence it follows from the definition cost functions that

$$c(\gamma) > c(\delta).$$

If C and D are of the same dimension, it is very reasonable to require that the given cost function c satisfy the condition

$$c(\gamma) = c(\delta).$$

In fact, each of the three special cost functions c_1, c_2, and c_3 in §2 satisfies this condition. Hereafter, we assume that the given cost function c satisfies this condition. Thus, in both instances, we have

$$c(\gamma) \geq c(\delta).$$

Now let us return to our study of any two distinct cubes in $M_1(f)$. Assume that C is dominated by D. According to the condition (i), D covers every point that could be covered by C. Because of condition (ii), the cost would not increase if we replaced C by D in any cubical cover of f. For these reasons, the row C may be removed from the reduced table of maximal cubes; however, if two or more cubes in $M_1(f)$ are of equal dominance, we will leave one of the corresponding rows in the table and remove the others. In Table II-6-3, 0**11 and *0*11 are dominated by **011, 01*1* is dominated by *101*, and 10*1* is dominated by 1*01*. Hence we check the four rows 0**11, *0*11, 01*1*, and 10*1* in the CHECK column.

(Note that, in column dominance, the columns of the *dominating points* are to be removed and that, in row dominance, the rows of the *dominated cubes* are to be removed.)

After having removed the checked rows and the checked columns from Table II-6-3, we obtain the *second reduced table of maximal cubes* for f as given in Table II-6-4.

A point $P \in F_2$ is said to be *secondary distinguished* iff it is contained in only one maximal cube of $M_2(f)$. In Table II-6-4, the points 10 and 18 are secondary distinguished. To mark a secondary distinguished point, we surround the lone 1 in its column by a broken-lined square.

A maximal cube $C \in M_2(f)$ is said to be *secondary essential* iff it contains a secondary distinguished point, say P, of F_2. Since C is the only maximal cube in $M_2(f)$ which contains P, C must be used if we want to cover F_2

TABLE II-6-4

$M_2(f)$ \ F_2	10	18	26	CHECK
**011	0	0	0	
101	1	0	1	√
1*01*	0	1	1	√
CHECK	√	√	√	

by cubes in $M_2(f)$. In Table II-6-4, the cubes $*101*$ and $1*01*$ are secondary essential; therefore, we check these rows in the CHECK column.

By a *secondary basic point* of F_2, we mean a point $P \in F_2$ that is contained in some secondary essential cube of $M_2(f)$. In the second reduced table of maximal cubes, the secondary basic points of F_2 can be determined as follows: A point $P \in F_2$ is secondary basic iff

$$\sum_{C \in E_2(f)} \alpha_{CP} \geq 1,$$

where $E_2(f)$ stands for the set of all secondary essential cubes in $M_2(f)$.

After finding the secondary basic points of F_2, we check the corresponding columns in the CHECK row. Having applied this procedure to Table II-6-4, we find that all columns are checked. Thus $E_2(f)$ covers F_2 and hence

$$\gamma = E(f) \cup E_2(f) = \{0*1**, *01**, 00**1, *101*, 1*01*\}$$

is a minimal cubical cover of f. This solves the minimization problem for this switching function.

In general, not all points of F_2 are secondary basic. When they are not, the process from Table II-6-2 to Table II-6-4 should be repeated again and again until it gives either a minimal cubical cover of f or a *cyclic table*, which is studied in the following section.

7. Methods on Cyclic Tables

The meaning of a *cyclic table* can be most conveniently described by an illustrative example. For this purpose, let us consider the switching function

$$f: Q^5 \to Q^*$$

defined by

$$f(x) = \begin{cases} 1, & (\text{if } x = 0, 4, 12, 16, 24, 28, 29, 31), \\ *, & (\text{if } x = 19, 27), \\ 0, & (\text{otherwise}). \end{cases}$$

Applying the tabular method of §4 to this switching function f, we obtain its set $M(f)$ of all maximal cubes of $K^*(f)$, namely, the following ten maximal cubes

00∗00, ∗0000, 0∗100, 1∗000, ∗1100, 11∗00, 1∗011, 1110∗, 11∗11, 111∗1.

On the other hand, the restricted on-set F of f is

$$F = f^{-1}(1) = \{0, 4, 12, 16, 24, 28, 29, 31\}.$$

Hence we obtain its table of maximal cubes, Table II-7-1.

TABLE II-7-1

$M(f)$ \ E	0	4	12	16	24	28	29	31	CHECK
00∗00	1	1	0	0	0	0	0	0	
∗0000	1	0	0	1	0	0	0	0	
0∗100	0	1	1	0	0	0	0	0	
1∗000	0	0	0	1	1	0	0	0	
∗1100	0	0	1	0	0	1	0	0	
11∗00	0	0	0	0	1	1	0	0	
1∗011	0	0	0	0	0	0	0	0	√
1110∗	0	0	0	0	0	1	1	0	
11∗11	0	0	0	0	0	0	0	1	
111∗1	0	0	0	0	0	0	1	1	
CHECK									

In Table II-7-1, there is no distinguished point of F and, therefore, no essential maximal cube and no basic point. However, there is a useless cube in $M(f)$, namely, 1∗011. After removing this row from the table, we obtain the first reduced table, Table II-7-2.

Applying the technique of dominance, we observe that there is no dominating point in F_1 and there is only one dominated cube in $M_1(f)$, namely, 11∗11, which is dominated by 111∗1. After removing the row 11∗11 from Table II-7-2, we obtain the second reduced table, Table II-7-3. Here the point 31 is a secondary distinguished point of F_2. Hence, the cube 111∗1 is a secondary essential maximal cube, and the two points 29 and 31 are secondary basic points of F_2. After removing the checked row and the checked columns from Table II-7-3, we obtain the third reduced table, Table II-7-4.

TABLE II-7-2

$M_1(f)$ \ F_1	0	4	12	16	24	28	29	31	CHECK
00*00	1	1	0	0	0	0	0	0	
*0000	1	0	0	1	0	0	0	0	
0*100	0	1	1	0	0	0	0	0	
1*000	0	0	0	1	1	0	0	0	
*1100	0	0	1	0	0	1	0	0	
11*00	0	0	0	0	1	1	0	0	
1110*	0	0	0	0	0	1	1	0	
11*11	0	0	0	0	0	0	0	1	√
111*1	0	0	0	0	0	0	1	1	
CHECK									

Applying the technique of dominance to Table II-7-4, we observe that there is no dominating point in F_3 and there is only one dominated cube in $M_3(f)$, namely, 1110*, which is dominated by *1100 and 11*00. After removing the row 1110* from Table II-7-4, we obtain the fourth reduced table, Table II-7-5. If there were a column in this table containing only one 1, the corresponding point of F_4 would be also called a *secondary distinguished point*, and the cube in $M_4(f)$ containing this point would be also called a *secondary essential maximal cube*.

TABLE II-7-3

$M_2(f)$ \ F_2	0	4	12	16	24	28	29	31	CHECK
00*00	1	1	0	0	0	0	0	0	
*0000	1	0	0	1	0	0	0	0	
0*100	0	1	1	0	0	0	0	0	
1*000	0	0	0	1	1	0	0	0	
*1100	0	0	1	0	0	1	0	0	
11*00	0	0	0	0	1	1	0	0	
1110*	0	0	0	0	0	1	1	0	
111*1	0	0	0	0	0	0	1	1	√
CHECK							√	√	

TABLE II-7-4

$M_3(f)$ $\diagdown$ F_3	0	4	12	16	24	28	CHECK
00*00	1	1	0	0	0	0	
*0000	1	0	0	1	0	0	
0*100	0	1	1	0	0	0	
1*000	0	0	0	1	1	0	
*1100	0	0	1	0	0	1	
11*00	0	0	0	0	1	1	
1110*	0	0	0	0	0	1	√
CHECK							

In Table II-7-5, there is no secondary essential row. Furthermore, there is no dominating column and no dominated row. Such a reduced table of maximal cubes is usually called a *cyclic table*.

On a cyclic table of maximal cubes, the methods of the preceding section are no longer helpful. There are various methods applicable to cyclic tables. In the remainder of this section, three of these methods are applied to Table II-7-5.

(a) THE BRANCHING METHOD

Assume that the i-th reduced table of maximal cubes for a given switching function f is cyclic. A point $P \in F_i$ is said to be of *order r* iff there are precisely r cubes in $M_i(f)$ which contain P. In other words, the order r

TABLE II-7-5

$M_4(f)$ $\diagdown$ F_4	0	4	12	16	24	28	CHECK
00*00	1	1	0	0	0	0	
*0000	1	0	0	1	0	0	
0*100	0	1	1	0	0	0	
1*000	0	0	0	1	1	0	
*1100	0	0	1	0	0	1	
11*00	0	0	0	0	1	1	
CHECK							

of a point $P \in F_i$ is given by

$$r = \sum_{C \in M_i(f)} \alpha_{CP}.$$

Since the table is cyclic, it follows that the order of every point of F_i is greater than 1. In Table II-7-5, it happens that every point of F_4 is of order 2.

The branching method on a cyclic table begins with the choice of an arbitrary point $P \in F_i$ of minimal order r. Let

$$C_1, C_2, \cdots, C_r$$

denote the r cubes of $M_i(f)$ which contain the point P. If we want to cover the points of F_i by means of the cubes in $M_i(f)$, then one of these r cubes must be selected. Hence our investigation naturally branches out into r cases in each of which one of these r cubes is selected. Let us illustrate this method by applying it to Table II-7-5.

Since, in Table II-7-5, every point in F_4 is of the minimal order 2, we can choose any of the six points in F_4. For example, let us choose the point 0. The two cubes in $M_4(f)$ which contain 0 are 00∗00 and ∗0000. Hence we branch out into two cases as follows.

If 00∗00 is selected, then the points 0 and 4 of F_4 are covered. Hence we may remove the row 00∗00, as well as the columns 0 and 4, from Table II-7-5. Doing so yields Table II-7-6. We can apply the technique of dominance to Table II-7-6 and obtain two dominated cubes in $M_5(f)$, namely, ∗0000 and 0∗100. By removing these two rows from Table II-7-6, we obtain Table II-7-7.

In Table II-7-7, we observe that the points 12 and 16 are secondary distinguished; therefore, the rows 1∗000 and ∗1100 are secondary essential, and all points of F_6 are secondary basic. Consequently, we

TABLE II-7-6

$M_5(f)$ \ F_5	12	16	24	28	CHECK
∗0000	0	1	0	0	√
0∗100	1	0	0	0	√
1∗000	0	1	1	0	
∗1100	1	0	0	1	
11∗00	0	0	1	1	
CHECK					

TABLE II-7-7

$M_6(f)$ $\diagdown$ F_6	12	16	24	28	CHECK
1*000	0	1	1	0	√
*1100	1	0	0	1	√
11*00	0	0	1	1	
CHECK	√	√	√	√	

obtain in this instance a cubical cover for the given switching function f, namely,

$$\gamma = \{111*1, 00*00, 1*000, *1100\}.$$

On the other hand, if *0000 is selected, a similar process gives us another cubical cover for f, namely,

$$\delta = \{111*1, *0000, 0*100, 11*00\}.$$

Consequently, either γ or δ must be a minimal cubical cover for f. In order to determine which is minimal, we must compare their costs $c(\gamma)$ and $c(\delta)$. For this particular example, we have

$$c(\gamma) = c(\delta)$$

in accordance with our new understanding about the cost function f in the preceding section. Hence both γ and δ are minimal cubical covers for f with respect to any given cost function c. This solves the minimization problem for the switching function defined at the beginning of the present section.

In general, it is possible for another cyclic table to result from the reductions of the table after the choice of a point P of the minimal order. If this happens, a similar branching process should be applied to the new cyclic table, and so on.

(*b*) METHOD OF BOOLEAN ALGEBRA

This method is also known as *Petrick's method*. As before, let us assume that the i-th reduced table of maximal cubes for a given switching function f is cyclic. Let

$$C_1, C_2, \cdots, C_l$$

denote the cubes in $M_i(f)$ and let

$$P_1, P_2, \cdots, P_m$$

denote the points in F_i. Also, we shall use the simpler notation

$$\alpha_{jk} = \alpha_{C_j P_k}$$

for every $j = 1, 2, \cdots, l$ and every $k = 1, 2, \cdots, m$.

For every point $x = x_1 \cdots x_l$ of the l-cube Q^l, define a subcollection γ_x of the collection $M_i(f)$ by the condition that, for every $j = 1, \cdots, l$, $C_j \in \gamma_x$ iff $x_j = 1$. Then we define a switching function

$$g : Q^l \rightarrow Q$$

of l variables by setting $g(x) = 1$ iff γ_x covers F_i. Thus we obtain the family

$$\mathscr{F} = \{\gamma_x \,|\, g(x) = 1\}$$

of all covers of F_i by cubes from $M_i(f)$.

To construct a Boolean expression for the switching function g, let us first define for every integer $k = 1, 2, \cdots, m$, a switching function

$$g_k : Q^l \rightarrow Q$$

of l variables by setting $g(x) = 1$ iff γ_x covers the point P_k of F_i. Consequently, g is the conjunction of the switching functions $g_1, g_2, \cdots, g_m$; in symbols,

$$g = g_1 g_2 \cdots g_m.$$

On the other hand, since γ_x covers P_k iff it contains at least one of the cubes containing P_k, it follows that $g_k(x) = 1$ iff $x_j = 1$ holds for at least one integer j satisfying $\alpha_{jk} = 1$. Consequently, g_k is the disjunction of all elementary switching functions x_j such that $\alpha_{jk} = 1$; in symbols,

$$g_k = \bigvee_{\alpha_{jk}=1} x_j.$$

This gives a Boolean expression for the switching function g as a conjunction of disjunctions of the elementary switching functions.

Applying this construction to Table II-7-5, we obtain $l = 6$, $m = 6$, and

$$g = (x_1 \vee x_2)(x_1 \vee x_3)(x_3 \vee x_5)(x_2 \vee x_4)(x_4 \vee x_6)(x_5 \vee x_6).$$

Developing this Boolean expression of g into a Boolean polynomial, we obtain

$$g = x_1 x_4 x_5 \vee x_2 x_3 x_6 \vee x_1 x_2 x_5 x_6 \vee x_1 x_3 x_4 x_6 \vee x_2 x_3 x_4 x_5.$$

By the definition of g, each term of this Boolean polynomial suggests a unique cover of F_4 with possibility of being maximal. In general, we should find them all and compare their costs. In Table II-7-5, however, since the six cubes are of the same dimension, each of the covers suggested by the first two terms of this Boolean polynomial is clearly of smaller cost than any of the covers suggested by last three terms. It suffices to consider the first two terms of this Boolean polynomial. The first term suggests the subcollection of $M_4(f)$ consisting of the first cube, the fourth cube, and the fifth cube; the second term suggests the subcollection consisting of the second cube, the third cube, and the sixth cube. Together with the secondary essential maximal cube $111*1$ already obtained in Table II-7-3, we obtain two cubical covers of f, namely,

$$\gamma = \{111*1, 00*00, 1*000, *1100\},$$
$$\delta = \{111*1, *0000, 0*100, 11*00\}.$$

Since γ and δ are of equal cost, each of them is a maximal cubical cover of f. Again, this solves the minimization problem for f.

(c) METHOD OF LINEAR PROGRAMMING

Let us assume, as before, that the i-th reduced table of maximal cubes for a given switching function f is cyclic, and let us use the notations established at the beginning of (b). For an arbitrary point $x = x_1 \cdots x_l$ of the l-cube Q^l, consider the subcollection γ_x of the collection $M_i(f)$ as defined in (b). By the definition of γ_x, it is clear that γ_x covers F_i iff

$$\sum_{j=1}^{l} \alpha_{jk} x_j \geq 1$$

holds for every $k = 1, 2, \cdots, m$.

This system of linear inequalities suggests possible application of linear programming. In order to apply linear programming, the cost function c must be *additive*, that is, the cost of a collection γ of cubes is the sum of the costs of the cubes in γ. In symbol,

$$c(\gamma) = \textstyle\sum_{C \in \gamma} c(C).$$

Throughout the remainder of the present section, we assume that c is additive. This assumption is very reasonable since each of the three special cost functions c_1, c_2, and c_3 in §2 is additive.

Under this additivity assumption on c, the cost $c(\gamma_x)$ of the subcollection γ_x of $M_i(f)$ corresponding to the point $x = x_1 \cdots x_l$ of Q^l is given by

$$c(\gamma_x) = \sum_{j=1}^{l} \alpha_j x_j,$$

where $\alpha_j = c(C_j)$ denotes the cost of the j-th cube C_j in $M_i(f)$. Hence the cost $c(\gamma_x)$ is a linear function of the coordinates of the point x.

Furthermore, we shall also assume that $\alpha_1, \cdots, \alpha_l$ are positive integers. As to the three special cost functions in §2, this condition is satisfied by c_1 and c_2 but not by c_3; however, this condition is not very restrictive. In fact, so long as $\alpha_1, \cdots, \alpha_l$ are positive rational numbers, we may multiply c by the common denominator d of $\alpha_1, \cdots, \alpha_l$ and obtain a new cost function

$$c' = dc,$$

with integral $\alpha_j' = d\alpha_j$ for every $j = 1, 2, \cdots, l$ and without changing the minimal cubical covers.

Apply the standard methods of integer linear programming to find an l-tuple of nonnegative integers $(x_1, \cdots, x_l)$ which satisfies the inequalities

$$\sum_{j=1}^{l} \alpha_{jk} x_j \geq 1, \qquad (k = 1, 2, \cdots, m),$$

and minimizes the linear function

$$\sum_{j=1}^{l} \alpha_j x_j.$$

Let $(x_1, \cdots, x_l)$ denote any optimal solution of this standard integer linear programming problem. We have the following lemma.

LEMMA 7.1.   *For each* $j = 1, \cdots, l$, *we have* $x_j \in Q$, *that is,* x_j *is either* 1 *or* 0.

Proof.   To prove (7.1) by the indirect method, let us assume that there exists a positive integer $h \leq l$ such that $x_h > 1$. Define an l-tuple of nonnegative integers $(y_1, \cdots, y_l)$ by taking

$$y_j = \begin{cases} x_h - 1, & (\text{if } j = h), \\ x_j, & (\text{if } j \neq h). \end{cases}$$

We shall prove that $(y_1, \cdots, y_l)$ satisfies the inequalities

$$\sum_{j=1}^{l} \alpha_{jk} y_j \geq 1, \qquad (k = 1, 2, \cdots, m).$$

For this purpose, consider an arbitrary positive integer $k \leq m$. Since

$$\sum_{j=1}^{l} \alpha_{jk} x_j \geq 1,$$

there exists a positive integer $g \leq l$ such that $\alpha_{gk} = 1$ and $x_g \geq 1$. If $g \neq h$, we have

$$\sum_{j=1}^{l} \alpha_{jk} y_j \geq \alpha_{gk} y_g = \alpha_{gk} x_g \geq 1.$$

If $g = h$, then we have $y_h = x_h - 1 \geq 1$ and hence

$$\sum_{j=1}^{l} \alpha_{jk} y_j \geq \alpha_{hk} y_k \geq 1.$$

This proves that $(y_1, \cdots, y_l)$ satisfies the inequalities mentioned above. Since

$$\sum_{j=1}^{l} \alpha_j y_j = \sum_{j=1}^{l} \alpha_j x_j - \alpha_h < \sum_{j=1}^{l} \alpha_j x_j,$$

this contradicts our assumption that $(x_1, \cdots, x_l)$ is an optimal solution of the integer linear program described above. This contradiction completes the proof of (7.1). ‖

Because of (7.1), an arbitrary optimal solution $(x_1, \cdots, x_l)$ of the integer linear program described above gives a point

$$x = x_1 \cdots x_l$$

of the l-cube Q^l and hence determines a subcollection of $M_i(f)$. We have the following theorem.

THEOREM 7.2. *Together with the essential and the secondary essential maximal cubes already obtained, the subcollection γ_x of $M_i(f)$ constitutes a minimal cubical cover of f.*

Proof. Since $(x_1, \cdots, x_l)$ satisfies the inequalities

$$\sum_{j=1}^{l} \alpha_{jk} x_k \geq 1, \qquad (k = 1, 2, \cdots, m),$$

γ_x covers the F_i. It follows that, together with the essential and the secondary essential maximal cubes already obtained, γ_x makes a cubical cover γ of f. Since $(x_1, \cdots, x_l)$ minimizes

$$c(\gamma_x) = \sum_{j=1}^{l} \alpha_j x_j$$

and since the cost function c is additive, it follows that γ is minimal with respect to c. ‖

Thus, (7.2) solves our minimization problem.

For detailed expositions of integer linear programming, interested readers may refer to [Gomory 2] and [Pyne and McCluskey 1].

8. Minimization by Complement

Let n denote a given positive integer and consider a switching function

$$f: Q^n \to Q^*$$

of n variables, possibly with don't care points. The minimal cubical covers of f found by the methods presented in the preceding sections give us the optimal two-stage AND-OR networks representing f. Dually, f can also be mechanized by optimal two-stage OR-AND networks which can be obtained by completely dual methods. It is possible that the latter might be more economical than the former; therefore, it is worthwhile to compare their costs and to determine which of the two is the better.

Instead of developing dual methods, it is much simpler to apply the methods already developed in preceding sections by passing to the *complement*

$$f' : Q^n \to Q*$$

which is defined by

$$f'(x) = \begin{cases} 1 - f(x), & (\text{if } f(x) \neq *), \\ *, & (\text{if } f(x) = *). \end{cases}$$

This process can be most conveniently described by means of an illustrative example. Let us consider the switching function $f : Q^5 \to Q*$ defined by

$$f(x) = \begin{cases} 1, & (\text{if } x = 1, 3, 10, 11, 12, 15, 18, 19, 21, 23, 26), \\ *, & (\text{if } x = 4, 5, 6, 7, 13, 14, 20, 22, 25, 27), \\ 0, & (\text{if } x = 0, 2, 8, 9, 16, 17, 24, 28, 29, 30, 31), \end{cases}$$

studied in §6. The complement

$$g = f' : Q^5 \to Q*$$

of this switching function is defined by

$$g(x) = \begin{cases} 1, & (\text{if } x = 0, 2, 8, 9, 16, 17, 24, 28, 29, 30, 31), \\ *, & (\text{if } x = 4, 5, 6, 7, 13, 14, 20, 22, 25, 27), \\ 0, & (\text{if } x = 1, 3, 10, 11, 12, 15, 18, 19, 21, 23, 26). \end{cases}$$

Applying the tabular method of §4 to this switching function g, we obtain its set $M(g)$ of all maximal cubes of $K*(g)$, namely, the following fifteen maximal cubes:

0∗101,   00∗∗0,   ∗0∗00,   ∗∗000,   001∗∗,   ∗01∗0,   ∗100∗,   1∗00∗,

1∗∗00,   ∗∗110,   ∗1∗01,   1∗1∗0,   11∗0∗,   11∗∗1,   111∗∗.

On the other hand, the restricted on-set G of g is

$$G = g^{-1}(1) = \{0, 2, 8, 9, 16, 17, 24, 28, 29, 30, 31\}.$$

Hence we obtain its table of maximal cubes, Table II-8-1.

There are two distinguished points 2 and 17 in G. Hence the cubes 00∗∗0 and 1∗00∗ are essential, and the five points 0, 2, 6, 7, and 24 are basic. Furthermore, the cubes 0∗101, 001∗∗, and ∗01∗0 are useless. After removing the checked rows and the checked columns from Table II-8-1, we obtain the first reduced table, Table II-8-2.

TABLE II-8-1

M(g) \ G	0	2	8	9	16	17	24	28	29	30	31	CHECK
0*101	0	0	0	0	0	0	0	0	0	0	0	√
00**0	1	1	0	0	0	0	0	0	0	0	0	√
*0*00	1	0	0	0	1	0	0	0	0	0	0	
**000	1	0	1	0	1	0	1	0	0	0	0	
001**	0	0	0	0	0	0	0	0	0	0	0	√
*01*0	0	0	0	0	0	0	0	0	0	0	0	√
100	0	0	1	1	0	0	1	0	0	0	0	
1*00*	0	0	0	0	1	1	1	0	0	0	0	√
1**00	0	0	0	0	1	0	1	1	0	0	0	
**110	0	0	0	0	0	0	0	0	0	1	0	
*1*01	0	0	0	1	0	0	0	0	1	0	0	
1*1*0	0	0	0	0	0	0	0	1	0	1	0	
11*0*	0	0	0	0	0	0	1	1	1	0	0	
11**1	0	0	0	0	0	0	0	0	1	0	1	
111**	0	0	0	0	0	0	0	1	1	1	1	
CHECK	√	√			√	√	√					

TABLE II-8-2

M₁(g) \ G₁	8	9	28	29	30	31	CHECK
*0*00	0	0	0	0	0	0	√
**000	1	0	0	0	0	0	√
100	1	1	0	0	0	0	
1**00	0	0	1	0	0	0	√
**110	0	0	0	0	1	0	√
*1*01	0	1	0	1	0	0	
1*1*0	0	0	1	0	1	0	√
11*0*	0	0	1	1	0	0	√
11**1	0	0	0	1	0	1	√
111**	0	0	1	1	1	1	
CHECK							

In Table II-8-2, we have one dominating point in G_1 and seven dominated cubes in $M_1(g)$. After removing the checked rows and the checked column from this table, we obtain the second reduced table, Table II-8-3.

In Table II-8-3, we have two secondary essential cubes $*100*$ and $111**$ in $M_2(g)$. Since these two cubes cover G_2, we obtain a minimal cubical cover

$$\delta = \{00**0,\ 1*00*,\ *100*,\ 111**\}$$

TABLE II-8-3

G_2 $M_2(g)$	8	9	28	30	31	CHECK
$*100*$	1	1	0	0	0	√
$*1*01$	0	1	0	0	0	
$111**$	0	0	1	1	1	√
CHECK	√	√	√	√	√	

of the switching function $g = f'$. This cubical cover δ of f' suggests a Boolean expression

$$x_1'x_2'x_3' \vee x_1 x_3' x_4' \vee x_2 x_3' x_4' \vee x_1 x_2 x_3$$

for f' modulo the set

$$D = \{4, 5, 6, 7, 13, 14, 20, 22, 25, 27\}$$

of don't care points. Applying De Morgan's laws of (I, §4) to the complement of this Boolean expression of f', we obtain a Boolean expression

$$B = (x_1 \vee x_2 \vee x_5)(x_1' \vee x_3 \vee x_4)(x_2' \vee x_3 \vee x_4)(x_1' \vee x_2' \vee x_3')$$

for the given switching function f modulo the set D of don't care points.

If branch-type components are being used, the Boolean expression B gives a parallel-series relay-contact network for f as shown in Figure II-8-4. The total number of contacts used in this figure is 12, which is the number of literals in the Boolean expression B and is equal to the cost

$$c_1(\delta) = \sum_{C \in \delta} \mathrm{cod}(C)$$

of the minimal cubical cover δ of the complement $g = f'$ of f.

FIGURE II-8-4

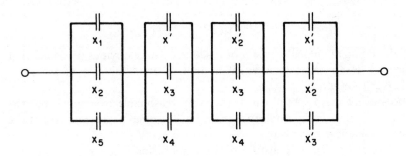

If gate-type components are being used, the Boolean expression B suggests a two-stage OR-AND network for f as shown in Figure II-8-5.

If the network is to be built directly from diodes, the total number of diodes is 16, which is the number of inputs to the gates and is equal to the cost

$$c_2(\delta) = b_1(\delta) + c_1(\delta) = b_1(\delta) + \sum_{C \in \delta} \text{cod}(C)$$

of the minimal cubical cover δ of the complement $g = f'$ of f.

FIGURE II-8-5

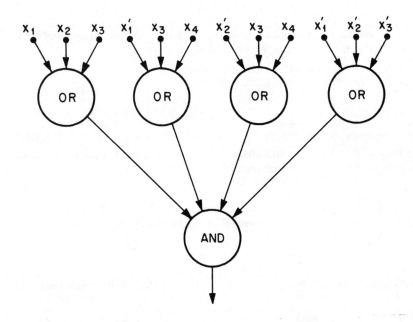

If the network is to be built from ready-made AND-gates and OR-gates, its cost would be equal to the cost

$$c_3(\delta) = b_1(\delta) + 1 + \varepsilon c_1(\delta)$$

of the minimal cubical cover δ of f' since we may obviously assume that the cost of an OR-gate is equal to that of an AND-gate of the same number of inputs.

Because of these special cases, it is very reasonable to assume that the cost to mechanize the Boolean expression B is equal to the cost $c(\delta)$ of the minimal cubical cover δ of f'.

At the end of §6, we constructed a minimal cubical cover

$$\gamma = \{0{*}1{**}, {*}01{**}, 00{**}1, {*}101{*}, 1{*}01{*}\}$$

of the same switching function f. The cost of the network suggested by γ is $c(\gamma)$. To compare $c(\gamma)$ and $c(\delta)$, we observe

$$b_1(\gamma) = 5, \qquad b_1(\delta) = 4, \qquad c_1(\gamma) = 13, \qquad c_1(\delta) = 12.$$

Hence we obtain

$$b_1(\delta) < b_1(\gamma), \qquad c_1(\delta) < c_1(\gamma).$$

According to our definition of a cost function c in §2, these imply

$$c(\delta) < c(\gamma)$$

and, therefore, the Boolean expression B of f suggests a cheaper network than that suggested by the minimal cubical cover γ of f.

The preceding example illustrates a *general minimization process*: For an arbitrarily given switching function

$$f : Q^n \to Q^*$$

of n variables, possibly with don't care points, we find a minimal cubical cover γ of f and a minimal cubical cover δ of the complement f' of f with respect to a given cost function. If

$$c(\gamma) \leq c(\delta),$$

then γ gives an optimal series-parallel, or two-stage AND-OR, network for f. If

$$c(\delta) \leq c(\gamma),$$

then δ gives an optimal parallel-series, or two-stage OR-AND, network for f.

9. Simultaneous Minimization

In designing a circuit for a certain computing operation, frequently one has to mechanize more than one switching function in one network, known as a *multiple-output circuit*. The present section is devoted to the minimization of these circuits.

Since every switching function of not more than n variables can be considered as of n variables in the obvious way, we can simplify this problem by assuming that the given switching functions are of the same number of variables. For this reason, let us consider an arbitrary collection

$$f_i : Q^n \to Q^*, \qquad (i = 1, 2, \cdots, m),$$

of m switching functions of n variables, possibly with don't care points. In order to mechanize these switching functions by means of gate-type components most economically, we consider for each $i = 1, \cdots, m$ a cubical cover γ_i of f_i. If a certain cube C belongs to two or more of these cubical covers, the same gate realizing C can be used for each of the corresponding switching functions. If we assume that the cost function c is *additive*, that is, the cost of the network is the sum of the costs of the different cubes in the covers γ_i, then this cost is equal to the cost $c(\gamma)$ of their union

$$\gamma = \bigcup_{i=1}^{m} \gamma_i.$$

This union γ will be called a *total cubical cover* of $f_1, \cdots, f_m$. Consequently, our problem is to find for each $i = 1, \cdots, m$ a cubical cover γ_i for the switching function f_i such that the cost $c(\gamma)$ of their union γ is minimal. Such a collection

$$\{\gamma_i \mid i = 1, 2, \cdots, m\}$$

of cubical covers of the switching functions f_i will be referred to as a *minimal collection*.

By a slight modification of the proof of (2.3), one can establish the following theorem.

THEOREM 9.1. *If a collection $\{\gamma_i \mid i = 1, \cdots, m\}$ of cubical covers for the switching functions f_i is minimal with respect to c and if C is a cube belonging precisely l of these cubical covers, say*

$$\gamma_{i_1}, \gamma_{i_2}, \cdots, \gamma_{i_l},$$

then C is a maximal cube for the conjunction

$$f_{i_1} f_{i_2} \cdots f_{i_l}.$$

Thus, in order to construct a minimal collection $\{\gamma_i \mid i = 1, \cdots, m\}$, we must find the maximal cubes of not only each switching function of the given collection

$$\mathscr{C} = \{f_1, f_2, \cdots, f_m\}$$

but also the conjunction of every subcollection of $\mathscr{C}$. To do so, we shall modify the tabular method in §4 by adjoining to the tables a column of *tags*. The tag in the row headed by a cube C, called the *tag* of C, is a character of m binary integers $\xi_1 \xi_2 \cdots \xi_m$ defined as follows:

$$\xi_i = \begin{cases} 1, & (if\ C \subset F_i^* = f_i^{-1}\{1, *\}), \\ 0, & (\text{otherwise}). \end{cases}$$

The coordinates of C will be called the *identifier* of C.

TABLE II-9-1

POINT	IDENTIFIER				TAG			CHECK
x	x_1	x_2	x_3	x_4	f_1	f_2	f_3	
2	0	0	1	0	1	1	0	√
8	1	0	0	0	1	0	1	√
3	0	0	1	1	1	1	0	√
5	0	1	0	1	1	1	0	√
6	0	1	1	0	0	1	1	√
9	1	0	0	1	1	0	1	√
10	1	0	1	0	1	1	0	√
7	0	1	1	1	1	1	1	√
11	1	0	1	1	1	1	0	√
13	1	1	0	1	1	0	1	√
14	1	1	1	0	0	1	1	√
15	1	1	1	1	1	1	1	√

This process can be most conveniently described by means of an illustrative example. For this purpose, let us consider three given switching functions

$$f_1, f_2, f_3 : Q^4 \to Q^*$$

of four variables defined as follows:

$$f_1(x) = \begin{cases} 1, & \text{(if } x = 2, 3, 5, 8, 9, 10, 11, 13) \\ *, & \text{(if } x = 7, 15), \\ 0, & \text{(if } x = 0, 1, 4, 6, 12, 14); \end{cases}$$

$$f_2(x) = \begin{cases} 1, & \text{(if } x = 2, 3, 5, 6, 10, 11, 14) \\ *, & \text{(if } x = 7, 15), \\ 0, & \text{(if } x = 0, 1, 4, 8, 9, 12, 13); \end{cases}$$

$$f_3(x) = \begin{cases} 1, & \text{(if } x = 6, 8, 9, 13, 14), \\ *, & \text{(if } x = 7, 15), \\ 0, & \text{(if } x = 0, 1, 2, 3, 4, 5, 10, 11, 12). \end{cases}$$

According to the rules of §4 and the modification mentioned above, we obtain the table of the points of the union

$$F^* = F_1^* \cup F_2^* \cup F_3^*$$

of the extended on-sets $F_i^* = f_i^{-1}\{1, *\}$ given in Table II-9-1. Applying the method described in §4, we obtain the table of 1-cubes given in Table II-9-2. The tag of any 1-cube $\{p, q\}$ is the coordinatewise product of the tags of p and q. A point in Table II-9-1 is checked iff it is contained in a 1-cube in Table II-9-2 *with the same tag*. Applying the method of §4 to Table II-9-2, we obtain the table of 2-cubes given in Table II-9-3. The tag of any 2-cube $\{p, q, r, s\}$ is the coordinatewise product of the tags of $\{p, q\}$ and $\{r, s\}$. A 1-cube in Table II-9-2 is checked iff it is contained in a 2-cube in Table II-9-3 *with the same tag*. Applying the method presented in §4 to Table II-9-3, we obtain the table of 3-cubes given in Table II-9-4. The tag of $\{2, 3, 6, 7, 10, 11, 14, 15\}$ is the coordinatewise product of the tags of $\{2, 3, 6, 7\}$ and $\{10, 11, 14, 15\}$. A 2-cube in Table II-9-3 is checked iff it is contained in a 3-cube in Table II-9-4 *with the same tag*.

TABLE II-9-2

1-CUBE	IDENTIFIER				TAG			CHECK
C	x_1	x_2	x_3	x_4	f_1	f_2	f_3	
{ 2, 3}	0	0	1	*	1	1	0	√
{ 2, 6}	0	*	1	0	0	1	0	√
{ 2, 10}	*	0	1	0	1	1	0	√
{ 8, 9}	1	0	0	*	1	0	1	
{ 8, 10}	1	0	*	0	1	0	0	√
{ 3, 7}	0	*	1	1	1	1	0	√
{ 3, 11}	*	0	1	1	1	1	0	√
{ 5, 7}	0	1	*	1	1	1	0	
{ 5, 13}	*	1	0	1	1	0	0	√
{ 6, 7}	0	1	1	*	0	1	1	√
{ 6, 14}	*	1	1	0	0	1	1	√
{ 9, 11}	1	0	*	1	1	0	0	√
{ 9, 13}	1	*	0	1	1	0	1	
{10, 11}	1	0	1	*	1	1	0	√
{10, 14}	1	*	1	0	0	1	0	√
{ 7, 15}	*	1	1	1	1	1	1	
{11, 15}	1	*	1	1	1	1	0	√
{13, 15}	1	1	*	1	1	0	1	
{14, 15}	1	1	1	*	0	1	1	√

TABLE II-9-3

2-CUBE	IDENTIFIER				TAG			CHECK
C	x_1	x_2	x_3	x_4	f_1	f_2	f_3	
{ 2, 3, 6, 7}	0	*	1	*	0	1	0	√
{ 2, 3, 10, 11}	*	0	1	*	1	1	0	
{ 2, 6, 10, 14}	*	*	1	0	0	1	0	√
{ 8, 9, 10, 11}	1	0	*	*	1	0	0	
{ 3, 7, 11, 15}	*	*	1	1	1	1	0	
{ 5, 7, 13, 15}	*	1	*	1	1	0	0	
{ 6, 7, 14, 15}	*	1	1	*	0	1	1	
{ 9, 11, 13, 15}	1	*	*	1	1	0	0	
{10, 11, 14, 15}	1	*	1	*	0	1	0	√

TABLE II-9-4

3-CUBE	IDENTIFIER	TAG	CHECK
C	x_1 x_2 x_3 x_4	f_1 f_2 f_3	
{2, 3, 6, 7, 10, 11, 14, 15}	* * 1 *	0 1 0	

In view of the rule about checking the cubes, it is clear that the unchecked cubes in Tables II-9-1 through II-9-4 are the maximal cubes for the switching functions f_1, f_2, f_3 and their various conjunctions. In Table II-9-5, we list all of these maximal cubes. The FUNCTION column gives the switching functions for which the cubes are maximal.

The tables of maximal cubes defined in §6 for these switching functions can be naturally put together as in Table II-9-6. The vacant spaces in the incidence matrices in this table are considered to be filled with zeros. Thus we obtain four essential cubes, namely,

$$*01*, \quad *11*, \quad 100*, \quad 01*1.$$

These cubes cover the basic points checked in the CHECK row of Table II-9-6. Furthermore, the cube *111 is useless.

TABLE II-9-5

MAXIMAL CUBE	IDENTIFIER	TAG	FUNCTION
C	x_1 x_2 x_3 x_4	f_1 f_2 f_3	
{2, 3, 6, 7, 10, 11, 14, 15}	* * 1 *	0 1 0	f_2
{2, 3, 10, 11}	* 0 1 *	1 1 0	f_1f_2
{8, 9, 10, 11}	1 0 * *	1 0 0	f_1
{3, 7, 11, 15}	* * 1 1	1 1 0	f_1f_2
{5, 7, 13, 15}	* 1 * 1	1 0 0	f_1
{6, 7, 14, 15}	* 1 1 *	0 1 1	f_2f_3
{9, 11, 13, 15}	1 * * 1	1 0 0	f_1
{8, 9}	1 0 0 *	1 0 1	f_1f_3
{5, 7}	0 1 * 1	1 1 0	f_1f_2
{9, 13}	1 * 0 1	1 0 1	f_1f_3
{7, 15}	* 1 1 1	1 1 1	$f_1f_2f_3$
{13, 15}	1 1 * 1	1 0 1	f_1f_3

TABLE II-9-6

CUBE	$F_1 = f_1^{-1}(1)$								$F_2 = f_2^{-1}(1)$							$F_3 = f_3^{-1}(1)$					CHECK
	2	3	5	8	9	10	11	13	2	3	5	6	10	11	14	6	8	9	13	14	
* * 1 *	[1]	1				1	1		1	1		1	1	1	1	1				[1]	✓
* 0 1 *	1	1				1	1		1	1			1	1							
1 0 * *		1		1	1	1	1						1	1			1	1			
* * 1 1		1					1			1				1							
* 1 * 1			1					1			1								1		✓
* 1 1 *												1			1	[1]				1	✓
1 * * 1					1		1	1						1				1	1		✓
1 0 0 *				1	1												[1]	1			✓
0 1 * 1			1								[1]										✓
1 * 0 1					1			1										1	1		
* 1 1 1																					
1 1 * 1								1											1		
CHECK	✓	✓	✓	✓	✓	✓	✓	✓	✓	✓	✓	✓	✓	✓	✓	✓	✓	✓	✓	✓	

Removing the checked rows and the checked columns from Table II-9-6, we obtain the first reduced table, Table II-9-7. Here we have one dominating column and three useless rows; however, we may apply the branching method to this table. Since 1∗01 and 11∗1 are of the same cost, we may choose either of them. Finally, to form a largest total cubical cover of the minimal cost, we must include every cube in Table II-9-5 of

TABLE II-9-7

CUBE	F_1	F_3	CHECK
	13	13	
∗ ∗ 1 ∗			√
1 0 ∗ ∗			√
∗ ∗ 1 1			√
∗ 1 ∗ 1	1		
1 ∗ ∗ 1	1		
1 ∗ 0 1	1	1	
1 1 ∗ 1	1	1	
CHECK	√		

cost 0, namely, the cube ∗∗1∗ which is represented by x_3. Consequently, we obtain two largest total cubical covers

$$\gamma = \{∗∗1∗, ∗01∗, ∗11∗, 100∗, 01∗1, 1∗01\},$$

$$\delta = \{∗∗1∗, ∗01∗, ∗11∗, 100∗, 01∗1, 11∗1\},$$

of the same minimal cost for the given switching functions f_1, f_2, and f_3.

For definiteness, let us consider the total cubical cover γ. A cubical cover γ_i of f_i consisting of cubes in γ for each $i = 1, 2, 3$, remains to be found. In the meantime, we want each γ_i to consist of as few cubes as possible.

To find γ_1, consider the incidence table of γ and F_1 as given in Table II-9-8, which is a part of Table II-9-6. Here we have four essential cubes in γ which cover all points of F_1; therefore, we obtain

$$\gamma_1 = \{∗01∗, 100∗, 01∗1, 1∗01\}.$$

To find γ_2, consider the incidence table of γ and F_2 as given in Table II-9-9, which is also a part of Table II-9-6. Here we have one essential

TABLE II-9-8

γ \ F_1	2	3	5	8	9	10	11	13	CHECK
* * 1 *									
* 0 1 *	[1]	[1]				[1]	[1]		√
* 1 1 *									
1 0 0 *				[1]	1				√
0 1 * 1			[1]						√
1 * 0 1					1			[1]	√
CHECK	√	√	√	√	√	√	√	√	

TABLE II-9-9

γ \ F_2	2	3	5	6	10	11	14	CHECK
* * 1 *	1	1		1	1	1	1	√
* 0 1 *	1	1			1	1		
* 1 1 *				1			1	
1 0 0 *								
0 1 * 1			[1]					√
1 * 0 1								
CHECK	√	√	√	√	√	√	√	

TABLE II-9-10

γ \ F_3	6	8	9	13	14	CHECK
* * 1 *						
* 0 1 *						
* 1 1 *	[1]				[1]	√
1 0 0 *		[1]	1			√
0 1 * 1						
1 * 0 1			1	[1]		√
CHECK	√	√	√	√	√	

cube in γ, namely, $01*1$. The cubes $100*$ and $1*01$ are useless. The cubes $*01*$ and $*11*$ are dominated by $**1*$. Therefore, we obtain

$$\gamma_2 = \{**1*, 01*1\}.$$

To find γ_3, consider the incidence table of γ and F_3 as given in Table II-9-10, also a part of Table II-9-6. Here we have three essential cubes in γ which cover all points of F_3; therefore, we obtain

$$\gamma_3 = \{*11*, 100*, 1*01\}.$$

These cubical covers γ_1, γ_2, and γ_3 suggest the following Boolean expressions

$$f_1 \equiv x_2' x_3 \lor x_1 x_2' x_3' \lor x_1' x_2 x_4 \lor x_1 x_3' x_4,$$
$$f_2 \equiv x_3 \lor x_1' x_2 x_4,$$
$$f_3 \equiv x_2 x_3 \lor x_1 x_2' x_3' \lor x_1 x_3' x_4,$$

for these switching functions modulo the set $D = \{7, 15\}$ of don't care points. A network for these Boolean polynomials with gate-type components is given in Figure II-9-11.

FIGURE II-9-11

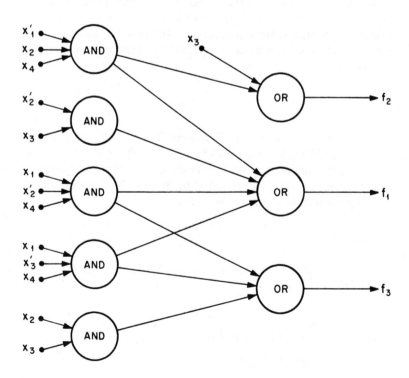

If we consider the total cubical cover δ instead of γ, we should obtain the cubical covers

$$\delta_1 = \{*01*, 100*, 01*1, 11*1\},$$
$$\delta_2 = \{**1*, 01*1\},$$
$$\delta_3 = \{*11*, 100*, 11*1\}$$

for the switching functions f_1, f_2, f_3, respectively. The network suggested by these cubical covers is the same as in Figure II-9-11 except that the inputs to the fourth AND gate, counting from the top, are changed into x_1, x_2, and x_4.

The method of the present section is based on our assumption that the given cost function c is *additive*, in other words, that the cost of the network is the sum of the costs of the AND-gates and hence does not depend on the number of inputs to the OR-gates. However, our choice of the cubical covers γ_1, γ_2, γ_3 from the total cover γ also takes care of the case where the changeable part of the cost of the network is dominated by the costs of the AND-gates with slight contribution from the number of inputs to the OR-gates. This dominance occurs when the network is to be built from ready-made AND-gates and OR-gates.

If the number of inputs to the OR-gates contributes considerably to the cost of the network, then essential rows in Table II-9-6 must be considered separately for each switching function. Interested readers may refer to [Mc, pp. 160–165] for a more complicated method of handling the table of maximal cubes.

Exercises

1. For each of the switching functions (a)–(e) of four variables listed below, find the maximal cubes by means of the map method and then construct a minimal cubical cover either directly from the map or by means of the methods presented in §6 and §7. Do the same for its complement and compare their costs:

(a) $f(x) = \begin{cases} 1, & (\text{if } x = 1, 5, 6, 7, 11, 12, 13, 15), \\ 0, & (\text{otherwise}); \end{cases}$

(b) $f(x) = \begin{cases} 1, & (\text{if } x = 2, 3, 5, 7, 8, 10, 12), \\ 0, & (\text{otherwise}); \end{cases}$

(c) $f(x) = \begin{cases} 1, & (\text{if } x = 3, 5, 7, 11), \\ *, & (\text{if } x = 6, 15), \\ 0, & (\text{otherwise}); \end{cases}$

$$(d)\ f(x) = \begin{cases} 1, & (\text{if } x = 0, 2, 5, 12, 13, 15), \\ *, & (\text{if } x = 6, 7, 8, 9), \\ 0, & (\text{otherwise}); \end{cases}$$

$$(e)\ f(x) = \begin{cases} 1, & (\text{if } x = 1, 4, 5), \\ *, & (\text{if } x = 2, 3, 6, 7, 8, 9, 12, 13), \\ 0, & (\text{otherwise}). \end{cases}$$

2. For each of the switching functions (a)–(d) of five variables listed below, find the maximal cubes by means of the tabular method and then construct a minimal cubical cover by the methods presented in §6 and §7. Do the same for its complement and compare their costs:

$$(a)\ f(x) = \begin{cases} 1, & (\text{if } x = 9, 11, 12, 13, 14, 15, 16, 18), \\ 0, & (\text{otherwise}); \end{cases}$$

$$(b)\ f(x) = \begin{cases} 1, & (\text{if } x = 0, 1, 2, 3, 6, 7, 10, 11, 18, 19), \\ 0, & (\text{otherwise}); \end{cases}$$

$$(c)\ f(x) = \begin{cases} 1, & (\text{if } x = 3, 5, 7, 11, 12, 29, 31), \\ *, & (\text{if } x = 1, 2, 6, 10, 28), \\ 0, & (\text{otherwise}); \end{cases}$$

$$(d)\ f(x) = \begin{cases} 1, & (\text{if } x = 8, 9, 10, 11, 17, 24, 26, 30), \\ *, & (\text{if } x = 0, 1, 2, 3, 6), \\ 0, & (\text{otherwise}). \end{cases}$$

3. For each of the switching functions (a)–(c) of six variables listed below, find the maximal cubes by means of the tabular method and then construct a minimal cubical cover by the methods given in §6 and §7. Do the same for its complement and compare their costs:

$$(a)\ f(x) = \begin{cases} 1, & (\text{if } x = 0, 5, 7, 8, 10, 15, 21, 26, 31, 32, 59, 62), \\ *, & (\text{if } x = 3, 19, 28, 35, 47, 63), \\ 0, & (\text{otherwise}); \end{cases}$$

$$(b)\ f(x) = \begin{cases} 1, & (\text{if } x = 8, 10, 17, 21, 25, 41, 44, 46, 56, 58), \\ *, & (\text{if } x = 9, 11, 19, 23, 27, 43, 45, 47, 57, 59), \\ 0, & (\text{otherwise}); \end{cases}$$

$$(c)\ f(x) = \begin{cases} 1, & (\text{if } x = 3, 5, 7, 11, 12, 29, 31), \\ *, & (\text{if } x = 1, 2, 6, 10, 28), \\ 0, & (\text{otherwise}). \end{cases}$$

4. Consider the switching function $f: Q^7 \to Q^*$ of seven variables defined by its Boolean expression

$$f = x_1'x_2'x_4'x_6'x_7' \lor x_1'x_4'x_6'x_7 \lor x_1'x_2x_4'x_5 \lor x_2'x_3x_5'x_6$$
$$\lor x_1x_2'x_3'x_4'x_5x_6 \lor x_1x_2x_3x_4x_6'x_7' \lor x_1'x_2'x_3x_4x_6x_7$$

with the points of the cube 1001**1 as don't care points. Find its maximal cubes by means of the consensus method and then construct a minimal cubical cover by the methods given in §6 and §7.

5. FACE OPERATORS. Let C denote an arbitrary cube in Q^n with co-ordinates $c_1 \cdots c_n$. For every positive integer $i \le n$, we define its *i-th upper face* $\partial_i^1(C)$ and its *i-th lower face* $\partial_i^0(C)$ by setting

$$\partial_i^1(C) = \begin{cases} c_1 \cdots c_{i-1}1c_{i+1} \cdots c_n, & \text{(if } c_i = *), \\ \square, & \text{(if } c_i \ne *), \end{cases}$$

$$\partial_i^0(C) = \begin{cases} c_1 \cdots c_{i-1}0c_{i+1} \cdots c_n, & \text{(if } c_i = *), \\ \square, & \text{(if } c_i \ne *). \end{cases}$$

If $c_i = *$, prove that

$$C = \partial_i^1(C) \cup \partial_i^0(C)$$

and that, for any subset F of Q^n, $C \in K(F)$ implies $\partial_i^1(C) \in K(F)$ and $\partial_i^0(C) \in K(F)$. [Roth 1.]

6. COFACE OPERATORS. Let F be any subset of Q^n and consider an arbitrarily given cube C in the cubical complex $K(F)$ and with co-ordinate $c_1 \cdots c_n$. For every positive integer $i \le n$, we define its *i-th coface* $\delta_i(C)$ *of* C *in* $K(F)$ as follows: In $c_i = *$, we set

$$\delta_i(C) = \square$$

If $c_i \ne *$, we obtain a cube

$$C^{(i)} = c_1 \cdots c_{i-1}*c_{i+1} \cdots c_n$$

in Q^n and we define

$$\delta_i(C) = \begin{cases} C^{(i)}, & \text{(if } C^{(i)} \in K(F)), \\ \square, & \text{(if } C^{(i)} \notin K(F)). \end{cases}$$

Prove that C is maximal in $K(F)$ iff $\delta_i(C) = \square$ holds for every $i = 1, 2, \cdots, n$. Hence maximal cubes in $K(F)$ are called *elementary cocycles*. [Roth 1.]

7. INTERSECTION OF CUBES. By means of the cap products given in Table II-5-1, show that the set-theoretic intersection $C \cap D$ of any

two cubes C and D in Q^n, with coordinates $c_1 \cdots c_n$ and $d_1 \cdots d_n$, respectively, can be determined as follows:

$$C \cap D = \square \quad \text{iff} \quad c_i \cap d_i = \square$$

holds for some positive integer $i \leq n$; otherwise, $C \cap D$ is the cube in Q^n whose j-th coordinate is $c_j \cap d_j$ for every $j = 1, \cdots, n$. By the *cap product* of any two collections γ and δ of cubes in Q^n, we mean the collection

$$\gamma \cap \delta = \{C \cap D \mid C \in \gamma \quad \text{and} \quad D \in \delta\}$$

of the pairwise intersections $C \cap D$ for all $C \in \gamma$ and all $D \in \delta$. Prove that the cap product is commutative and associative.

8. SHARP OPERATIONS. To define these operations, we first define the *sharp products* of elements in Q^* by means of the accompanying table. Let C and D denote any two cubes in Q^n with coordinates

$\#$	1	0	$*$
1	$\square$	$\times$	$\square$
0	$\times$	$\square$	$\square$
$*$	0	1	$\square$

$c_1 \cdots c_n$ and $d_1 \cdots d_n$. Define their *sharp product* $C \# D$ as follows. If $c_i \# d_i$ is a cross $\times$ for some i, then the cubes C and D are disjoint. In this case, let

$$C \# D = C.$$

Otherwise, we have $c_i \# d_i \neq \times$ for all $i \in N = \{1, 2, \cdots, n\}$. In this case, let

$$M = \{i \in N \mid c_i \# d_i \neq \square\}.$$

For every $i \in M$, let E_i denote the cube in Q^n whose coordinates are obtained from those of the cube C by replacing c_i by $c_i \# d_i$. Then define

$$C \# D = \{E_i \mid i \in M\}.$$

Prove that $C \# D$ is the collection of the maximal cubes of the cubical complex formed by the set $C \backslash D$ of all vertices of C not in D. For every collection γ of cubes in Q^n, define

$$\gamma \# D = \bigcup_{C \in \gamma} C \# D.$$

Establish the following commutativity relation

$$(\gamma \# D_1) \# D_2 = (\gamma \# D_2) \# D_1$$

for any two cubes D_1 and D_2 in Q^n. Thus we may define the *sharp product* $\gamma \# \delta$ of any two collections γ and δ of cubes in Q^n by induction on the number of cubes in δ, namely,

$$\gamma \# \delta = (\gamma \# D) \# (\delta \backslash \{D\}).$$

Verify that the sharp product is, in general, noncommutative and nonassociative. [Roth 1].

9. ESSENTIAL MAXIMAL CUBES.   Consider an arbitrary switching function

$$f : Q^n \to Q^*$$

possibly with don't care points. Prove that the following three statements are equivalent:
   (a) A maximal cube $C \in M(f)$ is essential.
   (b) $C \# [M(f)\backslash\{c\}]$ covers at least one point of $F = f^{-1}(1)$.
   (c) The cap product $C \cap K(f)$ is not empty and is not contained in the cubical complex $K(W)$ of the subset W of Q^n defined by

$$\mu = \{D \in M(f) \,|\, D \neq C \quad \text{and} \quad C \cap D \neq \Box\},$$
$$w = \bigcup_{D \in \mu} D.$$

Each of the conditions (b) and (c) can be applied to find the core $E(f)$ of f when the set $M(f)$ of maximal cubes was constructed by means of the consensus method. See [Roth 2] and [Mi, Vol. I, pp. 165, 175].

10. Let γ and δ denote any two collections of cubes in Q^n and let

$$F = \bigcup_{C \in \gamma} C, \qquad G = \bigcup_{D \in \delta} D.$$

Prove that $F \subset G$ iff $\gamma \# \delta = \Box$.

11. COVERING PROBLEM.   Let γ and δ denote any two collections of cubes in Q^n satisfying $\gamma \# \delta = \Box$. By the *covering problem* with respect to a given cost function c, we mean the problem of finding a subcollection δ_0 of δ of the minimal cost $c(\delta_0)$ which satisfies $\gamma \# \delta_0 = \Box$. The cubes in γ will be referred to as the *column cubes* and those in δ will be called the *row cubes* of the problem. Consider an arbitrarily given switching function

$$f : Q^n \to Q^*,$$

possibly with don't care points, and let γ denote a collection of cubes in Q^n satisfying

$$\bigcup_{C \in \gamma} C = F = f^{-1}(1).$$

Prove that every solution δ_0 to the covering problem (γ, δ), where $\delta = M(f)$ stands for the set of all maximal cubes of f, is a minimal cubical cover for f with respect to the given cost function c.

12. FIRST REDUCED PROBLEM. Consider an arbitrary covering problem (γ, δ) with respect to a given cost function c. A row cube $D \in \delta$ is said to be *essential* iff

$$\gamma \cap [D \# (\delta \backslash \{D\})] \neq \square.$$

Here, $\cap$ denotes the cap product as defined in Exercise 7. The subcollection ε of δ which consists of all essential cubes in δ is called the *core* of δ. Prove that the core ε of δ is contained in every solution δ_0 of the covering problem. Let

$$\gamma' = \gamma \# \varepsilon, \qquad \delta' = \delta \backslash \varepsilon.$$

Prove that the condition $\gamma' \# \delta' = \square$ is satisfied. The covering problem (γ', δ') with respect to the given cost function c will be referred to as the *first reduced problem* of the given covering problem (γ, δ). If the given cost function c is additive, prove that δ_0 is a solution to the covering problem (γ, δ) iff $\delta_0 \backslash \varepsilon$ is a solution to the first reduced problem (γ', δ').

13. SECOND REDUCED PROBLEM. Consider the first reduced problem (γ', δ') of an arbitrarily given covering problem (γ, δ) with respect to an additive cost function c. Let A and B denote any two cubes in γ'. We say that A *dominates* B iff, for an arbitrary subcollection σ of δ', $B \# \sigma = \square$ implies $A \# \sigma = \square$. Let γ'' denote a minimal subcollection of γ' such that every cube in $\gamma' \backslash \gamma''$ *dominates* at least one cube in γ''. Next, let A and B denote any two cubes in δ'. We say that A *dominates* B iff $c(A) \leq c(B)$ and $C \cap B \subset C \cap A$ holds for every $C \in \gamma'$. Let δ'' denote a minimal subcollection of δ' such that every cube in $\delta' \backslash \delta''$ is *dominated* by at least one cube in δ''. Prove $\gamma'' \# \delta'' = \square$. The covering problem (γ'', δ'') is called the *second reduced problem* of the given covering problem (γ, δ). Prove that every solution δ_0'' to the second reduced problem (γ'', δ'') is also a solution to the first reduced problem (γ', δ') and hence $\delta_0'' \cup \varepsilon$ constitutes a solution to the given covering problem (γ, δ) with ε standing for the core of δ.

14. HIGHER REDUCED PROBLEMS. Consider an arbitrarily given covering problem (γ, δ) with respect to an additive cost function c. The first reduced problem of the second reduced problem (γ'', δ'') of (γ, δ) will be called the *third reduced problem* of (γ, δ) and will be denoted by $(\gamma^{(3)}, \delta^{(3)})$. The second reduced problem of (γ'', δ'') will be called the *fourth reduced problem* of (γ, δ) and will be denoted by $(\gamma^{(4)}, \delta^{(4)})$. In general, let n denote any positive integer and assume that the $2n$-th reduced problem $(\gamma^{(2n)}, \delta^{(2n)})$ of (γ, δ) has already been constructed. Then the first reduced problem of $(\gamma^{(2n)}, \delta^{(2n)})$ is defined

to be the $(2n + 1)$-th *reduced problem* of (γ, δ) and the second reduced problem of $(\gamma^{(2n)}, \delta^{(2n)})$ is defined to be the $(2n + 2)$-th *reduced problem* of (γ, δ). This completes the inductive definition of the higher reduced problems of (γ, δ). Prove the existence of an integer $n \geq 0$ such that one of the following two situations occurs:
(a) The core ε_{2n} of $\delta^{(2n)}$ covers $\gamma^{(2n)}$, that is,

$$\gamma^{(2n)} \,\#\, \varepsilon_{2n} = \square.$$

In this case, we obtain a solution

$$\delta_0 = \varepsilon \cup \varepsilon_2 \cup \cdots \cup \varepsilon_{2n}$$

of the given covering problem (γ, δ).

(b) $(\gamma^{(2n)}, \delta^{(2n)}) = (\gamma^{(2n+1)}, \delta^{(2n+1)}) = (\gamma^{(2n+2)}, \delta^{(2n+2)})$.

In this case, no further reduction can simplify the problem. See next exercise.

15. BRANCHING METHOD. A covering problem (γ, δ) with respect to an additive cost function c is said to be *irreducible*, or *cyclic*, iff

$$(\gamma, \delta) = (\gamma', \delta') = (\gamma'', \delta'')$$

and hence all of the reduced problems of (γ, δ) are identical with (γ, δ). To solve an irreducible problem (γ, δ), one may apply the *branching method* described as follows. Choose an arbitrary cube $D \in \delta$, preferably of minimal cost $c(D)$. If D is used to cover a part of γ, we obtain a new covering problem

$$p_1 = (\gamma \,\#\, D, \delta \backslash \{D\}).$$

On the other hand, if D is not used to cover a part of γ, we also obtain a new covering problem

$$p_2 = (\gamma, \delta \backslash \{D\}).$$

Solve both p_1 and p_2. Let δ_1 and δ_2 denote solutions to the problems p_1 and p_2, respectively. Compare the costs of the collections $\delta_1 \cup \{D\}$ and δ_2. Prove that the one with smaller cost is a solution to the given problem (γ, δ). [Roth 2.]

16. Apply the method described in Exercises 11–15 to find a minimal cubical cover for the switching function of seven variables given in Exercise 4.

17. Let $n = 3k$ and consider the collection γ of cubes in Q^n defined as follows. A cube C of Q^n is in γ iff C has k 1's, k 0's, and k *'s in its coordinates. This collection γ defines a switching function $f : Q^n \to Q$ without don't care points, namely,

$$f^{-1}(1) = \bigcup_{C \in \gamma} C.$$

Prove that $M(f) = \gamma$ and hence f has

$$\binom{3k}{k}\binom{2k}{k}\binom{k}{k} = \frac{(3k)!}{(k!)^3}$$

maximal cubes. This indicates the complexity of the algorithms in §§4–7 and in Exercises 11–15 when n is even moderately large. See [Mi, Vol. I, p. 181].

18. DISJUNCTION OF BASIC GATES. For an arbitrary positive integer n, let $\mathcal{B}$ denote a given collection of switching functions of n variables, called *basic gates*, such that $\mathcal{B}$ contains every function that can be represented by a single minterm. For example, $\mathcal{B}$ may be the collection of all threshold functions of n variables. Each basic gate $\beta \in \mathcal{B}$ has a cost $c(\beta)$. Now consider an arbitrarily given switching function

$$f : Q^n \to Q^*,$$

possibly with don't care points. Our problem is to find a certain number of basic gates $\beta_1, \cdots, \beta_m \in \mathcal{B}$ such that

$$f \equiv \beta_1 \vee \beta_2 \vee \cdots \vee \beta_m$$

modulo $D = f^{-1}(*)$ and that the total cost

$$c(\beta_1, \cdots, \beta_m) = \sum_{i=1}^m c(\beta_i)$$

is minimal. For this purpose, let $F^* = f^{-1}\{1, *\}$ and consider the subcollection

$$L(f) = \{\beta \in \mathcal{B} \mid \beta^{-1}(1) \subset F^*\}$$

of $\mathcal{B}$. Define a partial order $\prec$ in $L(f)$ as follows: For any two basic gates α and β in $L(f)$, $\alpha \prec \beta$ iff we have

$$c(\alpha) \geq c(\beta), \qquad \alpha^{-1}(1) \subset \beta^{-1}(1).$$

Let $M(f)$ denote the basic gates in $L(f)$ which are maximal with respect to this partial order $\prec$. Verify that the methods in §§6–7 can be generalized to this problem. [Roth-Wagner 1.]

19. CONJUNCTION OF BASIC GATES. Assume that the collection $\mathcal{B}$ of basic gates satisfies the condition that, for every $\beta \in \mathcal{B}$, we have $\beta' \in \mathcal{B}$ and $c(\beta') = c(\beta)$. For an arbitrary switching function

$$f : Q^n \to Q^*,$$

possibly with don't care points, find basic gates $\alpha'_1, \cdots, \alpha'_l \in \mathcal{B}$ such that

$$f' \equiv \alpha'_1 \vee \alpha'_2 \vee \cdots \vee \alpha'_l$$

modulo $D = f^{-1}(*)$ and that the total cost

$$c(\alpha'_1, \cdots, \alpha'_l) = \sum_{i=1}^{l} c(\alpha'_i)$$

is minimal. By means of De Morgan's formulas, prove that

$$f \equiv \alpha_1 \wedge \alpha_2 \wedge \cdots \wedge \alpha_l$$

modulo D with total cost

$$c(\alpha_1, \cdots, \alpha_l) = c(\alpha'_1, \cdots, \alpha'_l).$$

As in §8, this cost $c(\alpha_1, \cdots, \alpha_l)$ should be compared with the cost $c(\beta_1, \cdots, \beta_m)$ in the preceding exercise.

20. Generalize the method in §9 to the simultaneous minimization of a given collection

$$f_i : Q^n \to Q^*, \qquad (i = 1, 2, \cdots, m),$$

of switching functions as disjunctions of basic gates.

Chapter III

DECOMPOSITION ALGORITHMS

In view of the main objective of designing more efficient electronic computers, logical designers in recent years have shown strong interest in the realization of switching functions by networks of more complicated devices than the classical AND and OR gates. With a given list of allowable logical devices, it is desirable to obtain the most economic network of allowable devices realizing a given switching function. This leads us to our general minimization problem as stated in §10. With the aid of a reduction theorem and the consideration of the total degree of a decomposition, our problem with reasonable cost structures can be solved by iterated search for simple decompositions with respect to disjunctive or nondisjunctive partitions of variables. At each stage, we shall make use of Ashenhurst's fundamental theorem and our own generalization to the nondisjunctive cases. The algorithms are described and illustrated in all details. Locally, the algorithm of assigning values 0 or 1 to the *'s in the partition matrix is given in §7. Then, the global algorithm of finding an optimal decomposition is given in §11.

I. Decompositions of Switching Functions

A given switching function of n variables can frequently be decomposed into a composite function of several essentially simpler switching functions. Such decomposition sometimes leads to designs for more economical switching circuits to realize the given switching function. As an illustrative example, let us consider the switching function f of four variables given by

$$f^{-1}(0) = \{0, 1, 2, 3, 4, 5, 9, 11, 13\},$$
$$f^{-1}(1) = \{6, 7, 8, 10, 12, 14, 15\}.$$

This switching function f has a decomposition given by

$$f(x) = \mu\{\&(x_2, x_3), \oslash(x_1, x_4), \vee[x_1, \&(x_2, x_3)]\}$$

for every point $x = x_1 x_2 x_3 x_4$ of the 4-cube Q^4, where

$$\mu : Q^3 \to Q, \qquad \vee : Q^2 \to Q, \qquad \oslash : Q^2 \to Q, \qquad \& : Q^2 \to Q$$

TABLE III-1-1

x	x_1	x_2	$\vee(x)$	$\vardiamond(x)$	$\&(x)$
0	0	0	0	0	0
1	0	1	1	1	0
2	1	0	1	1	0
3	1	1	1	0	1

TABLE III-1-2

x	x_1	x_2	x_3	$\mu(x)$
0	0	0	0	0
1	0	0	1	0
2	0	1	0	0
3	0	1	1	1
4	1	0	0	0
5	1	0	1	1
6	1	1	0	1
7	1	1	1	1

TABLE III-1-3

x	x_1	x_2	x_3	x_4	$\&(x_2, x_3)$	$\vardiamond(x_1, x_4)$	$\vee[x_1, \&(x_2, x_3)]$	$f(x)$
0	0	0	0	0	0	0	0	0
1	0	0	0	1	0	1	0	0
2	0	0	1	0	0	0	0	0
3	0	0	1	1	0	1	0	0
4	0	1	0	0	0	0	0	0
5	0	1	0	1	0	1	0	0
6	0	1	1	0	1	0	1	1
7	0	1	1	1	1	1	1	1
8	1	0	0	0	0	1	1	1
9	1	0	0	1	0	0	1	0
10	1	0	1	0	0	1	1	1
11	1	0	1	1	0	0	1	0
12	1	1	0	0	0	1	1	1
13	1	1	0	1	0	0	1	0
14	1	1	1	0	1	1	1	1
15	1	1	1	1	1	0	1	1

denote, respectively, the *majority*, the *OR*, the *exclusive OR*, and the *AND*, that is, switching functions defined by Tables III-1-1 and III-1-2.

This decomposition of the given switching function $f : Q^4 \to Q$ in terms of the simpler *component switching functions* μ, $\vee$, $\oslash$, and & can be verified by the correspondence table III-1-3.

FIGURE III-1-4

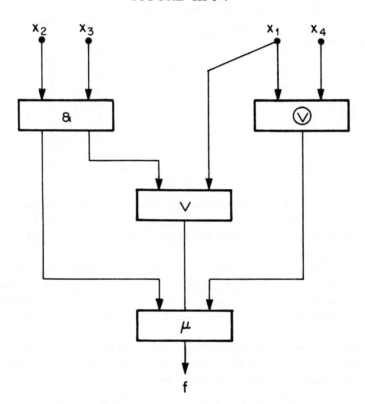

This decomposition of f can be represented by the Boolean graph in Figure III-1-4. This Boolean graph indicates a switching circuit realizing the given switching function f by means of four elementary logical devices, placed in the four black-boxes, realizing the four component switching functions μ, $\vee$, $\oslash$, and &.

As another example of decomposition, consider the switching function f of four variables given by

$$f^{-1}(0) = \{0, 1, 2, 4, 5, 6, 8, 9, 10, 12, 14\},$$
$$f^{-1}(1) = \{3, 7, 11, 13, 15\}.$$

This switching function f has a decomposition given by

$$f(x) = \delta\{\alpha(x_1, x_2, x_3), \beta(x_2, x_3, x_4), \gamma[\alpha(x_1, x_2, x_3), x_3, x_4]\}$$

for every point $x = x_1x_2x_3x_4$ of the 4-cube Q_4, where α, β, γ, and δ are switching functions of three variables defined by Table III-1-5.

TABLE III-1-5

x	x_1	x_2	x_3	$\alpha(x)$	$\beta(x)$	$\gamma(x)$	$\delta(x)$
0	0	0	0	1	1	1	1
1	0	0	1	0	1	1	1
2	0	1	0	1	1	1	1
3	0	1	1	0	0	0	0
4	1	0	0	1	1	1	1
5	1	0	1	0	0	1	0
6	1	1	0	0	1	1	0
7	1	1	1	0	0	0	0

This decomposition of f in terms of the component switching functions α, β, γ, and δ of three variables can be verified by Table III-1-6. It happens that the component switching functions α, β, γ, and δ are all linearly separable as defined in (I, §12).

This decomposition of f may be represented by the Boolean graph in Figure III-1-7. This Boolean graph indicates a switching circuit realizing f by means of four threshold devices, each with three inputs, placed in the four black-boxes realizing the linearly separable switching functions α, β, γ, and δ.

Finally, as an example with don't care points, let us consider the switching function f of four variables defined by Table III-1-8. Consider the switching function g of four variables defined by

$$g(x) = \phi[x_1, x_2, x_3, \psi(x_1, x_4)]$$

for every point $x = x_1x_2x_3x_4$ of the 4-cube Q^4, where

$$\phi : Q^4 \to Q, \qquad \psi : Q^2 \to Q$$

denote switching functions defined by

$$\phi^{-1}(0) = \{1, 2, 3, 4, 5, 6, 7, 9, 10, 11, 12, 14\},$$
$$\phi^{-1}(1) = \{0, 8, 13, 15\},$$
$$\psi^{-1}(0) = \{0, 3\},$$
$$\psi^{-1}(1) = \{1, 2\}.$$

TABLE III-1-6

x	x_1	x_2	x_3	x_4	$\alpha(x_1, x_2, x_3)$	$\beta(x_2, x_3, x_4)$	$\gamma[(x_1, x_2, x_3), x_3, x_4]$	$f(x)$
0	0	0	0	0	1	1	1	0
1	0	0	0	1	1	1	1	0
2	0	0	1	0	0	0	0	0
3	0	0	1	1	0	1	1	1
4	0	1	0	0	1	0	1	0
5	0	1	0	1	1	1	1	0
6	0	1	1	0	0	0	0	0
7	0	1	1	1	0	1	1	1
8	1	0	0	0	1	1	1	0
9	1	0	0	1	1	1	1	0
10	1	0	1	0	0	0	0	0
11	1	0	1	1	0	1	1	1
12	1	1	0	0	0	0	1	0
13	1	1	0	1	0	1	1	1
14	1	1	1	0	0	0	1	0
15	1	1	1	1	0	0	0	1

FIGURE III-1-7

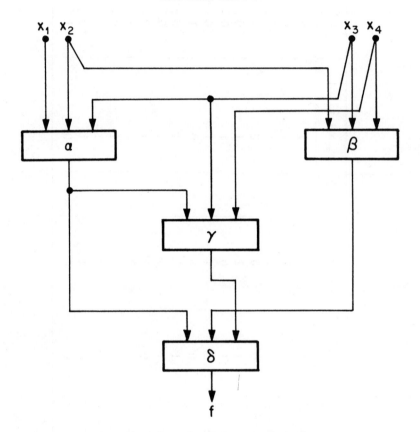

The table of correspondence of this switching function $g : Q^4 \to Q$ can be easily found in the form of Table III-1-9. Comparing Table III-1-8 with Table III-1-9, we obtain the relations

$$f^{-1}(0) \subset g^{-1}(0), \qquad f^{-1}(1) \subset g^{-1}(1).$$

In other words, for each point $x = x_1 x_2 x_3 x_4$ of Q^4 which is not a don't care point, we always have

$$f(x) = \phi[x_1, x_2, x_3, \psi(x_1, x_4)];$$

therefore, we say that we have obtained a decomposition of f by means of the component switching functions ϕ and ψ.

This decomposition of f can be represented by the Boolean graph in Figure III-1-10. This Boolean graph indicates a switching circuit realizing

TABLE III-1-8

x	x_1	x_2	x_3	x_4	$f(x)$
0	0	0	0	0	1
1	0	0	0	1	0
2	0	0	1	0	0
3	0	0	1	1	0
4	0	1	0	0	*
5	0	1	0	1	*
6	0	1	1	0	*
7	0	1	1	1	*
8	1	0	0	0	*
9	1	0	0	1	*
10	1	0	1	0	*
11	1	0	1	1	*
12	1	1	0	0	1
13	1	1	0	1	0
14	1	1	1	0	1
15	1	1	1	1	0

TABLE III-1-9

x	x_1	x_2	x_3	x_4	$\psi(x_1, x_4)$	$g(x)$
0	0	0	0	0	0	1
1	0	0	0	1	1	0
2	0	0	1	0	0	0
3	0	0	1	1	1	0
4	0	1	0	0	0	0
5	0	1	0	1	1	0
6	0	1	1	0	0	0
7	0	1	1	1	1	0
8	1	0	0	0	1	0
9	1	0	0	1	0	1
10	1	0	1	0	1	0
11	1	0	1	1	0	0
12	1	1	0	0	1	1
13	1	1	0	1	0	0
14	1	1	1	0	1	1
15	1	1	1	1	0	0

FIGURE III-1-10

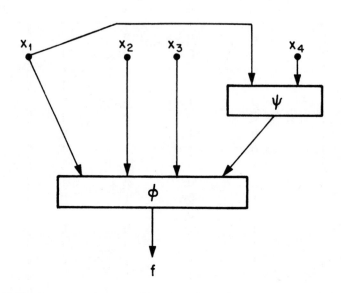

TABLE III-1-11

x	x_1	x_2	x_3	x_4	$\phi(x)$
0	0	0	0	0	1
1	0	0	0	1	0
2	0	0	1	0	0
3	0	0	1	1	0
4	0	1	0	0	*
5	0	1	0	1	*
6	0	1	1	0	*
7	0	1	1	1	*
8	1	0	0	0	*
9	1	0	0	1	*
10	1	0	1	0	*
11	1	0	1	1	*
12	1	1	0	0	0
13	1	1	0	1	1
14	1	1	1	0	0
15	1	1	1	1	1

f by means of two devices placed in the two black-boxes realizing the two component switching functions ϕ and ψ.

The inputs of the switching device ϕ are fed by the original variables x_1, x_2, x_3 and by the output of the device ψ. Hence, there are don't care points of Q^4 inherited from the original ones. In general, there also could be some new don't care points because some inputs are fed by the outputs of other devices. The don't care points of Q^4 for ϕ are shown in Table III-1-11; these are all inherited from the original don't care points for the given switching function f. In this particular example, we have no don't care point of Q^2 for the component switching function ψ.

2. Simple Decompositions

A special class of decompositions of switching functions called *simple decompositions* plays the basic role in the theory of decompositions. To define simple decompositions, we must introduce a general notion of a *partition of variables*. Let us consider a given set

$$X = \{x_1, \cdots, x_n\}$$

of n variables. By a *partition* of the set X, we mean an ordered pair of collections

$$Y = \{y_1, y_2, \cdots, y_s\}, \qquad Z = \{z_1, z_2, \cdots, z_t\}$$

of variables in X with repetitions allowed and

$$Y \cup Z = X;$$

that is to say, every variable x_k in X occurs at least once in at least one, and possibly in both, of Y and Z. This partition of X will be denoted by

$$Y \mid Z = y_1 y_2 \cdots y_s \mid z_1 z_2 \cdots z_t.$$

This notion of a partition of the variables in X includes those in [Ashenhurst 2] and [Hu 1] as special cases and is actually more general. In fact, in a general partition $Y \mid Z$ of X, not only may some y_i be the same variable x_k as some z_j, but also some y_i may be the same variable x_k as some y_j, or some z_i may be the same variable x_k as some z_j.

The integer s in the partition $Y \mid Z$ described above is called the *primary degree* of $Y \mid Z$; the integer t, the *secondary degree* of $Y \mid Z$. Since $Y \cup Z = X$, we must have

$$s + t \geq n.$$

The nonnegative integer

$$r = s + t - n$$

will be referred to as the *degree of repetition* of the partition $Y \mid Z$.

If $r = 0$, then Y and Z must be disjoint and the variables in Y and Z are all distinct. In this case, the partition $Y \mid Z$ is said to be *disjunctive* or *nonsingular*; otherwise, $Y \mid Z$ is said to be *nondisjunctive* or *singular*.

There are exactly 2^n disjunctive partitions of X [Ashenhurst 2, p. 77]. On the other hand, for each given $r > 0$, one can easily see that there are exactly

$$n^r \cdot 2^{n+r} = 2^n (2n)^r$$

partitions of X with r as the degree of repetition. For a given secondary degree t, there are exactly

$$C_t^n = \frac{n!}{t! \, (n - t)!}$$

disjunctive partitions of X with t as the secondary degree, and there are not more than

$$n^r C_t^{n+r} = \frac{(n + r)! \, n^r}{t! \, (n + r - t)!}$$

partitions of X with r as the degree of repetition and t as the secondary degree.

Now let us consider a given switching function

$$f : Q^n \to Q$$

of n variables $X = \{x_1, x_2, \cdots, x_n\}$. Let

$$Y \mid Z = \{y_1 y_2 \cdots y_s \mid z_1 z_2 \cdots z_t\}$$

be a partition of the set X. The given switching function

$$f(x_1, x_2, \cdots, x_n)$$

might possibly be expressed as a composite function

$$\phi[y_1, y_2, \cdots, y_s, \psi(z_1, z_2, \cdots, z_t)].$$

By this, we mean that there exist two switching functions

$$\phi : Q^{s+1} \to Q, \qquad \psi : Q^t \to Q$$

of $s + 1$ and t variables, respectively, such that for any point $(x_1, x_2, \cdots, x_n)$ of the n-cube Q^n the corresponding value of

$$\psi = \psi(z_1, z_2, \cdots, z_t),$$

substituted in $\phi(y_1, y_2, \cdots, y_s, \psi)$, gives the functional value $f(x_1, x_2, \cdots, x_n)$. If this statement is true, the switching functions ϕ and ψ are said to represent a *simple decomposition* of the given switching function f with respect to the partition $Y \mid Z$.

Usually we have some don't care points of Q^n for the given switching function f. If we do, then we say that the switching functions ϕ and ψ represent a simple decomposition of f with respect to the partition $Y \mid Z$ provided

$$f(x_1, x_2, \cdots, x_n) = \phi[y_1, y_2, \cdots, y_s, \psi(z_1, z_2, \cdots, z_t)]$$

holds for every point $(x_1, x_2, \cdots, x_n)$ of Q^n which is not a don't care point.

If the partition $Y \mid Z$ is disjunctive, the simple decomposition (ϕ, ψ) of f is said to be *disjunctive*; otherwise, it is said to be *singular* and the integer

$$r = s + t - n$$

is called the *degree of repetition* of the simple decomposition (ϕ, ψ). Finally, the integers s and t are called, respectively, the *primary degree* and the *secondary degree* of the simple decomposition (ϕ, ψ) of f.

As an example of simple decomposition, we have the third example in §1. In this example, the given switching function

$$f : Q^4 \to Q$$

is defined by Table III-1-6. The partition of variables concerned is

$$Y \mid Z = x_1 x_2 x_3 \mid x_1 x_4.$$

Then the switching functions

$$\phi : Q^4 \to Q, \qquad \psi : Q^2 \to Q$$

defined in §1 represent a singular simple decomposition (ϕ, ψ) of the given switching function f with degree of repetition $r = 1$.

As another example of simple decomposition, let us consider the switching function

$$f : Q^4 \to Q$$

of four variables defined by Table III-2-1. Consider the switching functions

$$\phi : Q^2 \to Q, \qquad \psi : Q^3 \to Q$$

defined by Tables III-2-2 and III-2-3. Consider the switching function g of four variables defined by

$$g(x) = \phi[x_1, \psi(x_2, x_3, x_4)]$$

for every point $x = x_1 x_2 x_3 x_4$ of the 4-cube Q^4. The table of correspondence of this switching function $g : Q^4 \to Q$ is given by Table III-2-4.

TABLE III-2-1

x	x_1	x_2	x_3	x_4	$f(x)$
0	0	0	0	0	1
1	0	0	0	1	0
2	0	0	1	0	0
3	0	0	1	1	0
4	0	1	0	0	0
5	0	1	0	1	0
6	0	1	1	0	1
7	0	1	1	1	1
8	1	0	0	0	0
9	1	0	0	1	1
10	1	0	1	0	1
11	1	0	1	1	1
12	1	1	0	0	1
13	1	1	0	1	1
14	1	1	1	0	0
15	1	1	1	1	0

TABLE III-2-2

x	x_1	x_2	$\phi(x)$
0	0	0	1
1	0	1	0
2	1	0	0
3	1	1	1

TABLE III-2-3

x	x_1	x_2	x_3	$\psi(x)$
0	0	0	0	0
1	0	0	1	1
2	0	1	0	1
3	0	1	1	1
4	1	0	0	1
5	1	0	1	1
6	1	1	0	0
7	1	1	1	0

TABLE III-2-4

x	x_1	x_2	x_3	x_4	$\psi(x_2, x_3, x_4)$	$g(x)$
0	0	0	0	0	0	1
1	0	0	0	1	1	0
2	0	0	1	0	1	0
3	0	0	1	1	1	0
4	0	1	0	0	1	0
5	0	1	0	1	1	0
6	0	1	1	0	0	1
7	0	1	1	1	0	1
8	1	0	0	0	0	0
9	1	0	0	1	1	1
10	1	0	1	0	1	1
11	1	0	1	1	1	1
12	1	1	0	0	1	1
13	1	1	0	1	1	1
14	1	1	1	0	0	0
15	1	1	1	1	0	0

Comparing Table III-2-1 with Table III-2-4, we obtain

$$f(x) = g(x) = \phi[x_1, \psi(x_2, x_3, x_4)]$$

for every point $x = x_1 x_2 x_3 x_4$ of Q^4. Hence we obtain a disjunctive simple decomposition (ϕ, ψ) of the given switching function f with respect to the partition

$$Y \mid Z = x_1 \mid x_2 x_3 x_4.$$

This simple decomposition (ϕ, ψ) of f is of primary degree $s = 1$ and secondary degree $t = 3$.

3. Reduction Theorem

The importance of simple decompositions of a given switching function

$$f : Q^n \to Q$$

of n variables results from a *reduction theorem* which says, roughly, that every decomposition of f can be obtained by composing a finite number of successive simple decompositions. To illustrate this reduction theorem, which will be established in the present section, let us first give an example.

For this purpose, let us consider the first example in §1. In this example, we have a switching function

$$f : Q^4 \to Q$$

of four variables defined by

$$f^{-1}(0) = \{0, 1, 2, 3, 4, 5, 9, 11, 13\}$$
$$f^{-1}(1) = \{6, 7, 8, 10, 12, 14, 15\}$$

and a decomposition of f given by

$$f(x) = \mu\{\&(x_2, x_3), \mathbb{V}(x_1, x_4), \vee[x_1, \&(x_2, x_3)]\}$$

for every point $x = x_1x_2x_3x_4$ of the 4-cube Q^4. This decomposition of f is illustrated by the Boolean graph given in Figure III-1-4.

In Figure III-1-4, let us first observe that neither of the inputs to the black-box & is an output of any other black-box in the graph. In other words, each of the variables of the component switching function & is an original variable of f. Such a component switching function of a decomposition is called a *primitive component switching function*.

Now, in Figure III-1-4, replace the black-box & by an independent variable denoted by the same symbol &. Thus we obtain a new Boolean graph with three inputs x_1, x_4, and & as given in Figure III-3-1.

Let us denote by $\phi_1 : Q^3 \to Q$ the switching function of three variables x_1, x_4, and & represented by the Boolean graph in Figure III-3-1. Then the correspondence table of ϕ_1 is as shown in Table III-3-2.

FIGURE III-3-1

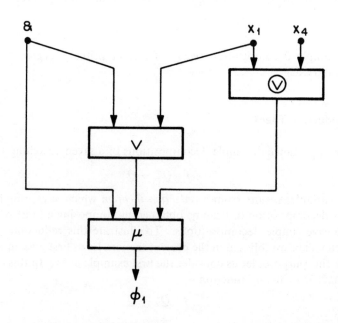

TABLE III-3-2

x	x_1	x_4	&	$\oslash(x_1, x_4)$	$\vee(x_1, \&)$	$\phi_1(x_1, x_4, \&)$
0	0	0	0	0	0	0
1	0	0	1	0	1	1
2	0	1	0	1	0	0
3	0	1	1	1	1	1
4.	1	0	0	1	1	1
5	1	0	1	1	1	1
6	1	1	0	0	1	0
7	1	1	1	0	1	1

Now let $\psi_1 : Q^2 \to Q$ denote the switching function deaned by

$$\psi_1(z_1, z_2) = \&(z_1, z_2)$$

for every point (z_1, z_2) of Q^2. Then, by comparing Figure III-1-4 with Figure III-3-1, we obtain

$$f(x) = \phi_1[x_1, x_4, \psi_1(x_2, x_3)]$$

for every point $x = x_1 x_2 x_3 x_4$ of Q^4. Thus we have obtained a disjunctive simple decomposition (ϕ_1, ψ_1) of f with respect to the partition $x_1 x_4 \mid x_2 x_3$.

Next, in Figure III-3-1, we observe that the component switching function $\oslash$ is primitive. By replacing the black-box $\oslash$ with an independent variable denoted by the same symbol $\oslash$, we obtain a new Boolean graph with three inputs x_1, &, and $\oslash$ as given in Figure III-3-3.

Let us denote by $\phi_2 : Q^3 \to Q$ the switching function of three variables x_1, &, and $\oslash$ represented by the Boolean graph in Figure III-3-3. Then the correspondence table of ϕ_2 is as shown in Table III-3-4.

Now let $\psi_2 : Q^2 \to Q$ denote the switching function defined by

$$\psi_2(z_1, z_2) = \oslash(z_1, z_2)$$

for every point (z_1, z_2) of Q^2. Then, by comparing Figure III-3-1 with Figure III-3-3, we have

$$\phi_1(x_1, x_4, \&) = \phi_2[x_1, \&, \psi_2(x_1, x_4)]$$

for every point $(x_1, x_4, \&)$ of Q^3. Thus we have obtained a singular simple decomposition (ϕ_2, ψ_2) of the switching function ϕ_1 with respect to the partition $x_1 \& \mid x_1 x_4$.

Finally, replace the primitive component switching function $\vee$ in Figure III-3-3 by an independent variable denoted by the same symbol $\vee$. Thus

FIGURE III-3-3

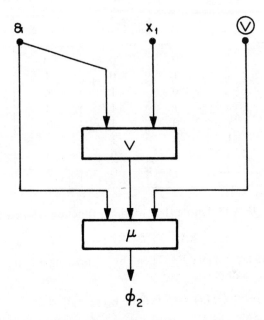

we obtain a new Boolean graph with inputs &, $\oslash$, and $\vee$ as shown in Figure III-3-5.

Let us denote by $\phi_3 : Q^3 \to Q$ the switching function of three variables &, $\oslash$, and $\vee$ represented by the Boolean graph in Figure III-3-5. Then ϕ_3 is obviously the majority function μ, that is,

$$\phi_3(\&, \oslash, \vee) = \mu(\&, \oslash, \vee)$$

for every point $(\&, \oslash, \vee)$ of Q^3. Now let $\psi_3 : Q^2 \to Q$ denote the switching

TABLE III-3-4

x	x_1	&	$\oslash$	$\vee(x_1, \&)$	$\phi_2(x_1, \&, \oslash)$
0	0	0	0	0	0
1	0	0	1	0	0
2	0	1	0	1	1
3	0	1	1	1	1
4	1	0	0	1	0
5	1	0	1	1	1
6	1	1	0	1	1
7	1	1	1	1	1

function defined by

$$\psi_3(z_1, z_2) = \vee(z_1, z_2)$$

for every point (z_1, z_2) of Q^2. Then, by comparing Figure III-3-3 with Figure III-3-5, we have

$$\phi_2(x_1, \&, \oslash) = \phi_3[\&, \oslash, \psi_3(x_1, \&)]$$

for every point $(x_1, \&, \oslash)$ of Q^3. Thus we have obtained a singular simple decomposition (ϕ_3, ψ_3) of the switching function ϕ_2 with respect to the partition $\&\oslash \mid x_1\&$.

FIGURE III-3-5

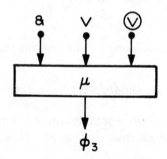

Thus, from the given decomposition of f, we have constructed a finite sequence

$$(\phi_1, \psi_1), \qquad (\phi_2, \psi_2), \qquad (\phi_3, \psi_3)$$

of simple decompositions, where

$$\psi_1 = \&, \qquad \psi_2 = \oslash, \qquad \psi_3 = \vee, \qquad \phi_3 = \mu$$

are exactly the four component switching functions in the given decomposition of f. Here (ϕ_1, ψ_1) is a simple decomposition of f; (ϕ_2, ψ_2) is a simple decomposition of ϕ_1; and (ϕ_3, ψ_3) is a simple decomposition of ϕ_2. Composing these three simple decompositions, we obtain

$$f(x) = \phi_1[x_1, x_4, \psi_1(x_2, x_3)]$$
$$= \phi_2[x_1, \psi_1(x_2, x_3), \psi_2(x_1, x_4)]$$
$$= \phi_3\{\psi_1(x_2, x_3), \psi_2(x_1, x_4), \psi_3[x_1, \psi_1(x_2, x_3)]\}$$
$$= \mu\{\&(x_2, x_3), \oslash(x_1, x_4), \vee[x_1, \&(x_2, x_3)]\}$$

for every point $x = x_1x_2x_3x_4$ of Q^4. This is exactly the given decomposition of f; therefore, the given decomposition of f with four component switching functions is the *composition* of three simple decompositions (ϕ_i, ψ_i),

$i = 1, 2, 3$, where ψ_1, ψ_2, ψ_3, and ϕ_3 are exactly the component switching functions of the given decomposition.

Our illustrative example given above suggests the following *reduction theorem* of decomposition.

THEOREM 3.1.   *Every decomposition of an arbitrarily given switching function*

$$f : Q^n \to Q$$

with $q + 1$ component switching functions is the composition of a sequence

$$(\phi_i, \psi_i), \qquad i = 1, 2, \cdots, q$$

of q simple decompositions such that

$$\psi_1, \psi_2, \cdots, \psi_q, \phi_q$$

are exactly the $q + 1$ component switching functions of the given decomposition of f.

Proof.   We shall prove the theorem by mathematical induction on the nonnegative integer q.

For the case $q = 0$, the given decomposition of f has only one component switching function which must be f itself. Hence, there is nothing to prove in this case.

Now let $q > 0$ and assume that the theorem has been proved for all decompositions with q component switching functions of any switching function. Consider an arbitrarily given decomposition D of a given switching function $f : Q^n \to Q$ with $q + 1$ component switching functions. At least one of the $q + 1$ component switching functions of D is primitive. Let $\psi_1 : Q^t \to Q$ be a primitive component switching function of D and let $z_1, \cdots, z_t$ denote the variables of ψ_1. Since ψ_1 is primitive, every z_j is some original variable x_k of f.

If, in the decomposition D of f (or, equivalently, in the Boolean graph of D), $\psi_1(z_1, \cdots, z_t)$ is replaced by an independent variable ψ_1, the decomposition D of f becomes a decomposition D_1 of a switching function $\phi_1 : Q^{s+1} \to Q$ with variables $y_1, \cdots, y_s$ and ψ_1, where $y_1, \cdots, y_s$ are those of $x_k's$ which appear in D outside of $\psi_1(z_1, \cdots, z_t)$. From this construction, it is obvious that

$$f(x) = \phi_1[y_1, \cdots, y_s, \psi_1(z_1, \cdots, z_t)]$$

for every point $x = x_1 x_2 \cdots x_n$ of Q^n. Thus, we obtain a simple decomposition (ϕ_1, ψ_1) of f. By the construction of D_1 and ϕ_1, D_1 is a decomposition of ϕ_1 which has q component switching functions, namely, the remaining q component switching functions of D.

By the inductive hypothesis, D_1 is the composition of $q - 1$ simple decompositions

$$(\phi_i, \psi_i), \qquad i = 2, \cdots, q,$$

such that $\psi_2, \cdots, \psi_q, \phi_q$ are exactly the q component switching functions of D_1. From the construction of D_1, it follows that D is the composition of the q simple decompositions

$$(\phi_i, \psi_i), \qquad i = 1, 2, \cdots, q$$

and that $\psi_1, \psi_2, \cdots, \psi_q, \phi_q$ are exactly the $q + 1$ component switching functions of the given decomposition D of f. This completes the inductive proof of (3.1). ‖

Because of the reduction theorem (3.1), it suffices to study only simple decompositions.

4. Total Degree of Repetition

Let us consider an arbitrarily given decomposition D of a given switching function

$$f : Q^n \rightarrow Q$$

of n variables $x_1, x_2, \cdots, x_n$ with $q + 1$ component switching functions. According to (3.1), there exists a sequence of simple decompositions

$$(\phi_i, \psi_i), \qquad i = 1, 2, \cdots, q,$$

such that $\psi_1, \psi_2, \cdots, \psi_q, \phi_q$ are exactly the $q + 1$ component switching functions of D and that D is the composition of these q simple decompositions, in symbols,

$$D = (\phi_q, \psi_q) \circ (\phi_{q-1}, \psi_{q-1}) \circ \cdots \circ (\phi_1, \psi_1).$$

Such a representation of the given decomposition D of f will be called a *factorization* of D into the *component simple decompositions* (ϕ_i, ψ_i), $i = 1, 2, \cdots, q$. From the proof of (3.1), it is obvious that D may have more than one factorization. In fact, every primitive component switching function of D can be chosen as the ψ_1.

Now let us investigate a certain given factorization

$$D = (\phi_q, \psi_q) \circ (\phi_{q-1}, \psi_{q-1}) \circ \cdots \circ (\phi_1, \psi_1)$$

of the given decomposition D of the switching function $f : Q^n \rightarrow Q$. For each $i = 1, 2, \cdots, q$, let s_i and t_i denote the primary degree and the secondary degree of the simple decomposition (ϕ_i, ψ_i) of the switching function ϕ_{i-1} with $\phi_0 = f$. Then ϕ_i is a switching function of $s_i + 1$ variables and ψ_i is a switching function of t_i variables. Let $s_0 = n - 1$.

In accordance with the definition in §2, the degree of repetition of the simple decomposition (ϕ_i, ψ_i) of ϕ_{i-1} is

$$r_i = s_i + t_i - (s_{i-1} + 1)$$
$$= s_i - s_{i-1} + t_i - 1$$

for every $i = 1, 2, \cdots, q$. Hence, the total sum of these q degrees r_i is

$$r = \sum_{i=1}^{q}(s_i - s_{i-1}) + \sum_{i=1}^{q}(t_i - 1)$$
$$= s_q - s_0 + \sum_{i=1}^{q}t_i - q$$
$$= p - q - n$$

where $p = t_1 + t_2 + \cdots + t_q + (s_q + 1)$ is the sum of the numbers of variables of the $q + 1$ component switching functions

$$\psi_1, \psi_2, \cdots, \psi_q, \phi_q$$

of the given decomposition D of f. Thus, we have proved the sum of the degrees of repetition of the simple decompositions in a factorization of D does not depend on the choice of the factorization D. For this reason, the nonnegative integer

$$r = p - q - n$$

will be called the total *degree of repetition* of the given decomposition D of f.

Section 10 below is concerned with decompositions of a given switching function $f : Q^n \rightarrow Q$ which consists of component switching functions each of t variables, where $t > 1$ is a preassigned integer; therefore, let us assume that D is a given decomposition of a switching function $f : Q^n \rightarrow Q$ with $q + 1$ component switching functions of t variables. In this case, the sum of the numbers of variables of the $q + 1$ component switching functions is

$$p = t(q + 1).$$

Hence the total degree r of repetition of this decomposition D of f is given by the following formula:

$$r = t(q + 1) - q - n$$
$$= (t - 1)(q + 1) - n + 1.$$

Solving this equation for the number $q + 1$ of component switching functions of the decomposition D of f, we obtain

$$q + 1 = \frac{n + r - 1}{t - 1} = \frac{r}{t - 1} + \frac{n - 1}{t - 1}.$$

By the *size* of a decomposition D of a given switching function f, we mean the number $S(D)$ of component switching functions of D. Thus, we have established the following theorem.

THEOREM 4.1. *If D is a decomposition of a switching function f of n variables with component switching functions of $t > 1$ variables, then the size $S(D)$ of D is given by*

$$S(D) = \frac{1}{t - 1} r(D) + \frac{n - 1}{t - 1}$$

where $r(D)$ denotes the total degree of repetition of D.

5. Ashenhurst's Fundamental Theorem

For each switching function $f : Q^n \to Q$ of n variables $X = \{x_1, x_2, \cdots, x_n\}$ and each disjunctive partition

$$Y \mid Z = y_1 y_2 \cdots y_s \mid z_1 z_2 \cdots z_t$$

of X, R. L. Ashenhurst introduced a *partition matrix* [Ashenhurst 2, p. 79]

$$M(f, Y \mid Z)$$

of f with respect to $Y \mid Z$ as follows: $M(f, Y \mid Z)$ is a matrix of 2^s rows and 2^t columns, in which the rows correspond to the 2^s binary integers $y = y_1 y_2 \cdots y_s$ in order, and the columns correspond to the 2^t binary integers $z = z_1 z_2 \cdots z_t$ in order. Each position in the matrix determines uniquely $y_1, y_2, \cdots, y_s$ and $z_1, z_2, \cdots, z_t$, and hence corresponds to a unique point $x = x_1 x_2 \cdots x_n$ of Q^n since $Y \mid Z$ is a disjunctive partition of X. Then the matrix $M(f, Y \mid Z)$ is defined by taking $f(x)$ to be the element at the position corresponding to $x = x_1 x_2 \cdots x_n$.

As an example of a partition matrix $M(f, Y \mid Z)$, let us consider the case $n = 4$ and the switching function

$$f : Q^4 \to Q$$

defined by

$$f^{-1}(0) = \{1, 2, 3, 4, 5, 6, 7, 8, 10, 11, 13, 15\},$$
$$f^{-1}(1) = \{0, 9, 12, 14\}.$$

Consider the partition

$$Y \mid Z = y_1 y_2 \mid z_1 z_2$$

where $y_1 = x_1$, $y_2 = x_2$, $z_1 = x_3$, and $z_2 = x_4$. Then the partition matrix $M(f, Y \mid Z)$ is shown in Table III-5-1.

The number of distinct row vectors in a partition matrix is defined as its *row multiplicity*, and similarly, the number of distinct column vectors is its *column multiplicity*. Thus, the partition matrix in Table III-5-1 has row multiplicity 4 and column multiplicity 4.

TABLE III-5-1

z y	0	1	2	3
0	1	0	0	0
1	0	0	0	0
2	0	1	0	0
3	1	0	1	0

Let μ and ν denote the row multiplicity and the column multiplicity of a partition matrix $M(f, Y \mid Z)$.

LEMMA 5.1. $\mu \leq 2^\nu$ and $\nu \leq 2^\mu$.

Proof. Let $\alpha_1, \alpha_2, \cdots, \alpha_\nu$ denote the ν distinct columns of $M(f, Y \mid Z)$. By the *reduced partition matrix* $M^*(f, Y \mid Z)$, we mean the 2^s by ν matrix formed by these ν columns. This matrix $M^*(f, Y \mid Z)$ has at most 2^ν distinct rows, since each row must correspond to one of the integers $0, 1, \cdots, 2^\nu - 1$ expressed in binary form. But the i-th row of $M(f, Y \mid Z)$ is formed systematically from the i-th row of $M^*(f, Y \mid Z)$ by putting as the j-th entry the i-th component of the particular α_k associated with the j-th column. Thus identical rows in $M^*(f, Y \mid Z)$ correspond to identical rows in $M(f, Y \mid Z)$. This implies $\mu \leq 2^\nu$. Similarly, we can prove $\nu \leq 2^\mu$. ‖

LEMMA 5.2. *For $\nu = 1$, it is necessary and sufficient that $\mu \leq 2$ and that no vectors other than 0 and 1 appear as row vectors.*

Proof. If $\nu = 1$, every row must have either entries all 0 or entries all 1, depending on the corresponding component of the single column vector α_1. Hence the condition is necessary. Conversely, if every row is all 0 or all 1, then all columns are identical and hence $\nu = 1$. ‖

LEMMA 5.3. *For $v = 2$, it is necessary and sufficient that $\mu \le 4$, that one nontrivial row vector β actually appear, and that no row vectors other than $0, 1, 1 - \beta$ appear in addition to β.*

Proof. Necessity. Assume $v = 2$. In this case, there are two distinct columns α_1 and α_2. The reduced matrix $M^*(f, Y | Z)$ may have rows 00, 01, 10, 11. Obviously, unless either 01 or 10 actually appeared, the two columns α_1 and α_2 would be identical, contrary to the assumption $v = 2$. We may assume without loss of generality that 01 actually appears. The row 01 of $M^*(f, Y | Z)$ corresponds to a nontrivial row β of $M(f, Y | Z)$. Then the rows 00, 11, 10 in $M^*(f, Y | Z)$ correspond to $0, 1, 1 - \beta$ in $M(f, Y | Z)$.

Sufficiency. Assume that the condition holds. Since a nontrivial row vector β appears in $M(f, Y | Z)$, it is obvious that $v \ge 2$. Since $\mu \le 4$ and the other rows are $0, 1, 1 - \beta$, it follows that $v \le 2$. Hence $v = 2$. ‖

Clearly, (5.2) and (5.3) hold also with the roles of columns and rows interchanged; the form of the lemmas given, however, is all that is needed in the proof of Theorem 5.4, *Ashenhurst's fundamental theorem.*

THEOREM 5.4. *A switching function $f : Q^n \to Q$ possesses a simple decomposition (ϕ, ψ) with respect to a disjunctive partition*

$$Y | Z = y_1 y_2 \cdots y_s | z_1 z_2 \cdots z_t$$

of the set $X = \{x_1, x_2, \cdots, x_n\}$ of the n variables iff the partition matrix $M(f, Y | Z)$ has column multiplicity $v \le 2$.

Proof. Sufficiency. First, let us assume $v = 2$. Then, by (5.3), $M(f, Y | Z)$ contains at least one nontrivial row vector β. This row vector β determines a switching function $\psi : Q^t \to Q$ by setting

$$\psi(z) = \beta_z, \qquad (z = z_1 z_2 \cdots z_t \in Q^t),$$

where β_z denotes the z-th component in the vector β. Define a switching function $\phi : Q^{s+1} \to Q$ as follows. Let $(y_1 y_2, \cdots, y_s, y_{s+1})$ denote an arbitrary point of the $(s + 1)$-cube Q^{s+1}. Let

$$y = y_1 y_2 \cdots y_s$$

and let R_y denote the y-th row in $M(f, Y | Z)$. By (5.3), R_y must be $0, 1, \beta$, or $1 - \beta$. We define ϕ by taking

$$\phi(y_1, y_2, \cdots, y_s, y_{s+1}) = \begin{cases} 0, & (\text{if } R_y = 0), \\ 1, & (\text{if } R_y = 1), \\ y_{s+1}, & (\text{if } R_y = \beta), \\ 1 - y_{s+1}, & (\text{if } R_y = 1 - \beta). \end{cases}$$

Then (ϕ, ψ) is a simple decomposition of f with respect to $Y | Z$.

Next, assume $v = 1$. Then, by (5.2), $M(f, Y \mid Z)$ contains no nontrivial row vector. In this case, we select $\psi : Q^t \to Q$ arbitrarily and define $\phi : Q^{s+1} \to Q$ as follows. Let $(y_1, y_2, \cdots, y_s, y_{s+1})$ be any point of Q^{s+1}. Let

$$y = y_1 y_2 \cdots y_s$$

and let R_y denote the y-th row in $M(f, Y \mid Z)$. We then define ϕ by taking

$$\phi(y_1, y_2, \cdots, y_s, y_{s+1}) = \begin{cases} 0, & (\text{if } R_y = 0), \\ 1, & (\text{if } R_y = 1). \end{cases}$$

Then (ϕ, ψ) is a simple decomposition of f with respect to $Y \mid Z$. Since ϕ is clearly independent of the variable y_{s+1}, it follows that f is independent of the variables $z_1, z_2, \cdots, z_t$.

Necessity. Assume that $v > 2$. Then $M(f, Y \mid Z)$ must contain two nontrivial row vectors β and γ such that

$$\gamma \neq \beta, \qquad \gamma \neq 1 - \beta.$$

Suppose these occur in the i-th row and the j-th row of $M(f, Y \mid Z)$. Then there exist four entries $e_{ik}, e_{il}, e_{jk}, e_{jl}$ in $M(f, Y \mid Z)$ such that

$$e_{ik} = e_{il}, \qquad e_{jk} \neq e_{jl}.$$

Let η_i and η_j denote the points of Q^s corresponding to the i-th row and the j-th row. Similarly, let ζ_k and ζ_l denote the points of Q^t corresponding to the k-th column and the l-th column. Suppose that there exists a simple decomposition (ϕ, ψ) of f with respect to $Y \mid Z$. Then we have either $\psi(\zeta_k) = \psi(\zeta_l)$ or $\psi(\zeta_k) \neq \psi(\zeta_l)$. If $\psi(\zeta_k) = \psi(\zeta_l)$, we have

$$e_{jk} = \phi[\eta_j, \psi(\zeta_k)] = \phi[\eta_j, \psi(\zeta_l)] = e_{jl},$$

which is impossible, since $e_{jk} \neq e_{jl}$. If $\psi(\zeta_k) \neq \psi(\zeta_l)$, we have

$$\phi[\eta_i, \psi(\zeta_k)] = e_{ik} = e_{il} = \phi[\eta_i, \psi(\zeta_l)].$$

Since $\psi(\zeta_k) \neq \psi(\zeta_l)$, it follows that

$$\phi[\eta_i, \psi(z)] = e_{ik}$$

for every $z \in Q^t$. This implies that the i-th row is trivial and contradicts the assumption that β is nontrivial. ‖

The sufficiency proof given above is constructive; in fact, it gives a precise method of constructing all simple decompositions (ϕ, ψ) of f with respect to $Y \mid Z$. Furthermore, we have also proved the following corollary.

COROLLARY 5.5. *The switching function* $f : Q^n \to Q$ *is independent of the variables* $Z = \{z_1, z_2, \cdots, z_t\}$ *iff the partition matrix* $M(f, Y \mid Z)$ *has column multiplicity* $v = 1$.

6. Cases with Don't Care Points

In our iteration method of solving the minimization problem given in §11, the switching function

$$f : Q^n \to Q$$

under consideration is usually the result of some previous step; therefore, there are frequently don't care points of Q^n for this switching function f. Let us assume that f is a given switching function of n variables

$$X = \{x_1, x_1, \cdots, x_n\}$$

with a given set of don't care points of Q^n. Let

$$Y \mid Z = \{y_1y_2 \cdots y_s \mid z_1z_2 \cdots z_t\}$$

be any disjunctive partition of X. We shall extend Ashenhurst's definition of the partition matrix $M(f, Y \mid Z)$ to this case as follows: $M(f, Y \mid Z)$ is a matrix of 2^s rows and 2^t columns, in which the rows correspond to the 2^s binary integers $y = y_1y_2 \cdots y_s$ in order, and the columns correspond to the 2^t binary integers $z = z_1z_2 \cdots z_t$ in order. Each position in the matrix determines uniquely $y_1, y_2, \cdots, y_s$ and $z_1, z_2, \cdots, z_t$, and hence corresponds to a unique point

$$x = x_1x_2 \cdots x_n$$

of Q^n. If this point x is a don't care point for f, we define the element in $M(f, Y \mid Z)$ at the position corresponding to x to be $*$; otherwise, we define it to be $f(x)$.

As an example, let us consider the case $n = 4$ and the switching function $f : Q^4 \to Q$ defined by the correspondence table given in Table III-1-8 with $*$'s standing for don't care points. Let

$$Y \mid Z = y_1y_2 \mid z_1z_2$$

be a disjunctive partition of X with $y_1 = x_1, y_2 = x_2, z_1 = x_3$, and $z_2 = x_4$. Then the partition matrix $M(f, Y \mid Z)$ is as shown in Table III-6-1.

As a second example, let us consider the case $n = 5$ and the switching function f of five variables $X = \{x_1, x_2, x_3, x_4, x_5\}$ defined by

$$f^{-1}(1) = \{0, 19, 26, 30\},$$
$$f^{-1}(0) = \{1, 4, 5, 8, 9, 12, 13, 18, 22, 23, 27, 31\},$$
$$f^{-1}(*) = \{2, 3, 6, 7, 10, 11, 14, 15, 16, 17, 21, 24, 25, 28, 29\}.$$

TABLE III-6-1

y \ z	0	1	2	3
0	1	0	0	0
1	*	*	*	*
2	*	*	*	*
3	1	0	1	0

Consider the disjunctive partition

$$Y \mid Z = y_1 y_2 y_3 \mid z_1 z_2$$

with $y_1 = x_1$, $y_2 = x_2$, $y_3 = x_3$, $z_1 = x_4$, and $z_2 = x_5$. Then the partition matrix $M(f, Y \mid Z)$ is as shown in Table III-6-2.

In §2, we defined that a simple decomposition (ϕ, ψ) of f with respect to $Y \mid Z$ is a pair of switching functions

$$\phi : Q^{s+1} \to Q, \qquad \psi : Q^t \to Q$$

such that

$$f(x) = \phi[y_1, y_2, \cdots, y_s, \psi(z_1, z_2, \cdots, z_t)]$$

holds for every point $x = x_1 x_2 \cdots x_n$ of Q^n which is not a don't care point. Ashenhurst's fundamental theorem (5.4) can be generalized to this case as follows.

TABLE III-6-2

y \ z	0	1	2	3
0	1	0	*	*
1	0	0	*	*
2	0	0	*	*
3	0	0	*	*
4	*	*	0	1
5	*	*	0	0
6	*	*	1	0
7	*	*	1	0

THEOREM 6.1. *A switching function*

$$f : Q^n \to Q$$

with don't are points of Q^n possesses a simple decomposition (ϕ, ψ) with respect to a disjunctive partition

$$Y \mid Z = y_1 y_2 \cdots y_s \mid z_1 z_2 \cdots z_t$$

of the set $X = \{x_1, x_2, \cdots, x_n\}$ of n variables iff the $*$'s in the partition matrix $M(f, Y \mid Z)$ can be assigned values 0 or 1 in such a way that its column multiplicity does not exceed 2.

Proof. Necessity. Assume that f has a simple decomposition (ϕ, ψ) with respect to $Y \mid Z$. Consider an arbitrary $*$ in the partition matrix $M(f, Y \mid Z)$ located at the row labeled $y = y_1 y_2 \cdots y_s$ and at the column labeled $z = z_1 z_2 \cdots z_t$. We assign to this $*$ in $M(f, Y \mid Z)$ the value

$$\phi[y_1, y_2, \cdots, y_s, \psi(z_1, z_2, \cdots, z_t)].$$

The matrix $\bar{M}$ thus obtained is obviously the partition matrix $M(g, Y \mid Z)$ of the switching function $g : Q^n \to Q$ defined by

$$g(x) = \phi[y_1, y_2, \cdots, y_s, \psi(z_1, z_2, \cdots, z_t)]$$

for every point $x = x_1 x_2 \cdots x_n$ with no don't care points. Since g possesses a simple decomposition (ϕ, ψ) with respect to $Y \mid Z$, it follows from (5.4) that $\bar{M} = M(g, T \mid Z)$ is of column multiplicity not exceeding 2.

Sufficiency. Assume that we assign values 0 or 1 to each of the $*$'s in $M(f, Y \mid Z)$ and obtain a matrix $\bar{M}$ of column multiplicity not exceeding 2. Define a switching function

$$g : Q^n \to Q$$

by taking $g(x)$ to be the element in $\bar{M}$ at the position corresponding to the point x of Q^n. Then we have

$$\bar{M} = M(g, Y \mid Z).$$

By (5.4), g possesses a simple decomposition (ϕ, ψ) with respect to $Y \mid Z$. Since

$$f(x) = g(x) = \phi[y_1, y_2, \cdots, y_s, \psi(z_1, z_2, \cdots, z_t)]$$

holds for every point $x = x_1 x_2 \cdots x_n$ of Q^n which is not a don't care point, (ϕ, ψ) is by definition a simple decomposition of f with respect to $Y \mid Z$. ∥

The preceding proof shows that every simple decomposition (ϕ, ψ) of f with respect to $Y \mid Z$ assigns precise values to the $*$'s in $M(f, Y \mid Z)$ in such a way that its column multiplicity does not exceed 2. Conversely, it also shows that every assignment of values 0 or 1 to the $*$'s in $M(f, Y \mid Z)$

in such a way that its column multiplicity does not exceed 2 gives rise to a simple decomposition (ϕ, ψ) of f with respect to $Y \mid Z$. A method of assigning values 0 or 1 to the $*$'s in $M(f, Y \mid Z)$ for this purpose is given in the following section.

Because of the given don't care points of Q^n for the given switching function f, the component switching functions

$$\phi : Q^{s+1} \to Q, \qquad \psi : Q^t \to Q$$

of any simple decomposition (ϕ, ψ) of f with respect to $Y \mid Z$ may inherit some don't care points from f. We are concerned with these in the remainder of the section.

By a *don't care column* in $M(f, Y \mid Z)$, we mean a column in $M(f, Y \mid Z)$ which consists of 2^s $*$'s. Similarly, by a *don't care row* in $M(f, Y \mid Z)$, we mean a row in $M(f, Y \mid Z)$ which consists of 2^t $*$'s. For example, the $M(f, Y \mid Z)$ in Table III-6-1 has two don't care rows.

Now let (ϕ, ψ) be an arbitrarily given simple decomposition of a given switching function $f : Q^n \to Q$ with don't care points with respect to a disjunctive partition

$$Y \mid Z = y_1 y_2 \cdots y_s \mid z_1 z_2 \cdots z_t$$

of the set $X = \{x_1, x_2, \cdots, x_n\}$ of n variables. Precise knowledge about the don't care points of the component switching functions ϕ and ψ inherited from f is essential for further decomposition of ϕ and for mechanization of ψ. These don't care points are given by the following two theorems.

THEOREM 6.2.   *A point* $z = z_1 z_2 \cdots z_t$ *of* Q^t *is a don't care point for the component switching function* ψ *iff the* z-th *column in the partition matrix* $M(f, Y \mid Z)$ *is a don't care column.*

THEOREM 6.3.   *A point* $(y_1, y_2, \cdots, y_s, y_{s+1})$ *of* Q^{s+1} *is a don't care point for the component switching function* ϕ *iff, in the row labeled* $y = y_1 y_2 \cdots y_s$ *in* $M(f, Y \mid Z)$, *the element in the column labeled* $z = z_1 z_1 \cdots z_t$ *is a* $*$ *if* $\psi(z) = y_{s+1}$.

7. Assignment of Values to $*$'s

Consider a given switching function

$$f : Q^n \to Q$$

of n variables $X = \{x_1, x_2, \cdots, x_n\}$ with given don't care points and a given disjunctive partition

$$Y \mid Z = y_1 y_2 \cdots y_s \mid z_1 z_2 \cdots z_t$$

TABLE III-7-1

∩	0	1	∗
0	0	□	0
1	□	1	1
∗	0	1	∗

of X. Let $M(f, Y \mid Z)$ denote the partition matrix of f with respect to $Y \mid Z$ as defined in the preceding section. In view of (6.1), we wish either to assign to the ∗'s in $M(f, Y \mid Z)$ values 0 or 1 in such a way that its column multiplicity does not exceed 2, or, alternatively, to prove the impossibility of doing so. In the present section, we describe a systematic method for accomplishing this task.

The elements in the partition matrix $M(f, Y \mid Z)$ are 0, 1, or ∗. We shall define an intersection operation ∩ between these elements by Table III-7-1, in which □ denotes the empty set. Now let

$$u = (u_0, u_1, \cdots, u_m), \qquad v = (v_0, v_1, \cdots, v_m)$$

be any two columns in $M(f, Y \mid Z)$, where $m = 2^s - 1$. We define the intersection $u \cap v$ of these two columns by

$$u \cap v = (u_0 \cap v_0, u_1 \cap v_1, \cdots, u_m \cap v_m).$$

Two columns u and v in $M(f, Y \mid Z)$ are said to be *compatible* iff $u \cap v$ contains no empty set sign □; otherwise, u and v are said to be *incompatible*. If u and v are incompatible, then it is impossible for them to become equal columns by assigning values 0 or 1 to the ∗'s in u and v.

To define the intersection of three or more columns in $M(f, Y \mid Z)$, let us expand Table III-7-1 to the version shown in Table III-7-2. (Note that the binary operation ∩ defined in the set $\{0, 1, ∗, □\}$ is both commutative

TABLE III-7-2

∩	0	1	∗	□
0	0	□	0	□
1	□	1	1	□
∗	0	1	∗	□
□	□	□	□	□

and associative.) Then the intersection

$$u_1 \cap u_2 \cap \cdots \cap u_k$$

of any number of columns $u_1, u_2, \cdots, u_k$ in $M(f, Y \mid Z)$ can be defined in the obvious way. If this intersection contains no empty set sign $\square$, the columns $u_1, u_2, \cdots, u_k$ are said to be *compatible;* otherwise, they are said to be *incompatible*. In the latter case, one can easily see that among these h columns there are u_i and u_j which are incompatible.

To start our algorithm, we form the intersection of pairs of columns in the partition matrix $M(f, Y \mid Z)$ and look for mutually incompatible columns in $M(f, Y \mid Z)$. In general, there are at least three columns in $M(f, Y \mid Z)$ such that any two of these are incompatible. For example, any two of the three columns in Table III-6-1 labeled 0, 1, and 2 are incompatible. In this case, the matrix obtained by assigning values 0 or 1 to the *'s in $M(f, Y \mid Z)$ always has column multiplicity of least 3. Hence, in this general case, there exists no simple decomposition of f with respect to $Y \mid Z$. This completes our task in this case.

In the remaining case, let us first assume that there are two columns u_1 and v_1 in $M(f, Y \mid Z)$ which are incompatible. Then, every other column in $M(f, Y \mid Z)$ must be compatible with at least one of these two columns and possibly with both. For example, in Table III-6-2, we have u_1 and v_1 as the columns labeled 0 and 1, respectively, and every other column is compatible both with u_1 and with v_1. Note, however, that the remaining two columns are incompatible.

Next, let $u_1, \cdots, u_h$ denote the columns in $M(f, Y \mid Z)$ incompatible with v_1 and let $v_1, \cdots, v_k$ denote the columns in $M(f, Y \mid Z)$ incompatible with u_1. In Table III-6-2 with u_1 and v_1 chosen as above, we have $h = 1$ and $k = 1$. If the h columns $u_1, \cdots, u_h$ are incompatible, then there are two incompatible columns, each of which is incompatible with v_1, and hence there exists no simple decomposition of f with respect to $Y \mid Z$. Similarly, we can dispose of the case where the k columns $v_1, \cdots, v_k$ are incompatible. Hence we will assume that both the h columns $u_1, \cdots, u_h$ and the k columns $v_1, \cdots, v_k$ are compatible.

In this case, let us replace each of the h columns $u_1, \cdots, u_h$ in $M(f, Y \mid Z)$ with their intersection

$$u_1 \cap u_2 \cap \cdots \cap u_h$$

and replace each of the k columns $v_1, \cdots, v_k$ in $M(f, Y \mid Z)$ with their intersection

$$v_1 \cap v_2 \cap \cdots \cap v_k.$$

The result of this operation is the same as assinging values 0 or 1 to some *'s in the columns $u_1, \cdots, u_h$ and $v_1, \cdots, v_k$ of $M(f, Y \mid Z)$. For economy of notation, we will retain $u_1, \cdots, u_h, v_1, \cdots, v_k$ and $M(f, Y \mid Z)$ to denote the new columns and the new matrix after this operation. Thus, we have in $M(f, Y \mid Z)$ two incompatible columns u_1 and v_1, together with

$$u_1 = u_2 = \cdots = u_h, \qquad v_1 = v_2 = \cdots = v_k.$$

After this operation, there may be some column in $M(f, Y \mid Z)$ other than these $h + k$ columns $u_1, \cdots, u_h, v_1, \cdots, v_k$ which is, incompatible with u_1 ot v_1. If there is, we repeat the operation and obtain a larger h, or a larger k, or both. After a finite number of iterations of this operation, there will be no other column in $M(f, Y \mid Z)$ which is incompatible with u_1 or v_1. Hereafter, we shall assume that no such column remains.

If $h + k = 2^t$, then there is no other column in $M(f, Y \mid Z)$, and hence $M(f, Y \mid Z)$ has column multiplicity 2. If there are still some $*$'s in u_1 or v_1, we may assign values 0 or 1 to them quite arbitrarily and we will get a simple decomposition of f for each of these assignments.

If $h + k < 2^t$, then there are

$$d = 2^t - h - k$$

columns in $M(f, Y \mid Z)$ other than the $h + k$ columns $u_1, \cdots, u_h$ and $v_1, \cdots, v_k$. Each of these d columns is compatible with both u_1 and v_1. For example, in Table III-6-2 with u_1 and v_1 chosen as above, we have $h = 1$, $k = 1$, and $d = 2$. The column labeled 2 and the column labeled 3 are compatible with u_1 and v_1.

In this case, let w denote one of these d columns in $M(f, Y \mid Z)$. Since w is compatible with both u_1 and v_1, we must branch out out algorithm and work out both of the following two alternative ways.

(1) Replace each of the $h + 1$ columns $u_1, \cdots, u_h, w$ with the intersection $u_1 \cap w$, and denote the new columns by $u_1, \cdots, u_{h+1}$. After this operation, there might be some column in $M(f, Y \mid Z)$, other than $v_1, \cdots, v_k$, which is incompatible with u_1. Hence, we can reapply this process and obtain larger h, or k, or both. After a finite number of these intersection and branching operations, we will obtain simple decompositions of f with respect to $Y \mid Z$, or prove that this alternative way does not lead to a simple decomposition of f.

(2) Replace each of the $k + 1$ columns $v_1, \cdots, v_k, w$ with the intersection $v_1 \cap w$, and repeat the steps outlined in (1). In this way, we may obtain all simple decompositions of f with respect to $Y \mid Z$, or prove that there is no such.

For an example of our branching operation, let us consider Table III-6-2. We have chosen u_1 as the column labeled 0 and v_1 as the column labeled 1.

Let w denote the column leveled 2. Then our process branches out into the following two parts:

(1) Replace each of the two columns u_1 and w by their intersection

$$u_1 \cap w = (1, 0, 0, 0, 0, 0, 1, 1).$$

Consider the remaining column w' which is labeled 3. Since w' and our new column $u_1 \cap w$ are incompatible, we replace each of the two columns v_1 and w' with their intersection

$$v_1 \cap w' = (0, 0, 0, 0, 1, 0, 0, 0).$$

Thus the partition matrix $M(f, Y \mid Z)$ in Table III-6-2 becomes the matrix given in Table III-7-3. Consequently, the $*$'s in $M(f, Y \mid Z)$ of Table

TABLE III-7-3

y \ z	0	1	2	3
0	1	0	1	0
1	0	0	0	0
2	0	0	0	0
3	0	0	0	0
4	0	1	0	1
5	0	0	0	0
6	1	0	1	0
7	1	0	1	0

III-6-2 have been assigned values 0 or 1 in such a way that the new matrix in Table III-7-3 has column multiplicity $\nu = 2$ and row multiplicity $\mu = 3$. By the method described in the sufficiency proof of (5.4), we obtain two simple decompositions (ϕ, ψ) of f with respect to $Y \mid Z$. In one of them,

$$\phi : Q^4 \to Q, \qquad \psi : Q^2 \to Q$$

are given by their on-sets

$$\psi^{-1}(1) = \{0, 2\}, \qquad \phi^{-1}(1) = \{1, 8, 13, 15\}.$$

In the other, these are given by

$$\psi^{-1}(1) = \{1, 3), \qquad \phi^{-1}(1) = \{0, 9, 12, 14\}.$$

(2) Replace each of the two columns v_1 and w with their intersection

$$v_1 \cap w = (0, 0, 0, 0, 0, 0, 1, 1).$$

Since the remaining column w' and our new column $v_1 \cap w$ are incompatible, we replace each of the two columns u_1 and w' with their intersection

$$u_1 \cap w' = (1, 0, 0, 0, 1, 0, 0, 0).$$

Thus the partition matrix $M(f, Y \mid Z)$ in Table III-6-2 becomes the matrix given in Table III-7-4.

Consequently, the *'s in $M(f, Y \mid Z)$ of Table III-6-2 have been assigned values 0 or 1 in such a way that the new matrix in Table III-7-4 is of

TABLE III-7-4

y \ z	0	1	2	3
0	1	0	0	1
1	0	0	0	0
2	0	0	0	0
3	0	0	0	0
4	1	0	0	1
5	0	0	0	0
6	0	1	1	0
7	0	1	1	0

column multiplicity $v = 2$ and of row multiplicity $\mu = 3$. By the method described in the sufficiency proof of (5.4), we obtain two simple decompositions (ϕ, ψ) of f with respect to $Y \mid Z$. In one of them,

$$\phi : Q^4 \to Q, \qquad \psi : Q^2 \to Q$$

are given by their on-sets

$$\psi^{-1}(1) = \{0, 3\}, \qquad \phi^{-1}(1) = \{1, 9, 12, 14\}.$$

In the other, they are given by

$$\psi^{-1}(1) = \{1, 2\}, \qquad \phi^{-1}(1) = \{0, 8, 13, 15\}.$$

Thus we have obtained all simple decompositions of f with respect to $Y \mid Z$. The component switching functions ϕ and ψ in these simple decompositions have no don't care points in accordance with the theorems (6.2) and (6.3).

Now let us return to our general algorithm. It remains to handle the case where every two columns in $M(f, Y \mid Z)$ are compatible. In this case, it follows that the 2^t columns

$$v_0, v_1, \cdots, v_m, \qquad (m = 2^t - 1),$$

in $M(f, Y \mid Z)$ are compatible. Hence we may replace each of these 2^t columns with their intersection

$$v = v_0 \cap v_1 \cap \cdots \cap v_m$$

and obtain a matrix of column multiplicity $\nu = 1$. By (5.5), f is independent of the variables $z_1, \cdots, z_t$.

8. Singular Simple Decompositions

Let $f : Q^n \to Q$ be an arbitrarily given switching function of n variables

$$X = \{x_1, x_2, \cdots, x_n\}$$

with or without don't care points, and consider any partition

$$Y \mid Z = y_1 y_2 \cdots y_s \mid z_1 z_2 \cdots z_t$$

of X with degree of repetition

$$r = s + t - n > 0.$$

In order to find the singular simple decompositions of f, we shall first construct a switching function g of $s + t$ variables

$$V = \{y_1, y_2, \cdots, y_s, z_1, z_2, \cdots, z_t\}$$

with don't care points of the $(s + t)$-cube Q^{s+t} as follows. Since $Y \mid Z$ is a partition of X, each point $x = x_1 x_2 \cdots x_n$ of Q^n determines uniquely $y_1, y_2, \cdots, y_s$ and $z_1, z_2, \cdots, z_t$; hence x corresponds to a unique point $\lambda(x)$ in Q^{s+t}. The assignment $x \to \lambda(x)$ defines a function

$$\lambda : Q^n \to Q^{s+t}$$

which is clearly one-to-one but not onto.

To construct the auxiliary switching function g, let us first specify the don't care points of Q^{s+t}. An arbitrary point

$$v = (y_1, \cdots, y_s, z_1, \cdots, z_t)$$

of Q^{s+t} is a don't care point iff one of the following conditions holds:
  (1) The point v is not contained in the image $\lambda(Q^n)$ in Q^{s+t}.
  (2) There is a don't care point x of Q^n for f such that $\lambda(x) = v$.
If α is the number of don't care points of Q^n for f, then the number of don't care points of Q^{s+t} is

$$\beta = 2^{s+t} - 2^n + \alpha.$$

To define the auxiliary switching function $g : Q^{s+t} \to Q$, let

$$v = (y_1, \cdots, y_s, z_1, \cdots, z_t)$$

be an arbitrary point of Q^{s+t} which is not a don't care point. Then, by the definition given above, there is a unique point x of Q^n such that $\lambda(x) = v$; furthermore, x is not a don't care point of Q^n for f. Now we define $g(v) = f(x)$. This completes the construction of g.

Now $Y \mid Z$ is a disjunctive partition of the set V of $s + t$ variables; therefore, the construction of the auxiliary switching function g reduces the study of singular simple decompositions of f with respect to $Y \mid Z$ to the study of disjunctive simple decompositions of g with respect to $Y \mid Z$. Precisely, for arbitrary switching functions

$$\phi : Q^{s+1} \to Q, \qquad \psi : Q^t \to Q,$$

(ϕ, ψ) is a simple decomposition of f with respect to $Y \mid Z$ iff (ϕ, ψ) is a simple decomposition of g with respect to $Y \mid Z$. Hence we can apply the methods developed in the last two sections to find all singular simple decompositions of f with respect to a given nondisjunctive partition $Y \mid Z$ of the set X of n variables.

In practice, we need the partition matrix $M(g, Y \mid Z)$ which is completely determined by f. This matrix will be referred to as the *partition matrix* of f with respect to the nondisjunctive partition $Y \mid Z$, and will be denoted by

$$M(f, Y \mid Z).$$

This partition matrix can be constructed directly from the given switching function f as follows: $M(f, Y \mid Z)$ is a matrix of 2^s rows and 2^t columns whose elements are 0, 1, or *. The rows in $M(f, Y \mid Z)$ correspond to the 2^s binary integers $y = y_1 y_2 \cdots y_s$, and the columns correspond to the 2^t binary integers $z = z_1 z_2 \cdots z_t$. Since $Y \mid Z$ is a partition of X, each point x of Q^n determines uniquely the binary integers $y = y_1 y_2 \cdots y_s$ and $z = z_1 z_2 \cdots z_t$. If x is not a don't care point of Q^n, we define the element at the y-th row and the z-th column as $f(x)$; otherwise, we define the element as *. In this way, we get the elements at 2^n positions in the matrix $M(f, Y \mid Z)$. Each of the remaining $2^{s+t} - 2^n$ positions in the matrix $M(f, Y \mid Z)$ corresponds to the pair $y = y_1 y_2 \cdots y_s$ and $z = z_1 z_2 \cdots z_t$ which can never occur simultaneously. Hence, at each of these remaining positions in $M(f, Y \mid Z)$, we write the don't care sign *. This completes the construction of $M(f, Y \mid Z)$ directly from f.

As an illustrative example, consider the case $n = 4$ and the switching function $f : Q^4 \to Q$ of the variables $X = \{x_1, x_2, x_3, x_4\}$ defined by

$$f^{-1}(1) = \{0, 9, 12, 14\}$$

with no don't care points of Q^4. Let

$$Y \mid Z = y_1 y_2 y_3 \mid z_1 z_2$$

be a nondisjunctive partition of X with $y_1 = x_1, y_2 = x_2, y_3 = x_3, z_1 = x_1$, and $z_2 = x_4$. Then the partition matrix $M(f, Y \mid Z)$ is exactly the same as that given in Table III-6-2.

If we apply (6.1) to the auxiliary switching function g and the disjunctive partition $Y \mid Z$ of the set V, we obtain the following generalization of Ashenhurst's fundamental theorem to singular simple decompositions [Hu 1].

THEOREM 8.1. *A switching function* $f : Q^n \to Q$ *with or without don't care points of* Q^n *possesses a simple decomposition* (ϕ, ψ) *with respect to a given partition*

$$Y \mid Z = y_1 y_2 \cdots y_s \mid z_1 z_2 \cdots z_t$$

of the set $X = \{x_1, x_2, \cdots, x_n\}$ *of n variables with degree of repetition*

$$r = s + t - n \geq 0$$

iff the *'s in the partition matrix* $M(f, Y \mid Z)$ *can be assigned values* 0 *or* 1 *in such a way that its column multiplicity does not exceed* 2.

As to the process of assigning values 0 or 1 to the *'s in $M(f, Y \mid Z)$, we can apply the algorithm described in §7. In this systematic way, we can find all simple decompositions of f with respect to a given partition $Y \mid Z$ or prove the nonexistence of such.

For the illustrative example given above, the algorithm has been worked out completely in §7, and four simple decompositions of f with respect to the given partition $Y \mid Z$ are obtained there.

9. Decomposition Charts

The algorithm for finding all possible simple decompositions of a given switching function with respect to a given partition of the variables as developed in the four preceding sections can be programmed for electronic computers, as well as worked out by manual calculation. For $n \leq 6$ at least, manual work is greatly facilitated by means of the *decomposition charts* printed for various partitions of the variables.

To define the decomposition charts, let us consider an arbitrarily given partition

$$Y \mid Z = y_1 y_2 \cdots y_s \mid z_1 z_2 \cdots z_t$$

of the set $X = \{x_1, x_2, \cdots, x_n\}$ of n variables with degree of repetition

$$r = s + t - n \geq 0.$$

By the *decomposition chart* of the given partition $Y \mid Z$, we mean the matrix

$$DC_n(Y \mid Z)$$

of 2^s rows and 2^t columns defined as follows. The rows correspond to the 2^s binary integers $y = y_1 y_2 \cdots y_s$ in order, and the columns correspond to the 2^t binary integers $z = z_1 z_2 \cdots z_n$ in order. Since $Y \mid Z$ is a partition of X, each point

$$x = x_1 x_2 \cdots x_n$$

of Q^n determines uniquely the binary integers $y = y_1 y_2 \cdots y_s$ and $z = z_1 z_2 \cdots z_t$. In this case, we define the element at the y-th row and the z-th column as the decimal integer that represents the binary integer x. Thus, we get the elements at 2^n positions in the matrix $DC_n(Y \mid Z)$. At each of the remaining

$$2^{s+t} - 2^n$$

positions in the matrix $DC_n(Y \mid Z)$, we write the don't care sign $*$. This completes the general definition of the decomposition charts.

The following theorem is obvious from the definition given above.

THEOREM 9.1. *For an arbitrary partition $Y \mid Z$ of $X = \{x_1, x_2, \cdots, x_n\}$, $DC_n(Z \mid Y)$ is the transpose of $DC_n(Y \mid Z)$, that is, $DC_n(Z \mid Y)$ can be obtained by interchanging the rows and the columns of $DC_n(Y \mid Z)$.*

Because of (9.1), it suffices to print decomposition charts of only one half of the partitions.

Decomposition charts for disjunctive partitions were introduced by R. L. Ashenhurst in [Ashenhurst 2]. He also considered the decomposition chart for the trivial partition $\square \mid X$ of X.

As an illustrative example of the decomposition charts, let us consider the case $n = 4$. Decomposition charts of seven of the nontrivial disjunctive partitions of

$$X = \{x_1, x_2, x_3, x_4\}$$

are given in Tables III-9-1 through III-9-7. The decomposition charts of the other nontrivial disjunctive partitions of the set $X = \{x_1, x_2, x_3, x_4\}$ can be obtained from these seven charts by permuting the rows, by permuting the columns, and by interchanging the rows with the columns.

For $n = 5$ and 6, then decomposition charts of nontrivial disjunctive partitions can be found in [Ashenhurst 2, pp, 83–84] and also in Curtis' book [Cu, pp. 174–181].

As an example of decomposition charts of nondisjunctive partitions, let us consider the partition

$$Y \mid Z = x_1 x_2 x_3 \mid x_1 x_4$$

TABLE III-9-1: $DC_4(x_1 \mid x_2 x_3 x_4)$

x_1 \\ $x_2 x_3 x_4$	0	1	2	3	4	5	6	7
0	0	1	2	3	4	5	6	7
1	8	9	10	11	12	13	14	15

TABLE III-9-2: $DC_4(x_2 \mid x_1 x_3 x_4)$

x_2 \\ $x_1 x_3 x_4$	0	1	2	3	4	5	6	7
0	0	1	2	3	8	9	10	11
1	4	5	6	7	12	13	14	15

TABLE III-9-3: $DC_4(x_3 \mid x_1 x_2 x_4)$

x_3 \\ $x_1 x_2 x_4$	0	1	2	3	4	5	6	7
0	0	1	4	5	8	9	12	13
1	2	3	6	7	10	11	14	15

TABLE III-9-4: $DC_4(x_4 \mid x_1 x_2 x_3)$

x_4 \\ $x_1 x_2 x_3$	0	1	2	3	4	5	6	7
0	0	2	4	6	8	10	12	14
1	1	3	5	7	9	11	13	15

TABLE III-9-5: $DC_4(x_1 x_2 \mid x_3 x_4)$

$x_1 x_2$ \\ $x_3 x_4$	0	1	2	3
0	0	1	2	3
1	4	5	6	7
2	8	9	10	11
3	12	13	14	15

TABLE III-9-6: $DC_4(x_1x_3 \mid x_2x_4)$

x_1x_3 \ x_2x_4	0	1	2	3
0	0	1	4	5
1	2	3	6	7
2	8	9	12	13
3	10	11	14	15

TABLE III-9-7: $DC_4(x_1x_4 \mid x_2x_3)$

x_1x_4 \ x_2x_3	0	1	2	3
0	0	2	4	6
1	1	3	5	7
2	8	10	12	14
3	9	11	13	15

TABLE III-9-8: $DC_4(x_1x_2x_3 \mid x_1x_4)$

$x_1x_2x_3$ \ x_1x_4	0	1	2	3
0	0	1	*	*
1	2	3	*	*
2	4	5	*	*
3	6	7	*	*
4	*	*	8	9
5	*	*	10	11
6	*	*	12	13
7	*	*	14	15

of the set $X = \{x_1, x_2, x_3, x_4\}$. According to the definition, its decomposition chart is obtained in Table III-9-8.

Whether or not decomposition charts of nondisjunctive partitions should be printed in advance for convenience depends on the individual logical designer. When he has made a decomposition chart of a certain nondisjunctive partition, he should have a few duplicate copies of it made for possible future use.

TABLE III-9-9: $DC_4(x_1 \mid x_2x_3x_4)$

x_1 \ $x_2x_3x_4$	0	1	2	3	4	5	6	7
0	0	①	2	③	④	5	6	⑦
1	⑧	9	10	⑪	12	⑬	14	⑮

TABLE III-9-10: $DC_4(x_2 \mid x_1x_3x_4)$

x_2 \ $x_1x_3x_4$	0	1	2	3	4	5	6	7
0	0	①	2	③	⑧	9	10	⑪
1	4	5	6	⑦	12	⑬	14	⑮

TABLE III-9-11: $DC_4(x_3 \mid x_1x_2x_4)$

x_3 \ $x_1x_2x_4$	0	1	2	3	4	5	6	7
0	0	①	④	5	⑧	9	12	⑬
1	2	③	6	⑦	10	⑪	14	⑮

TABLE III-9-12: $DC_4(x_4 \mid x_1x_2x_3)$

x_4 \ $x_1x_2x_3$	0	1	2	3	4	5	6	7
0	0	2	④	6	⑧	10	12	14
1	①	③	5	⑦	9	⑪	⑬	⑮

R. L. Ashenhurst used the decomposition charts to find all disjunctive simple decompositions for any given switching function of six variables at most. For example, let us consider the switching function

$$f : Q^4 \rightarrow Q$$

without don't care points defined by its on-set

$$f^{-1}(1) = \{1, 3, 4, 7, 8, 11, 13, 15\}.$$

In the decomposition charts in Tables III-9-1 through III-9-7, let us circle the numbers 1, 3, 4, 7, 8, 11, 13, 15 appearing in the matrices. Thus,

TABLE III-9-13: $DC_4(x_1x_2 \mid x_3x_4)$

x_3x_4 / x_1x_2	0	1	2	3
0	0	①	2	③
1	④	5	6	⑦
2	⑧	9	10	⑪
3	12	⑬	14	⑮

TABLE III-9-14: $DC_4(x_1x_3 \mid x_2x_4)$

x_2x_4 / x_1x_3	0	1	2	3
0	0	①	④	5
1	2	③	6	⑦
2	⑧	9	12	⑬
3	10	⑪	14	⑮

TABLE III-9-15: $DC_4(x_1x_4 \mid x_2x_3)$

x_2x_3 / x_1x_4	0	1	2	3
0	0	2	④	6
1	①	③	5	⑦
2	⑧	10	12	14
3	9	⑪	⑬	⑮

we obtain Tables III-9-9 through III-9-15. In the matrices of these seven tables, circled numbers are to be considered as 1's, and noncircled numbers, as 0's. In this way, we have obtained the partition matrices of the given switching function f with respect to the corresponding seven disjunctive partitions.

To find simple decompositions of f with respect to these disjunctive partitions, we must look for partition matrices with column multiplicity not exceeding 2. By an inspection of the Tables III-9-9 through III-9-15, we find that only one of these seven matrices is of column multiplicity not exceeding 2. This is the partition matrix

$$M(f, x_4 \mid x_1 x_2 x_3)$$

which is given by Table III-9-12 and is of column multiplicity 2. By the method given in the sufficiency proof of (5.4), this partition matrix $M(f, x_4 \mid x_1 x_2 x_3)$ gives rise to two simple decompositions (ϕ, ψ) of f with respect to the disjunctive partition $x_4 \mid x_1 x_2 x_3$. In one of them,

$$\phi : Q^2 \to Q, \qquad \psi : Q^3 \to Q$$

are given by their on-sets

$$\phi^{-1}(1) = \{1, 2\}, \qquad \psi^{-1}(1) = \{2, 4\}.$$

In the other, these are given by

$$\phi^{-1}(1) = \{0, 3\}, \qquad \psi^{-1}(1) = \{0, 1, 3, 5, 6, 7\}.$$

In view of (9.1), we should look for matrices in Tables III-9-9 through III-9-15 with row multiplicity not exceeding 2. Since the transposes of the matrices in Tables III-9-9 through III-9-12 give rise to only trivial decompositions of f, it suffices to study only Tables III-9-13 through III-9-15.

An inspection of Tables III-9-13 through III-9-15 reveals that only one of these three matrices is of row multiplicity not exceeding 2. This is the matrix in Table III-9-13 and is of row multiplicity 2. Given (9.1), it follows that the partition matrix

$$M(f, x_3 x_4 \mid x_1 x_2)$$

is the transpose of Table III-9-13 and hence is of column multiplicity 2. By the method given in the sufficiency proof (5.4), this partition matrix $M(f, x_3 x_4 \mid x_1 x_2)$ gives rise to two simple decompositions (ϕ, ψ) of f with respect to the disjunctive partition $x_3 x_4 \mid x_1 x_2$. In one of them,

$$\phi : Q^3 \to Q, \qquad \psi : Q^2 \to Q$$

are given by their on-sets

$$\phi^{-1}(1) = \{1, 2, 6, 7\}, \qquad \psi^{-1}(1) = \{1, 2\}.$$

In the other, these are given by

$$\phi^{-1}(1) = \{0, 3, 6, 7\}, \qquad \psi^{-1}(1) = \{0, 3\}.$$

Since the other disjunctive simple decompositions of f can be obtained by permuting some of the variables, we have essentially obtained all disjunctive simple decompositions of f. This completes our illustrative example.

To generalize Ashenhurst's method of decomposition charts to finding simple decompositions of an arbitrarily given switching function

$$f: Q^n \to Q$$

with or without don't care points and with respect to a given partition

$$Y \mid Z = y_1 y_2 \cdots y_s \mid z_1 z_2 \cdots z_t$$

of degree of repetition

$$r = s + t - n \geq 0,$$

let us consider the decomposition chart

$$DC_n(Y \mid Z)$$

as defined above. Consider the on-set $f^{-1}(1)$ of f and the set $f^{-1}(*)$ of all don't care points of Q^n for f. These are subsets of the n-cube Q^n considered as the set of all decimal integers $0, 1, \cdots, 2^n - 1$.

In the 2^s by 2^t matrix $DC_n(Y \mid Z)$, we circle every number that appears in the set $f^{-1}(1)$ and cross every number that appears in the set $f^{-1}(*)$. The circled numbers in $DC_n(Y \mid Z)$ are then considered as 1's, the crossed numbers are considered as $*$'s, and the remaining numbers are considered as 0's. The matrix obtained from $DC_n(Y \mid Z)$ in this way is obviously the partition matrix

$$M(f, Y \mid Z)$$

of the switching function f with respect to the partition $Y \mid Z$. Then we can apply the method in §§6–8 to finding all simple decompositions of f with respect to $Y \mid Z$.

As an illustrative example, consider the case $n = 4$ and the switching function $f: Q^4 \to Q$ of the variables $X = \{x_1, x_2, x_3, x_4\}$ defined by

$$f^{-1}(1) = \{0, 9, 12, 14\}$$

with no don't care points of Q^4. Let us find the simple decompositions of f with respect to the nondisjunctive partition

$$Y \mid Z = x_1 x_2 x_3 \mid x_1 x_4.$$

The decomposition chart of this partition is given in Table III-9-8. Since f has no don't care points, we simply circle the numbers 0, 9, 12, 14 in Table III-9-8 and obtain Table III-9-16. Since circled numbers are considered as 1's and uncircled numbers as 0's, Table III-9-16 coincides with Table III-6-2. Thus, the details in §§6–8 apply to this case, and the illustrative example is completed.

TABLE III-9-16

$x_1x_2x_3$ ╲ x_1x_4	0	1	2	3
0	⓪	1	*	*
1	2	3	*	*
2	4	5	*	*
3	6	7	*	*
4	*	*	8	⑨
5	*	*	10	11
6	*	*	⑫	13
7	*	*	⑭	15

10. Optimal Networks

The reduction theorem (3.1), together with the algorithms of finding simple decompositions developed in §§5–9, gives rise to an effective solution to the general minimization problem of realizing an arbitrarily given switching function by an optimal network with a prescribed list of allowable logical devices. The present section is devoted to defining the problem with various preliminary discussions. The main algorithm is presented in the next section.

As the prescribed list of allowable logical devices, let us consider any given set B of switching functions which is *functionally complete* in the sense of (I, §7). The switching functions in the set B are referred to as the *basic switching functions*, and the set B itself as the given *basis* of switching functions.

EXAMPLES OF BASES OF SWITCHING FUNCTIONS:

(1) The conjunction functions $\wedge$ and the disjunction functions $\vee$ of all finite numbers of variables, together with the complementation function $c : Q \to Q$ constitute a basis of switching functions. See (I, 7.1).

(2) The three switching functions

$$\wedge : Q^2 \to Q, \qquad \vee : Q^2 \to Q, \qquad c : Q \to Q$$

constitute a basis of switching functions. See (I, 7.2).

(3) The NAND function $\wedge' : Q^2 \to Q$ constitutes a basis of switching functions. See (I, 7.10).

(4) The NOR function $\vee' : Q^2 \to Q$ constitutes a basis of switching functions. See (I, 7.11).

(5) For any integer $t \geq 2$, the symmetric switching functions of not more than t variables constitute a basis of switching functions. See (I, 11.8).

(6) For any integer $t \geq 2$, the threshold functions of not more than t variables constitute a basis of switching functions. See (I, 12.4).

Since the given basis B of switching functions is functionally complete, every switching function

$$f : Q^n \to Q$$

has a decomposition with basic switching functions as its component switching functions. In other words, f can always be realized by a finite network of logical devices realizing some of the basic switching functions. Since every logical device has a cost, naturally we like to find an optimal (i.e., least expensive) network of basic logical devices to realize the given switching function f. This desire gives rise to the general minimization problem mentioned at the beginning of this section.

Precisely, for every basic switching function ψ in the given basis B, let

$$c(\psi)$$

denote the *cost* of ψ, that is, the price of the basic logical device which realizes the switching function ψ. By a *basic decomposition* of f, we mean a decomposition D of f such that every component switching function in D is a basic switching function. We define the *cost* of any basic decomposition D of as the sum

$$c(D) = \sum_{i=1}^{q} c(\psi_i)$$

of the costs of its component switching functions $\psi_1, \cdots, \psi_q$. Then our general minimization problem is to find an *optimal basic decomposition* of f with respect to this cost function, that is to say, to find a basic decomposition D of f such that its cost $c(D)$ is minimum.

If the basis B of switching functions is given by Example (1), then our general minimization problem reduces to the outstanding classical problem of finding an optimal Boolean expression for an arbitrarily given switching function f. In other words, this is the classical problem of realizing f by means of a cheapest multilevel network of AND-gates, OR-gates, and inversions.

If the basis B of switching functions is given by Example (6), then our general minimization problem reduces to a similar problem in threshold logic. See [H1, chap. viii].

In case the cost $c(\psi)$ of the basic switching functions $\psi \in B$ are arbitrarily given by a price list, it seems to me that we must find all basic decompositions of f with degree of repetition $r \geq 0$ up to a reasonably large number, depending on the price differentials, and compare their costs. Fortunately, in practice, at least one of the following cases almost always can be applied.

(*a*) If the basic logical devices are ready-made, it is a common practice of the logical designers to neglect the price differentials of the devices and to measure the cost of a network by the number of these devices. In this case, the cost $c(D)$ of a basic decomposition D reduces to the size $S(D)$ of D, that is, the number of component functions in D. In symbols, we have

$$c(D) = S(D).$$

This can be further modified as follows. Since it is practically impossible to build too many inputs into a single basic logical device, we may assume the existence of an integer t that each basic switching function is of not more than t variables. Next, since every switching function of $s < t$ variables can be considered as a switching function of t variables which is independent of the last $t - s$ variables, we may assume that every basic switching function is of exactly t variables. Then it follows from (4.1) that we have

$$c(D) = S(D) = \frac{1}{t-1}\, r(D) + \frac{n-1}{t-1}$$

for every basic decomposition D of any switching function f of n variables. Consequently, *a basic decomposition D is optimal iff its degree of repetition $r(D)$ is minimal.*

(*b*) An interesting, although rather artificial, case is that the cost of a basic logical device is measured by its number of inputs minus one. In this case, the cost $c(D)$ of a basic decomposition of a switching function $f : Q^n \to Q$ with $q + 1$ component switching functions is given by

$$c(D) = p - (q + 1) = p - q - 1,$$

where p denotes the sum of the numbers of variables of the $q + 1$ component switching functions in D. On the other hand, the degree of repetition $r(D)$ of D is given by

$$r(D) = p - q - n$$

according to a formula in §4. Hence we obtain

$$c(D) = r(D) + n - 1.$$

Consequently, *a basic decomposition D is optimal iff its degree of repetition $r(D)$ is minimal.*

(*c*) Frequently, the cost of a basic logical device is approximately proportional to the number of inputs to the device. For example, if the basic switching functions are as given by Example (1) and are to be realized by gate-type devices built directly from diodes, and so on, the cost is usually measured by the number of inputs to the device as explained in (II, §2). In this case, the cost $c(D)$ of a basic decomposition of a switching function $f : Q^n \rightarrow Q$ with $q + 1$ component switching functions is measured by the sum p of variables of the $q + 1$ component switching functions in D. Using

$$r(D) = p - q - n, \qquad S(D) = q + 1,$$

we obtain

$$c(D) = p = r(D) + q + n = r(D) + S(D) + n - 1.$$

Consequently, *a basic decomposition D is optimal iff $r(D) + S(D)$ is minimal.* Since $S(D)$ frequently increases with $r(D)$, there is a good chance that a basic decomposition D with minimal $r(D)$ is also optimal.

In view of the preceding three cases (*a*)–(*c*), I believe that, in the general problem of finding an optimal network for a given switching function f, we should first find a basic decomposition D of f with minimal degree of repetition $r(D)$. An algorithm for this purpose is given in the following section.

Although handicapped by the absence of the reduction theorem (3.1), R. L. Ashenhurst managed to study complex decompositions by means of a number of auxiliary theorems. These auxiliary theorems are given in Exercises 9–15 at the end of this chapter. Based on these auxiliary theorems of Ashenhurst, a very complicated algorithm was developed by H. A. Curtis in his book [Cu] for decompositions of a certain type.

On the other hand, J. P. Roth and his group at I.B.M. elaborately developed systematic methods for the general minimization problem, first only for Boolean trees and finally for arbitrary Boolean graphs, without using Ashenhurst's theory of decompositions. Their works can be found in [Roth-Wagner 1, Roth 3, and Roth-Karp 1]. Further development of the minimization problem and work related to that of Ashenhurst-Curtis are given by R. M. Karp in his paper [Karp 1].

11. Minimization Algorithm

Consider an arbitrarily given switching function

$$f : Q^n \rightarrow Q$$

of n variables $X = \{x_1, \cdots, x_n\}$ with or without don't care points and let B denote any given *basis*, that is, a functionally complete set of switching functions. The switching functions in B are called *basic switching functions*.

In the preceding section we have shown that the general minimization problem frequently reduces to the problem of finding a *basic decomposition* D of f with minimal degree of repetition $r(D)$. Here, as defined in the preceding section, a basic decomposition of f means a decomposition of f in which all component switching functions are basic. For convenience, this last problem is referred to as the *reduced minimization problem*. Our reduction theorem (3.1), together with the algorithms for finding simple decompositions in §§5-8, enables us to formulate an algorithm for the reduced minimization problem which is presented here.

The first step in the algorithm is the search for a disjunctive simple decomposition (ϕ, ψ) of f where ψ must be a basic switching function. For this purpose, let us arrange the disjunctive partitions

$$Y \mid Z = y_1 y_2 \cdots y_s \mid z_1 z_2 \cdots z_t, \qquad t = n - s,$$

of $X = \{x_1, \cdots, x_n\}$ in the order of the integer s followed by the lexicographical order of the variables in Y. For example, if $n = 4$, then the disjunctive partitions of $X = \{x_1, x_2, x_3, x_4\}$ are ordered as follows:

$$x_1 \mid x_2 x_3 x_4, \ x_2 \mid x_1 x_3 x_4, \ x_3 \mid x_1 x_2 x_4, \ x_4 \mid x_1 x_2 x_3;$$

$$x_1 x_2 \mid x_3 x_4, \ x_1 x_3 \mid x_2 x_4, \ x_1 x_4 \mid x_2 x_3, \ x_2 x_3 \mid x_1 x_4, \ x_2 x_4 \mid x_1 x_3, \ x_3 x_4 \mid x_1 x_2;$$

$$x_1 x_2 x_3 \mid x_4, \ x_1 x_2 x_4 \mid x_3, \ x_1 x_3 x_4 \mid x_2, \ x_2 x_3 x_4 \mid x_1.$$

We start with the first disjunctive partition $Y_1 \mid Z_1$ of the variables $X = \{x_1, \cdots, x_n\}$ and form the partition matrix $M(f, Y_1 \mid Z_1)$. Then we apply the algorithm in §7 to this partition matrix and search for simple decompositions of f with respect to $Y_1 \mid Z_1$. If f has no simple decomposition with respect to $Y_1 \mid Z_1$, we go on to the next disjunctive partition $Y_2 \mid Z_2$ of X and so on.

In general, let us assume that we are studying the i-th disjunctive partition

$$Y_i \mid Z_i = y_1 y_2 \cdots y_s \mid z_1 z_2 \cdots z_t$$

of X. We form the partition matrix $M(f, Y_i \mid Z_i)$ and apply the algorithm in §7 to this partition matrix. If f has no simple decomposition with respect to $Y_i \mid Z_i$, we go on to the next disjunctive partition $Y_{i+1} \mid Z_{i+1}$. Otherwise, we construct the simple decompositions of f with respect to $Y_i \mid Z_i$ for all possible assignments of values 0 or 1 to the *'s in $M(f, Y_i \mid Z_i)$ in such a way that its column multiplicity does not exceed 2. Then we arrange the simple decompositions in the order they were constructed, say

$$(\alpha, \beta), (\gamma, \delta), \cdots, (\phi, \psi), (\rho, \theta), \cdots, (\xi, \eta).$$

Next, we begin with (α, β). If β is not a basic switching function, we discard (α, β) and proceed to study (γ, δ), and so on. In general, let us assume that we are studying the simple decomposition (ϕ, ψ). If ψ is not in the basis B, we discard (ϕ, ψ) and proceed to study (ρ, θ). If ψ is in the basis B, then we enter (ϕ, ψ) into a list $D(0, 1)$ of decompositions of f of *total degree* 0 (of repetition) and of *order* 1. In this case, we investigate ϕ as described below.

Here, ϕ is a switching function of $s + 1$ variables. If ϕ is in the given basis B, then we have already obtained a basic decomposition (ϕ, ψ) with minimal total degree of repetition and thus out reduced minimization problem is solved. Otherwise, we repeat our algorithm so far with n replaced by $s + 1$, f replaced by ϕ, and $X = \{x_1, \cdots, x_n\}$ replaced by $Y = \{y_1, \cdots, y_{s+1}\}$. If ϕ has no disjunctive simple decomposition of the form (λ, μ), where $\mu \in B$, we proceed to study (ρ, θ). On the other hand, if, with respect to some disjunctive partition $U \mid V$ of the set Y according to the algorithm, we find a simple decomposition (λ, μ) of ϕ with $\mu \in B$, then we enter the decomposition

$$(\lambda, \mu) \circ (\phi, \psi)$$

of f into a list $D(0, 2)$ of decompositions of f of total degree 0 and order 2 and repeat for λ the algorithm we applied to ϕ.

After a finite number of iterations of this process, we shall either have found a basic decomposition of f with minimum total degree of repetition, or shall have entered a number of decompositions

$$D = (\phi_q, \psi_q) \circ (\phi_{q-1}, \psi_{q-1}) \circ \cdots \circ (\phi_1, \psi_1)$$

of f into the lists

$$D(0, q), \quad q = 1, 2, \cdots,$$

and have proceeded to study the next disjunctive simple decomposition (ρ, θ) of f with respect to $Y_i \mid Z_i$ as for (ϕ, ψ). In this way, we shall either find a basic decomposition of f with minimum total degree of repetition, or shall dispose of all disjunctive simple decompositions of f with respect to $Y_i \mid Z_i$ and enter a number of decompositions of f into the lists $D(0, q)$, $q = 1, 2, \cdots$.

In the latter case, we proceed to the next disjunctive partition $Y_{i+1} \mid Z_{i+1}$ of the set X and repeat the process we carried out for $Y_i \mid Z_i$. In this way, we shall either find a basic decomposition of f with minimum total degree of repetition, or dispose of all disjunctive partitions of X and complete the lists $D(0, q)$, $q = 1, 2, \cdots$. For completeness, let $D(0, 0)$ denote the list that consists of the trivial decomposition of f itself.

If we have not yet solved the problem, we must consider decompositions of f with a higher degree of repetition. For this purpose, let us first consider the largest integer q such that $D(0, q)$ is not empty. We arrange the decompositions of f in the list $D(0, q)$ in the order in which they were entered. Then we consider the first decomposition

$$D = (\phi_q, \psi_q) \circ (\phi_{q-1}, \psi_{q-1}) \circ \cdots \circ (\phi_1, \psi_1)$$

in the list $D(0, q)$, assuming that ϕ_q is a switching function of m variables $W = \{w_1, \cdots, w_m\}$. (Note that $\phi_q = f$ if $q = 0$.) Next we consider the nondisjunctive partitions

$$U \mid V = u_1 u_2 \cdots u_s \mid v_1 v_2 \cdots v_t$$

of W with degree of repetition $s + t - m = 1$ and arrange these partitions of W in the order of the integer s followed by the lexicographical order of the variables in U. Starting with the first partition $U_1 \mid V_1$ of W, we form the partition matrix $M(\phi_q, U_1 \mid V_1)$ as in §8. Then we apply the algorithm in §7 to this partition matrix and search for simple decompositions of ϕ_q with respect to $U_1 \mid V_1$. If q_q has no simple decomposition with respect to $U_1 \mid V_1$, we proceed to the next partition $U_2 \mid V_2$ in order, and so on.

In general, let us assume that we are studying the i-th partition

$$U_i \mid V_i = u_1 u_2 \cdots u_s \mid v_1 v_2 \cdots v_t$$

of W with $s + t - m = 1$. We form the partition matrix $M(\phi_q, U_i \mid V_i)$ as in §8 and apply the algorithm in §7 to this partition matrix. If ϕ_q has no simple decomposition with respect to $U_i \mid V_i$, then we proceed to the next partition $U_{i+1} \mid V_{i+1}$ of W. Otherwise, we construct the simple decompositions of ϕ_q with respect to $U_i \mid V_i$ for all possible assignments of values 0 or 1 to *'s in $M(\phi_q, U_i \mid V_i)$ in such a way that its column multiplicity does not exceed 2. Then we arrange these simple decompositions of ϕ_q in the order in which they were constructed, say

$$(\alpha, \beta), (\gamma, \delta), \cdots, (\phi, \psi), (\rho, \theta), \cdots, (\xi, \eta).$$

Next, we begin with (α, β). If β is not a basic switching function, we discard (α, β) and proceed to study (γ, δ), and so on. In general, let us assume that we are studying the simple decomposition (ϕ, ψ) of ϕ_q with respect to $U_i \mid V_i$. If ψ is not in the basis B, then we discard (ϕ, ψ) and proceed to study (ρ, θ). If ψ is in the basis B, then we enter the decomposition

$$(\phi, \psi) \circ (\phi_q, \psi_q) \circ (\phi_{q-1}, \psi_{q-1}) \circ \cdots \circ (\phi_1, \psi_1)$$

into a list $D(1, q + 1)$ of decompositions of f of total degree 1 and of order $q + 1$ and investigate ϕ as follows. If ϕ is in the given basis B, then we obtain a basic decomposition

$$D = (\phi, \psi) \circ (\phi_q, \psi_q) \circ (\phi_{q-1}, \psi_{q-1}) \circ \cdots \circ (\phi_1, \psi_1)$$

with minimum total degree of repetition $r = 1$, and thus our problem is solved. Otherwise, we apply our process of searching for disjunctive simple decompositions to ϕ. If ϕ has no disjunctive simple decomposition of the form (λ, μ) with $\mu \in B$, then we proceed to study (ρ, θ). On the other hand, if there are disjunctive simple decompositions of ϕ of the form (λ, μ) with $\mu \in B$, we enter the decompositions

$$(\lambda, \mu) \circ (\phi, \psi) \circ (\phi_q, \psi_{q-1}) \circ (\phi_{q-1}, \psi_{q-1}) \circ \cdots \circ (\phi_1, \psi_1)$$

into a list $D(1, q + 2)$ and repeat with λ the algorithm we applied to ϕ.

After a finite number of iterations of this process, we shall either have found a basic decomposition of f with minimum total degree of repetition $r = 1$, or shall have entered a number of decompositions

$$D = (\phi_p, \psi_p) \circ (\phi_{p-1}, \psi_{p-1}) \circ \cdots \circ (\phi_1, \psi_1)$$

of f into the lists $D(1, p)$ with $p = 1, 2, \cdots$. In the latter case, we proceed to study (ρ, θ). In this way, we shall either solve the problem, or shall have disposed of all simple decompositions of ϕ_q with respect to $U_i \mid V_i$. In the latter case, we proceed to the next partition $U_{i+1} \mid V_{i+1}$ of W.

Thus, we shall either solve the problem, or dispose of all partitions of W of degree of repetition 1. In the latter case, we proceed to the decomposition E of f which stands next to D in the list $D(0, q)$ and repeat the process as we did for D. In this way, we shall either have solved the problem, or shall have studied all decompositions of f in the list $D(0, q)$ and have entered a number of decompositions of f into the lists $D(1, p), p = 1, 2, \cdots$.

If we have not yet solved the problem, we proceed to the next nonempty list $D(0, q'), q' < q$, and repeat the process as we did for the list $D(0, q)$. In this way, we shall either have solved the problem, or shall have studied all lists $D(0, q), q = 0, 1, 2, \cdots$, and entered a number of decompositions of f into the lists

$$D(1, q), \qquad q = 1, 2, \cdots.$$

If we have not yet solved the problem, we must consider decompositions of f with degree of repetition 2. For this purpose, we first consider the decompositions in the lists $D(1, q)$ and repeat the process we carried out for the lists $D(0, q)$. In this way, we shall either solve the problem, or enter a number of decompositions of f into new lists

$$D(2, q), \qquad q = 1, 2, \cdots.$$

In the latter case, we proceed to study the decompositions of f in the lists $D(0, q)$, say

$$D = (\phi_q, \psi_q) \circ (\phi_{q-1}, \psi_{q-1}) \circ \cdots \circ (\phi_1, \psi_1),$$

by considering the simple decompositions (ϕ, ψ) of ϕ_q with degree of repetition 2, and then looking for successive disjunctive decompositions of ϕ. In this way, we shall either solve the problem, or shall complete the lists $D(2, q)$ for each $q = 1, 2, \cdots$.

In general, for any $r > 1$, we proceed to construct the lists

$$D(r, q), \quad q = 1, 2, \cdots,$$

when we fail to solve the problem after the completion of the lists $D(r - 1, q)$. Since B is functionally complete, it follows that basic decompositions of f with minimum total degree of repetition do exist and our process will terminate. This completes our minimization algorithm.

The preceding formulation of our minimization algorithm is given for the most general case in such a way that the reader can apply it to his own particular problem without much difficulty. Certainly, many improvements can be made for various special cases. A few examples of these improvements are given below.

(1) If the given switching function f is of not more than six variables, then the decomposition charts described in §9 can be used to save the designer's time if he must work by manual calculation.

(2) If the given basis B contains no switching function of t variables, then we don't have to consider any partition of secondary degree t. In particular, if every basic switching function is of t variables, then it suffices to study only partitions of secondary degree t.

(3) If the switching functions in the basis B are given by their numbers of variables and their on-sets, then whether or not a particular simple decomposition (ϕ, ψ) should be discarded can be determined by inspection from the partition matrix during the process of constructing (ϕ, ψ).

(4) If the given switching function f is independent of some of its variables, one should find these variables by means of (5.5) and get rid of them.

In the preceding algorithm, we work on the lists $D(r, q)$, for a fixed $r \geq 0$, in the decreasing order of q. My reason for suggesting this approach is that in the decompositions of f with higher order q, the switching functions to be worked on are usually of fewer variables and hence less complicated. However, if there are big differences in the numbers of variables of the basic switching functions and if decompositions of f with smaller q at minimum r are desired, one should work on the lists $D(r, q)$ in the increasing order of q.

Our general minimization problem is to minimize the cost of a network of basic logical devices which realizes an arbitrarily given switching function f, not to minimize the cost of finding such a network. In special cases, existing special methods can certainly provide a solution to this problem at less cost.

The preceding algorithm was first designed for finding optimal threshold networks in [H1, chap. viii].

Finally, for any given integer $p \geq 0$, the preceding algorithm can be easily modified to find all basic decompositions of a switching function f with total degree of repetition $r \leq p$.

12. Illustrative Example

As an illustrative example of our minimization algorithm, let us consider the set B of all sixteen switching functions of two variables. By (I,7.10) or (I,7.11), the set B is functionally complete and hence can be used as our basis. Assume that the basic logical devices realizing these sixteen switching functions of two variables are of the same cost. Hence, according to (*a*) in §10, a basic decomposition D of an arbitrarily given switching function

$$f : Q^n \to Q,$$

with or without don't care points, is optimal iff its total degree of repetition $r(D)$ is a minimum. Therefore, we may apply the minimization algorithm given in §11.

For example, let us apply the algorithm to the switching function

$$f : Q^4 \to Q$$

of four variables $X = \{x_1, x_2, x_3, x_4\}$, with no don't care point and defined by its on-set

$$f^{-1}(1) = \{0, 1, 2, 3, 4, 5, 6, 9, 11, 13, 15\}.$$

As remarked in (1) of §11, we shall make use of the decomposition charts of §9. By (2) of §11, it suffices to study only the partitions of secondary degree 2. Thus we circle the numbers in Tables III-9-5 through III-9-7 which appear in the on-set $f^{-1}(1)$ and obtain Tables III-12-1 through III-12-3. Hence, $M(f, x_1x_2 \mid x_3x_4)$ is of column multiplicity 3 and row multiplicity 3, $M(f, x_1x_3 \mid x_2x_4)$ is of column multiplicity 3 and row multiplicity 3, and $M(f, x_1x_4 \mid x_2x_3)$ is of column multiplicity 2 and row multiplicity 3. By (5.4) and its sufficiency proof, there are only two nondisjunctive simple

TABLE III-12-1: $DC_4(x_1x_2 \mid x_3x_4)$

x_1x_2 \ x_3x_4	0	1	2	3
0	⓪	①	②	③
1	④	⑤	⑥	7
2	8	⑨	10	⑪
3	12	⑬	14	⑮

TABLE III-12-2: $DC_4(x_1x_3 \mid x_2x_4)$

x_1x_3 \ x_2x_4	0	1	2	3
0	⓪	①	④	⑤
1	②	③	⑥	7
2	8	⑨	12	⑬
3	10	⑪	14	⑮

TABLE III-12-3: $DC_4(x_1x_4 \mid x_2x_3)$

x_1x_4 \ x_2x_3	0	1	2	3
0	⓪	②	④	⑥
1	①	③	⑤	7
2	8	10	12	14
3	⑨	⑪	⑬	⑮

decompositions (ϕ, ψ) of f with $\psi \in B$, namely, the two simple decompositions (α, β) and (γ, δ) of f with respect to the partition $x_1x_4 \mid x_2x_3$. Here,

$$\alpha : Q^3 \to Q, \qquad \beta : Q^2 \to Q, \qquad \gamma : Q^3 \to Q, \qquad \delta : Q^2 \to Q$$

are switching functions without don't care points and given by

$$\alpha^{-1}(1) = \{0, 1, 2, 6, 7\},$$
$$\beta^{-1}(1) = \{3\},$$
$$\gamma^{-1}(1) = \{0, 1, 3, 6, 7\},$$
$$\delta^{-1}(1) = \{0, 1, 2\}.$$

TABLE III-12-4: $DC_3(y_1 \mid y_2 y_3)$

y_1 \ $y_2 y_3$	0	1	2	3
0	⓪	①	②	3
1	4	5	⑥	⑦

TABLE III-12-5: $DC_3(y_2 \mid y_1 y_3)$

y_2 \ $y_1 y_3$	0	1	2	3
0	⓪	①	4	5
1	②	3	⑥	⑦

TABLE III-12-6: $DC_3(y_3 \mid y_1 y_2)$

y_3 \ $y_1 y_2$	0	1	2	3
0	⓪	②	4	⑥
1	①	3	5	⑦

Note that $\beta = \wedge$ and $\delta = \wedge'$. This completes the list $D(0, 1)$ which consists of (α, β) and (γ, δ).

Next let us search for disjunctive simple decompositions of the switching function

$$\alpha : Q^3 \rightarrow Q$$

of three variables $Y = \{y_1, y_2, y_3\}$ in the form (ϕ, ψ) with $\psi \in B$. For this purpose, we circle the numbers in the decomposition charts $DC_3(y_1 \mid y_2 y_3)$, $DC_3(y_2 \mid y_1 y_3)$, and $DC_3(y_3 \mid y_1 y_2)$ which appear in the on-set $\alpha^{-1}(1)$ of α. Thus we obtain Tables III-12-4 through III-12-6. Each of the three partition matrices $M(\alpha, y_1 \mid y_2 y_3)$, $M(\alpha, y_2 \mid y_1 y_3)$, and $M(\alpha, y_3 \mid y_1 y_2)$ is of column multiplicity 3. Hence α has no disjunctive simple decomposition (ϕ, ψ) with $\psi \in B$.

Similarly, γ has no disjunctive simple decomposition (ϕ, ψ) with $\psi \in B$. In fact, γ is the switching function obtained by complementing the last variable y_3.

TABLE III-12-7: $DC_3(y_1y_2 \mid y_1y_3)$

y_1y_2 \ y_1y_3	0	1	2	3
0	⓪	①	*	*
1	②	3	*	*
2	*	*	4	5
3	*	*	⑥	⑦

TABLE III–12–8: $DC_3(y_1y_2 \mid y_2y_3)$

y_1y_2 \ y_2y_3	0	1	2	3
0	⓪	①	*	*
1	*	*	②	3
2	4	5	*	*
3	*	*	⑥	⑦

TABLE III-12-9: $DC_3(y_1y_3 \mid y_2y_3)$

y_1y_3 \ y_2y_3	0	1	2	3
0	⓪	*	②	*
1	*	①	*	3
2	4	*	⑥	*
3	*	5	*	⑦

This proves that f has no basic decomposition with total degree of repetition $r = 0$. Hence we must look for basic decompositions of total degree of repetition $r = 1$.

Let us search for singular simple decompositions of α with degree of repetition 1. For this purpose, clearly it suffices to consider the decomposition charts $DC_3(y_1y_2 \mid y_1y_3)$, $DC_3(y_1y_2 \mid y_2y_3)$, and $DC_3(y_1y_3 \mid y_2y_3)$. Having circled the numbers that appear in $\alpha^{-1}(1)$ we obtain Tables III-12-7 through III-12-9.

Let us work on Table III-12-7. Considering the circled numbers as 1's and the uncircles numbers as 0's, we obtain the partition matrix $M(\alpha, y_1y_2 \mid y_1y_3)$ as in Table III-12-10. To find simple decompositions of α

TABLE III-12-10: $M(\alpha, y_1y_2 \mid y_1y_3)$

y_1y_2 \ y_1y_3	0	1	2	3
0	1	1	*	*
1	1	0	*	*
2	*	*	0	0
3	*	*	1	1

with respect to the partition $y_1y_2 \mid y_1y_3$, we must assign values 0 or 1 to the *'s in Table III-12-10 in such a way that the resulting matrix shall be of column multiplicity not exceeding 2. This can be done either by inspection or by the algorithm in §7. By inspection, we can easily see that one of the possible ways of assigning values 0 or 1 to the *'s in Table III-12-10 is that given by Table III-12-11.

The matrix in Table III-12-11 is of column multiplicity 2. By the sufficiency proof of (5.4), we obtain two simple decompositions of α from Table III-12-11, one which is (λ, μ) with

$$\lambda : Q^3 \to Q, \qquad \mu : Q^2 \to Q$$

given by their on-sets

$$\lambda^{-1}(1) = \{0, 1, 2, 4, 6, 7\},$$
$$\mu^{-1}(1) = \{1, 2, 3\}.$$

Note that μ is the disjunction function $\vee$. The other simple decomposition of α given by Table III-12-11 can be obtained by complementing μ and the last variable in λ.

Next let us search for disjunctive simple decompositions of the switching function λ of three variables $W = \{w_1, w_2, w_3\}$. For this purpose, it suffices

TABLE III-12-11: $M(\alpha, y_1y_2 \mid y_1y_3)$

y_1y_2 \ y_1y_3	0	1	2	3
0	1	1	1	1
1	1	0	0	0
2	1	0	0	0
3	1	1	1	1

TABLE III-12-12: $M(\lambda, w_1 \mid w_2w_3)$

w_1 \ w_2w_3	0	1	2	3
0	⓪	①	②	3
1	④	5	⑥	⑦

TABLE III-12-13: $M(\lambda, w_2 \mid w_1w_3)$

w_2 \ w_1w_3	0	1	2	3
0	⓪	①	④	5
1	②	3	⑥	⑦

TABLE III–12–14: $M(\lambda, w_3 \mid w_1w_2)$

w_3 \ w_1w_2	0	1	2	3
0	⓪	②	④	⑥
1	①	3	5	⑦

to investigate the partition matrices $M(\lambda, w_1 \mid w_2w_3)$, $M(\lambda, w_2 \mid w_1w_3)$, and $M(\lambda, w_3 \mid w_1w_2)$. These can be easily constructed by circling the numbers in the decomposition charts that appear in $\lambda^{-1}(1)$ and are given in Tables III-12-12 through III-12-14. Since $M(\lambda, w_3 \mid w_1w_2)$ is of column multiplicity 2, it follows from the sufficiency proof of (5.4) that λ has two simple decompositions with respect to the partition $w_3 \mid w_1w_2$, one of which is (ϕ, ψ) with

$$\phi : Q^2 \to Q, \qquad \psi : Q^2 \to Q$$

given by their on-sets

$$\phi^{-1}(1) = \{0, 1, 2\},$$
$$\psi^{-1}(1) = \{1, 2\}.$$

Note that ϕ is the NAND function $\wedge'$ and ψ is the exclusive OR function $\ⓥ$. The other simple decomposition of λ with respect to $w_3 \mid w_1w_2$ can be obtained by complementing ψ and the last variable in ϕ. Since both ϕ

and ψ are in our basis B, we obtain an optimal basic decomposition

$$D = (\phi, \psi) \circ (\lambda, \mu) \circ (\alpha, \beta)$$

of the given switching function $f : Q^4 \to Q$ with component switching functions

$$\phi = \wedge', \qquad \psi = \oslash, \qquad \mu = \vee, \qquad \beta = \wedge.$$

Hence, for every point $x = x_1 x_2 x_3 x_4$ of Q^4, we have

$$f(x) = \wedge'\{\vee [x_1 \wedge (x_2, x_3)], \oslash(x_1, x_4)\}.$$

This decomposition D of f describes an optimal network of 2-input logical devices for f as shown by the Boolean graph given in Figure III-12-15.

FIGURE III-12-15

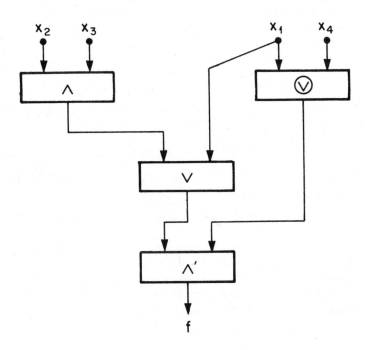

For the purpose of illustration, we have given in the preceding example far more details than necessary for the usual practice of a logical designer. For example, Tables III-12-7 through III-12-10 are given to show how the decomposition charts of nondisjunctive partitions can be applied to specific problems. In practice, Table III-12-7 would be enough for finding the simple decomposition (λ, μ) of α. Another worked-out example can be found in [H1, pp. 308–312]. Other examples are given as exercises at the end of this chapter for the interested readers to work out.

Exercises

1. Construct decomposition charts of not more than six variables for all disjunctive partitions in the form described in §9. Order a number of duplicate copies of these charts and keep the masters for further duplication.

2. Construct decomposition charts of not more than four variables for all nondisjunctive partitions of degree of repetition $r \leq 2$. Order a number of duplicate copies of these charts and keep the masters for further duplication.

3. By using decomposition charts, find all decompositions of the following switching functions with total degree of repetition $r = 0$ and with component switching functions of at least two variables:

   (a) the switching function f of five variables without don't care points and defined by its on-set

$$f^{-1}(1) = \{4, 7, 8, 11, 13, 14, 23, 27, 28, 29, 30\},$$

   (b) the switching function f of five variables with $\{1, 5, 23, 25, 30, 31\}$ as its don't care points and defined by its on-set

$$f^{-1}(1) = \{4, 8, 10, 16, 21, 27, 28\},$$

   (c) the switching function f of six variables with $\{7, 17, 51, 58, 63\}$ as its don't care points and defined by its on-set

$$f^{-1}(1) = \{0, 3, 6, 10, 13, 15, 21, 24, 28, 34, 36, 41, 43, 55\}.$$

4. By using decomposition charts, find all decompositions of the following switching functions with total degree of repetition $r \leq 2$ and with component switching functions of at least two variables:

   (a) the switching function f of three variables without don't care points and defined by its on-set

$$f^{-1}(1) = \{0, 2, 3, 4, 5, 6\},$$

   (b) the switching function f of four variables without don't care points and defined by its on-set

$$f^{-1}(1) = \{6, 7, 8, 9, 10, 11, 13, 15\},$$

   (c) the switching function f of four variables with $\{0, 4, 8, 12\}$ as its don't care points and defined by its on-set

$$f^{-1}(1) = \{6, 7, 9, 10, 11, 13, 15\}.$$

5. Construct an optimal network of 2-input NAND-gates for each of the following switching functions:

(a) the switching function f of three variables without don't care points and defined by its on-set

$$f^{-1}(1) = \{5, 6, 7\},$$

(b) the switching function f of four variables without don't care points and defined by its on-set

$$f^{-1}(1) = \{0, 1, 2, 3, 4, 5, 6, 8, 9, 11, 15\},$$

(c) the switching function f of four variables with $\{0, 4, 8, 12\}$ as it is don't care points and defined by its on-set

$$f^{-1}(1) = \{1, 2, 3, 5, 6, 9, 11, 15\}.$$

6. Construct an optimal network of 2-input NOR-gates for each of the following switching functions:

(a) the switching function f of three variables without don't care points and defined by its on-set

$$f^{-1}(1) = \{3, 6, 7\},$$

(b) the switching function f of four variables without don't care points and defined by its on-set

$$f^{-1}(1) = \{4, 5, 6, 7, 8, 12, 13, 14, 15\},$$

(c) the switching function f of four variables with $\{1, 4, 7, 10, 13\}$ as its don't care points and defined by its on-set

$$f^{-1}(1) = \{5, 6, 8, 12, 14, 15\}.$$

7. Let our basis B consist of the three switching functions

$$c : Q \to Q, \qquad \wedge : Q^2 \to Q, \qquad \vee : Q^2 \to Q.$$

Assume that the cost of c is zero and that the costs of $\wedge$ and $\vee$ are positive and equal. Construct an optimal basic network for each of the switching functions in Exercises 5 and 6.

8. Let our basis B consist of all symmetric switching functions and assume that the cost of a symmetric device is measured by its number of inputs minus 1. Construct an optimal network with symmetric devices for each of the switching functions in Exercises 5 and 6. Discuss modifications that must be made if

(a) the costs of all symmetric devices are equal,

(b) the cost of a symmetric device is measured by the number of its inputs.

9. Establish *Ashenhurst's Auxiliary Theorem* 1: If a nondegenerate switching function f of n variables $X = \{x_1, \cdots, x_n\}$ has a simple decomposition (α, β) with respect to a disjunctive partition $Y \mid Z$ of X and a simple decomposition (γ, δ) with respect to a disjunctive partition $U \mid V$ of X satisfying $U \subset Y$ and hence $V \supset Z$, then δ has a uniquely determined simple decomposition (ϕ, ψ) with respect to the disjunctive partition $V \backslash Z \mid Z$ of V and satisfying $\psi = \beta$. Furthermore, the switching function ϕ is nondegenerate. [Ashenhurst 2, p. 95; Cu, p. 275.]

10. Establish *Ashenhurst's Auxiliary Theorem* 2: If a nondegenerate switching function f of n variables $X = \{x_1, \cdots, x_n\}$ has a simple decomposition (α, β) with respect to a disjunctive partition

$$Y \mid Z = y_1 y_2 \cdots y_s \mid z_1 z_2 \cdots z_t$$

of X and a simple decomposition (γ, δ) with respect to the disjunctive partition $Z \mid Y$, then there exists a uniquely determined switching function

$$g : Q^2 \to Q$$

of two variables such that

$$f(x) = g[\delta(y_1, y_2, \cdots, y_s), \beta(z_1, z_2, \cdots, z_t)]$$

holds for every point $x = x_1 x_2 \cdots x_n$ of the n-cube Q^n. Furthermore, the switching function g is nondegenerate. [Ashenhurst 2, p. 96; Cu, p. 277.]

11. Establish *Ashenhurst's Auxiliary Theorem* 3: If a nondegenerate switching function f of n variables $X = \{x_1, \cdots, x_n\}$ has a simple decomposition (α, β) with respect to a disjunctive partition

$$Y \mid Z = y_1 y_2 \cdots y_s \mid z_1 z_2 \cdots z_t$$

and a simple decomposition (γ, δ) with respect to a disjunctive partition

$$U \mid V = u_1 u_2 \cdots u_p \mid v_1 v_2 \cdots v_q$$

satisfying

$$Y \cap U = \{w_1, \cdots, w_m\}, \qquad Z \cap V = \square,$$

then there exists a uniquely determined switching function

$$g : Q^{m+2} \to Q$$

of $m + 2$ variables such that

$$f(x) = g[w_1, \cdots, w_m, \delta(v_1, \cdots, v_q), \beta(z_1, \cdots, z_t)]$$

holds for every point $x = x_1 x_2 \cdots x_n$ of the n-cube Q^n. Furthermore, the switching function g is nondegenerate. [Ashenhurst 2, p. 97; Cu, p. 280.]

12. Establish *Ashenhurst's Auxiliary Theorem* 4: If a nondegenerate switching function f of n variables $X = \{x_1, \cdots, x_n\}$ has a simple decomposition (α, β) with respect to a disjunctive partition

$$Y \mid Z = y_1 y_2 \cdots y_s \mid z_1 z_2 \cdots z_t$$

and a simple decomposition (γ, δ) with respect to a disjunctive partition

$$U \mid V = u_1 u_2 \cdots u_p \mid v_1 v_2 \cdots v_q$$

satisfying

$$Y \cap U = \square, \qquad Z \cap V = \{w_1, w_2, \cdots, w_m\},$$

then there exist three switching functions

$$\phi : Q^m \to Q, \qquad \psi : Q^p \to Q, \qquad \chi : Q^s \to Q$$

satisfying

$$f(x_1, \cdots, x_n) = \phi(w_1, \cdots, w_m) \,\#\, \psi(u_1, \cdots, u_p) \,\#\, \chi(y_1, \cdots, y_s),$$

where the operation $\#$ is uniquely determined as $\wedge$, $\vee$, or $\varovee$. Furthermore, the switching functions ϕ, ψ, χ are nondegenerate, uniquely determined if $\#$ is $\wedge$ or $\vee$, and to within complementation if $\#$ is $\varovee$. [Ashenhurst 2, p. 98; Cu, p. 282.]

13. Establish *Ashenhurst's Auxiliary Theorem* 5: If a nondegenerate switching function f of n variables $X = \{x_1, \cdots, x_n\}$ has a simple decomposition (α, β) with respect to a disjunctive partition $Y \mid Z$ of X and a simple decomposition (γ, δ) with respect to a disjunctive partition $U \mid V$ satisfying

$$Y \cap U = \{w_1, \cdots, w_m\},$$
$$Z \cap V = \{a_1, \cdots, a_p\},$$
$$Z \backslash V = \{b_1, \cdots, b_q\},$$
$$V \backslash Z = \{c_1, \cdots, c_r\},$$

then there exist switching functions

$$\phi : Q^p \to Q, \qquad \psi : Q^q \to Q, \qquad \chi : Q^r \to Q, \qquad g : Q^{m+1} \to Q$$

satisfying

$$f(x_1, \cdots, x_n) = g[w_1, \cdots, w_m, \phi(a_1, \cdots, a_p) \,\#\, \psi(b_1, \cdots, b_q) \,\#\, \chi(c_1, \cdots, c_r)],$$

where the operation $\#$ is uniquely determined as $\wedge$, $\vee$, or $\varovee$. Furthermore, the switching functions ϕ, ψ, χ, and g are nondegenerate,

ϕ, ψ, χ are uniquely determined to within complementation, and g is uniquely determined to within complementation of the last variable. [Ashenhurst 2, p. 100; Cu, p. 286.]

14. Generalize Ashenhurst's auxiliary theorems in Exercises 9–13 to cases where more than two disjunctive simple decompositions of a switching function are given. [Ashenhurst 2, pp. 102–103; Cu, pp. 290–292.]

15. Generalize Ashenhurst's auxiliary theorems in Exercises 9–14 to cases where the simple decompositions of f may be singular. [Ashenhurst 1; Cu, pp. 386–398.]

Chapter IV

SEQUENTIAL MACHINES
AND AUTOMATA

The theory of sequential switching circuits or sequential machines, which are abstract models of electronic computers, was initiated independently by [Huffman 1] and [Moore 1] around 1954. Since then, it has undergone remarkable growth. Most of its known results and historical developments can be found in the existing books on the subject, for example, [Gil], [Gin], [Ha], [H–S], [Mc], and [Mi, vol. ii]. My objective in this chapter is to organize this considerable body of engineers' contributions into a branch of pure mathematics, in particular, a branch of abstract algebra. As another algebraic structure, I present the theory in the usual modern algebraic fashion, that is, in the form of machines, submachines, homomorphisms, quotient machines, and so on, in uniformized terminology and notation. As I did for switching functions and their Boolean expressions in Chapter I, I differentiate the meaning of automata from that of sequential machines. In Chapter I, we saw that a switching function can be represented by many different Boolean expressions. Similarly, an automaton can be realized by many different sequential machines. This differentiation simplifies the theory at several points.

I. Automata

The output $f(x)$ of any logical device D that realizes a switching function

$$f : Q^n \to Q$$

of n variables depends only on its present inputs

$$x = x_1 x_2 \cdots x_n \in Q^n.$$

These logical devices are called *combinational circuits*. Most devices used in electronic computers are combinational circuits; however, there are also many devices whose outputs depend not only on the present inputs but, in general, also on the entire past history of inputs. The latter logical devices are called *automata*.

With the purpose of formulating a precise mathematical definition for automata with n inputs, let us first introduce a few preliminary notions. The 2^n points of the n-cube Q^n will be called the *input words* of n variables. Thus an input word

$$w = x_1 x_2 \cdots x_n$$

is a symbol which is the juxtaposition of n elements of the set

$$Q = \{0, 1\}.$$

By an *input tape* of n variables, we mean a finite sequence

$$\tau = (w_1, w_2, \cdots, w_q)$$

of input words $w_1, w_2, \cdots, w_q$ of n variables. The number q of input words in an input tape τ is defined as the *length* $\lg(\tau)$ of the input tape τ. In symbols, we have

$$\lg(\tau) = \lg(w_1, w_2, \cdots, w_q) = q.$$

We shall use $\square$ to denote the *empty input tape*. Then we have $\lg(\tau) = 0$ iff $\tau = \square$.

Consider the infinite set

$$T_n = T(Q^n)$$

of all possible input tapes of n variables. Define a binary operation as follows. Let

$$\xi = (u_1, u_2, \cdots, u_p), \qquad \eta = (v_1, v_2, \cdots, v_q)$$

denote arbitrary input tapes of n variables. By the *product* of ξ and η, we mean the input tape $\xi\eta$ of n variables obtained from ξ and η by concatenation; that is,

$$\xi\eta = (u_1, u_2, \cdots, u_p, v_1, v_2, \cdots, v_q).$$

The following properties of this binary operation in T_n are obvious.

PROPOSITION 1.1.   *The product in T_n is associative, that is,*

$$\xi(\eta\zeta) = (\xi\eta)\zeta$$

holds for arbitrary input tapes ξ, η, ζ of n variables.

PROPOSITION 1.2.   *The empty input tape $\square$ is a unit for the product in T_n, that is,*

$$\square\tau = \tau = \tau\square$$

holds for every input tape τ of n variables.

PROPOSITION 1.3. *For any two input tapes ξ and η of n variables, we have*
$$\lg(\xi\eta) = \lg(\xi) + \lg(\eta).$$

Because of (1.1), T_n is a *semigroup* as defined in [H2, p. 96]. Since T_n has a unit $\square$ by (1.2), it is also a *monoid* as defined in [H2, p. 97]. In fact, T_n is the *free monoid* generated by the 2^n elements of Q^n as defined in [H3, p. 34]. On the other hand, the product in T_n is clearly not commutative.

The mathematical definition of automata is as follows: By an *automaton* of n variables, we mean a function
$$A : T_n \to Q$$
from the infinite set T_n of all possible input tapes of n variables into the set
$$Q = \{0, 1\}.$$
For any given input tape $\tau \in T_n$, the value
$$A(\tau) \in Q$$
is called the corresponding *output* of the automaton A.

As an illustrative example, let us consider the device shown in the diagram in Figure IV-1-1. Here, $\bigotimes$ stands for the exclusive OR function

FIGURE IV-1-1

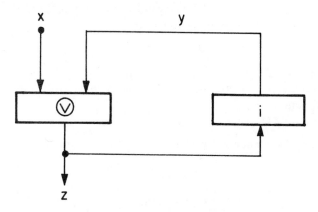

and i stands for the identity function. This diagram does not represent a combinational circuit because it contains a feedback loop.

Assume that this circuit is operated by pulsewise signals to the single input x. Since $n = 1$, the input words are 0's and 1's, and the input tapes are finite sequences of 0's and 1's. Assume that we have been provided with a machine that can read our input tapes at a uniform speed, say, one input word per unit time. The machine is to send a pulse to the input x as soon as it reads a 1 in the tape. The duration of the pulse is much shorter than one unit of time. Since $\bigvee(1, 0) = 1$ and $\bigvee(1, 1) = 0$, every pulse to the input x changes y into $z = 1 - y$. Because of this feature, the device is called a *reverser*. A certain delaying device is built in the box indicated by i to make sure that the inner state y changes after the pulse has passed away and before the possible next pulse arrives.

To see that this device is an automaton, let us assume that the *initial state* of y is 0, that is, y has the value 0 when the device is turned on. We feed an arbitrary input tape

$$\tau = (w_1, w_2, \cdots, w_q)$$

to the machine. Then the first 1 in the tape τ changes y from 0 to 1, the second from 1 to 0, the third from 0 to 1, and so on. After the whole tape τ has been read by the machine, the final output on z will be $A(\tau)$ which is 1 or 0 according as the number of 1's in the tape τ is odd or even. Mathematically, it can be expressed as follows:

$$\begin{aligned} A(\tau) &= w_1 \oplus w_2 \oplus \cdots \oplus w_q \\ &= w_1 + w_2 + \cdots + w_q \bmod 2. \end{aligned}$$

Here, $\oplus$ stands for mod 2 addition while $+$ denote the usual addition. Because of this feature, the device is also called a *serial* mod 2 *adder*. Since the final output $A(\tau) \in Q$ is determined for every input tape $\tau \in T_1$, the assignment $\tau \to A(\tau)$ defines a function

$$A : T_1 \to Q.$$

According to our definition, A is an automaton of one variable.

As another example of automata, let us consider an arbitrarily given switching function

$$f : Q^n \to Q$$

of n variables. We define a function

$$A_f : T_n \to Q$$

by setting

$$A_f(\tau) = f(w_q)$$

for every input tape

$$\tau = (w_1, w_2, \cdots, w_q)$$

of n variables. Since every input word is a point of Q^n, this function A_f is well defined. According to our definition, A_f is an automaton of n variables and will be referred to as the *induced automaton* of the given switching function f.

The preceding definition of A_f is very natural. In fact, if we feed the input words in the tape

$$\tau = (w_1, w_2, \cdots, w_q)$$

in the given order to the n inputs $x_1, x_2, \cdots, x_n$ of any machine that realizes the switching function f, the final output reading on the machine will certainly be

$$A_f(\tau) = f(w_q)$$

which is the output for the last input word w_q on the input tape τ.

On the other hand, let us consider an arbitrarily given automaton

$$A : T_n \to Q$$

of n variables. Since every point w of the n-cube Q^n can be considered as an input tape (w) that consists of w as its lone input word, we may define a function

$$f_A : Q^n \to Q$$

by setting

$$f_A(w) = A(w)$$

for every point $w \in Q^n$. This switching function f_A will be referred to as the *restriction* of the automaton A on the n-cube Q^n. Conforming with the customary notation in mathematics, we shall also denote this restriction of A by

$$f_A = A \mid Q^n.$$

Every switching function $f : Q^n \to Q$ of n variables is the restriction of some automaton $A : T_n \to Q$ of n variables. Precisely, we have the following proposition which is obvious.

PROPOSITION 1.4. *For every switching function $f : Q^n \to Q$, we have*

$$A_f \mid Q^n = f.$$

Not every automaton is induced by some switching function. For example, the serial mod 2 adder

$$A : T_1 \to Q$$

defined above is not induced by any switching function of one variable. To verify this assertion by contradiction, assume that A were induced by a switching function $f : Q^1 \to Q$. Then we would have

$$A(0, 1) = f(1) = A(1, 1).$$

This is impossible because $A(0, 1) = 1$ and $A(1, 1) = 0$. Thus our assertion is verified. Consequently, the notion of automata is a nontrivial generalization of that of switching functions.

Just as switching functions of n variables may have don't care points of Q^n, an automaton of n variables may have *don't care tapes* in T_n. In fact, some of the input tapes in T_n may never occur in normal operation. For example, if the input signals come in the form of pulses, one can hardly arrange two pulses to arrive at different inputs at exactly the same time. In this case, no input word containing two or more 1's can ever occur in any workable input tape. By an *automaton of n variables, possibly with don't care tapes*, we mean a function

$$A : T_n \to Q^*$$

from the set T_n of all possible input tapes of n variables into the set

$$Q^* = \{1, 0, *\}.$$

The inverse image

$$A^{-1}(*) = \{\tau \in T_n \mid A(\tau) = *\}$$

is called the *set of don't care tapes* for the automaton A.

Each of the automata defined above has only one output. Multi-output automata can be easily defined as follows. By an *automaton with n inputs and m outputs*, we mean a function

$$A : T_n \to Q^m$$

from the set T_n of all input tapes of n variables into the m-cube Q^m. For each integer $i = 1, 2, \cdots, m$, let

$$p_i : Q^m \to Q$$

denote the switching function of m variables defined by

$$p_i(y) = y_i$$

for every point $y = y_1 \cdots y_m$ of Q^m. Then the composition

$$A_i = p_i \circ A : T_n \to Q$$

of A and p_i defined by

$$A_i(\tau) = p_i[A(\tau)]$$

for each input tape $\tau \in T_n$ is an automaton with only one output for every integer $i = 1, 2, \cdots, m$, and we have

$$A(\tau) = A_1(\tau)A_2(\tau) \cdots A_m(\tau) \in Q^m$$

for every $\tau \in T_n$. In the terminology of set theory, A is the *Cartesian product*

$$A = A_1 \times A_2 \times \cdots \times A_m$$

of the m automata $A_1, A_2, \cdots, A_m$, [H3, p. 13]; therefore, it suffices to study the mathematical theory of automata with only one output.

For further generalization, we may replace the set Q^n of input words by an arbitrarily given set W, and the set Q of output values by another set V. Let $T(W)$ denote the set of all finite sequences of points in W. Then the functions

$$A : T(W) \to V$$

are called *abstract automata* with W as the set of *input words* and V as the set of *output values*. If W and V are finite sets, these abstract automata can be reduced to ordinary automata, possibly with don't care tapes, as follows. We assume that the numbers of elements in W and V are p and q, respectively, and choose least integers n and m satisfying

$$p \le 2^n, \qquad q \le 2^m.$$

Then we can consider W and V as subsets of Q^n and Q^m, respectively, by selecting some injective (i.e., one-to-one) functions

$$i : W \to Q^n, \qquad j : V \to Q^m.$$

This having been done, $T(W)$ becomes a subset of $T_n = T(Q^n)$ and the composed function

$$j \circ A : T(W) \to Q^m$$

can be considered as an ordinary automaton with n inputs, m outputs, and set-theoretic difference

$$T_n \backslash T(W)$$

as its set of don t care tapes.

2. Sequential Machines

Having defined the mathematical notion of automata, we naturally come to the problem of realizing any given automaton

$$A : T_n \to Q$$

of n variables by means of a certain machine M. Since the output $A(\tau)$ depends on the whole tape τ which is the entire past history of inputs, the machine M must be able to preserve information about the previous input words. For this purpose, the concept of *states* was introduced by the pioneers of sequential machines. The *state* of the machine M corresponds to some memory of the past input words and changes while further input words on the tape τ are fed into M.

As to the final output reading $A(\tau)$ on the machine M after the whole tape τ has been fed into M, there are two types of machines, namely, the *Moore machines* and the *Mealy machines*. In a Moore machine, the final output reading depends only on the final state of the machine. In a Mealy machine, the final output reading depends not only on the final state of the machine but also on the final input word on the tape. Since these two types of machines are equivalent according to Exercise 13 at the end of this chapter, we shall consider only Moore-type machines.

As a result of the preceding discussion, we are now in a better position to define the abstract mathematical concept of a sequential machine. By a *sequential machine with n inputs*, we mean a set S together with a function

$$M : S \times Q^n \to S$$

from the Cartesian product $S \times Q^n$ into the set S. The elements of the set S are called the *states* of the machine and the function M is called the *transition function* of the machine. Here, the *Cartesian product* $S \times Q^n$ of the two sets S and Q^n is the set of all ordered pairs (a, w) with $a \in S$ and $w \in Q^n$ as defined in [H2, p. 24].

Since the transition function

$$M : S \times Q^n \to S$$

of a sequential machine gives the complete information about the machine, it will be used to denote the machine itself.

Now let us consider an arbitrarily given sequential machine

$$M : S \times Q^n \to S.$$

For every nonempty input tape $\tau \in T_n$, let τ' denote the input tape obtained by deleting the last input word on τ. Then, for every state $a \in S$ and every input tape $\tau \in T_n$, we can define a state $a\tau \in S$ inductively by setting

$$a\tau = \begin{cases} a, & (\text{if } \tau = \Box), \\ M(a\tau', w_q), & (\text{if } \tau \neq \Box), \end{cases}$$

where w_q denotes the last input word on the tape τ.

The following two propositions are obvious.

PROPOSITION 2.1. *For every state $a \in S$, we have*

$$a\Box = a.$$

PROPOSITION 2.2. *For every state $a \in S$ and any two input tapes $\sigma, \tau \in T_n$, we have*

$$a(\sigma\tau) = (a\sigma)\tau.$$

In other words, the monoid T_n of all input tapes of n variables operates on the right of the set S of states.

The assignment $(a, \tau) \to a\tau$ defines a function

$$M^* : S \times T_n \to S$$

from the Cartesian product $S \times T_n$ into the set S. Since

$$aw = M(a, w)$$

holds for every $a \in S$ and every $w \in Q^n$, M^* is an extension of the transition function M. Consequently, M^* will be referred to as the *extended transition function* of the sequential machine M.

In engineering, the initial state of a sequential machine means the state of the machine when it is turned on. Mathematically, the *initial state* of a sequential machine

$$M : S \times Q^n \to S$$

means only an arbitrarily chosen element a of its set S of all states.

In engineering, the output function of a Moore machine with S as its set of states means the function

$$f : S \to Q$$

from S into the set $Q = \{0, 1\}$ such that the output reading on the machine is $f(a)$ while the machine is in the state a. Mathematically the *output function* of a sequential machine

$$M : S \times Q^n \to S$$

means only an arbitrarily chosen function

$$f : S \to Q.$$

Now let us assume that a sequential machine

$$M : S \times Q^n \to S$$

together with an initial state $a \in S$ and an output function $f : S \to Q$ is arbitrarily given. We can define an automaton

$$A : T_n \to Q$$

by taking

$$A(\tau) = f(a\tau)$$

for every input tape $\tau \in T_n$. This automaton A is said to be the *behavior* of the sequential machine M with respect to the initial state $a \in S$ and the output function $f : S \to Q$; in symbols, we have

$$A = \beta(M, a, f).$$

We shall also say that the system (M, a, f) *realizes* the automaton A.

Next, let us consider the question whether every automaton of n variables can be realized by sequential machine. This will be answered affirmatively by means of the free sequential machine of n variables. By the *free sequential machine* of n variables, we mean the function

$$F_n : T_n \times Q^n \to T_n$$

defined by

$$F_n(\tau, w) = \tau w$$

for every $\tau \in T_n$ and every $w \in Q^n$. Here, on the right side of the equation, w stands for the input tape in T_n which consists of w as its lone input word and, therefore, τw is the input tape in T_n obtained by adding w into the input tape τ as the last input word.

Since the set of states in the free sequential machine F_n is the set T_n of all input tapes of n variables, every automaton

$$A : T_n \to Q$$

is by definition an output function of F_n. Since $\square\tau = \tau$ holds for every $\tau \in T_n$, the following proposition is obvious.

PROPOSITION 2.3. *For every automaton $A : T_n \to Q$ of n variables, we have*

$$A = \beta(F_n, \square, A).$$

Consequently, we have the following corollary of (2.3).

COROLLARY 2.4. *Every automaton can be realized by a sequential machine.*

This corollary reduces the study of automata to the study of sequential machines.

3. Submachines

Let us consider an arbitrarily given sequential machine

$$M : S \times Q^n \to S$$

of n variables. A subset R of the set S of states is said to be *closed* with respect to the machine M iff

$$M(R \times Q^n) \subset R,$$

that is, $M(a, w) \in R$ holds for every $a \in R$ and every $w \in Q^n$. The following proposition is obvious.

PROPOSITION 3.1. *A subset R of S is closed with respect to the machine M iff*

$$a\tau \in R$$

holds for every state $a \in R$ *and every input tape* $\tau \in T_n$.

As an illustrative example of closed subsets of states, let $n = 1$,

$$S = \{a_0, a_1, a_2, a_3\},$$

and consider the sequential machine $M : S \times Q \to S$ defined by Table IV-3-1. Table IV-3-1 is usually called the *state table* of the given sequential

TABLE IV-3-1

$M(a, w)$ \ a	w 0	1
a_0	a_1	a_0
a_1	a_1	a_0
a_2	a_1	a_0
a_3	a_3	a_3

machine M. It can also be shown figuratively by the diagram in Figure IV-3-2.

The diagram in Figure IV-3-2 is called the *state diagram*, or the *Moore graph*, of the given sequential machine M. From this diagram, one can easily see that each of the following subsets of S is closed with respect to the given sequential machine M:

$$\{a_0, a_1, a_2\}, \quad \{a_0, a_1\}, \quad \{a_3\}.$$

FIGURE IV-3-2

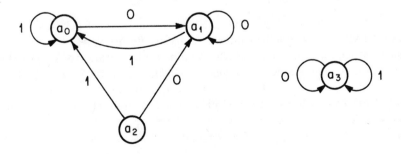

Now let us consider an arbitrarily given closed subset R of S with respect to a sequential machine

$$M : S \times Q^n \to S.$$

Since $M(a, w) \in R$ holds for every $a \in R$ and every $w \in Q^n$, we may define a function

$$L : R \times Q^n \to R$$

by taking

$$L(a, w) = M(a, w)$$

for every $a \in R$ and every $w \in Q^n$. According to our definition in §2, L is a sequential machine of n variables with R as its set of states. Hereafter, L is called the *submachine* of M on the closed subset R of S; in symbols,

$$L = M \mid R.$$

Let $f : S \to Q$ denote an arbitrary output function of the given sequential machine M. Consider the restriction

$$g = f \mid R : R \to Q$$

of f on the closed subset R of S. Then g is an output function of the submachine L. The practical interest in submachines is raised by the following proposition.

PROPOSITION 3.2.   *For every state $a \in R$, we have*

$$\beta(M, a, f) = \beta(L, a, g).$$

Proof. Let $A = \beta(M, a, f)$ and $B = \beta(L, a, g)$. We have to prove $A(\tau) = B(\tau)$ for every input tape τ in T_n. For this purpose, let $\tau \in T_n$ be arbitrarily given. Since $a \in R$, it follows from (3.1) that $a\tau \in R$. Since g is the restriction of f on R, we have $f(a\tau) = g(a\tau)$. Consequently, we obtain

$$A(\tau) = f(a\tau) = g(a\tau) = B(\tau).$$

This completes the proof of (3.2). ‖

In other words, (3.2) says that the submachine L of M behaves exactly as M itself. This practical interest suggests the problem of finding the smallest submachine of M which contains a given state $a \in S$. For this purpose, we shall define the *component machine* M_a of the given sequential machine M as follows. Let $a, b \in S$ be any two states. We say that b is *accessible from a* by means of M iff there exists an input tape $\tau \in T_n$ such that

$$a\tau = b.$$

This relation is clearly reflexive and transitive but not always symmetric. Hence, in general, this is not an equivalence relation as defined in [H2, p. 30].

For an arbitrarily given state $a \in S$, subset S_a of S consisting of all states in S which are accessible from a by means of M is said to be the *component* of a in S with respect to M. For example, let $S = \{a_0, a_1, a_2, a_3\}$ and consider the sequential machine M of one variable defined in the diagram in Figure IV-3-1. Then we have the components

$$S_{a_0} = \{a_0, a_1\}, \qquad S_{a_1} = \{a_0, a_1\},$$
$$S_{a_2} = \{a_0, a_1, a_2\}, \qquad S_{a_3} = \{a_3\}.$$

LEMMA 3.3. *For every state* $a \in S$, *the component* S_a *is a closed subset of* S *with respect to* M *and contains* a.

Proof. Since $a\square = a$, a is accessible from itself. This proves that S_a contains the state a. To prove that S_a is a closed subset of S, let b denote an arbitrary state in S_a. Since b is accessible from a, there exists an input tape $\sigma \in T_n$ with $b = a\sigma$. This implies that

$$b\tau = (a\sigma)\tau = a(\sigma\tau) \in S_a$$

holds for every input tape $\tau \in T_n$. Since this is true for every state $b \in S_a$, it follows that S_a is a closed subset of S. This completes the proof of (3.3). ‖

Because of (3.3), we have a submachine

$$M_a = M \mid S_a : S_a \times Q^n \to S_a$$

of the given sequential machine M on the closed subset S_a of S. This submachine M_a of M will be referred to as the *component machine* of M determined by the state $a \in S$. Its usefulness is indicated by the following proposition.

PROPOSITION 3.4. *The component machine* M_a *of a given sequential machine*

$$M : S \times Q^n \to S$$

determined by a state $a \in S$ *is the smallest submachine of* M *containing the state* a.

Proof. Since M_a is a submachine of M containing the state a by (3.3), it remains to prove that M_a is contained in every submachine of M containing the state a. For this purpose, let

$$L = M \mid R : R \times Q^n \to R$$

denote an arbitrary submachine of M with $a \in R$. We need to prove

$$S_a \subset R.$$

For this purpose, let b denote any state in S_a. By definition of S_a, there exists an input tape $\tau \in T_n$ with $b = a\tau$. Since $a \in R$ and R is closed, this implies $b \in R$. Since b is any state in S_a, we have $S_a \subset R$. This completes the proof of (3.4). ‖

4. Homomorphisms

Consider any two sequential machines

$$L : R \times Q^n \to R, \qquad M : S \times Q^n \to S$$

of n variables. By a *homomorphism* from the machine L into the machine M, we mean a function

$$h : R \to S$$

from the set R of states in the machine L into the set S of states in the machine M such that

$$h[L(a, w)] = M[h(a), w]$$

holds for every state $a \in R$ and every input word $w \in Q^n$. For example, if R is a closed subset of S with respect to the machine M and L is the submachine of M on R, then the *inclusion function*

$$i : R \to S$$

defined by $i(a) = a \in S$ for every state $a \in R$ is clearly a homomorphism of L into M. This homomorphism i will be referred to as the *inclusion homomorphism* of the submachine L of M into the machine M itself. In particular, if $R = S$ and $L = M$, then i is said to be the *identity homomorphism* of the machine M.

PROPOSITION 4.1.   *A function* $h : R \to S$ *is a homomorphism from the machine* L *into the machine* M *iff*

$$h(a\tau) = [h(a)]\tau$$

holds for every state $a \in R$ *and every input tape* $\tau \in T_n$.

Having borrowed the terminology of a homomorphism from modern algebra, we should certainly feel free to use the related algebraic terms for various special homomorphisms defined as follows.

A homomorphism $h : R \to S$ from the machine L into the machine M is said to be an *epimorphism* iff h is *surjective* (i.e., iff h is onto). h is said to be a *monomorphism* iff h is *injective* (i.e., iff h is one-to-one). h is said to be an *isomorphism* iff h is *bijective* (i.e., iff h is both onto and one-to-one). Homomorphisms from a machine into itself are called *endomorphisms* and isomorphisms from a machine onto itself are called *automorphisms*. For example, the inclusion homomorphism i from a submachine L of a machine M into the machine M itself is a monomorphism and i is not an epimorphism unless $L = M$. The identity homomorphism i of a machine M is both a monomorphism and an epimorphism; therefore, i is an isomorphism and also an automorphism.

LEMMA 4.2.   *For any homomorphism* $h : R \to S$ *from the machine L into the machine M, the subset*

$$h(R) = \{h(a) \in S \mid a \in R\}$$

of S is closed with respect to the machine M.

Proof. Let $b \in h(R)$ and $\tau \in T_n$ be arbitrarily given. Since $b \in h(R)$, there exists a state $a \in R$ with $h(a) = b$. By (4.1), we have

$$b\tau = [h(a)]\tau = h(a\tau) \in h(R).$$

Since b and τ are arbitrarily given, this implies that $h(R)$ is closed according to (3.1). ‖

Because of (4.2), we obtain a submachine $M \mid h(R)$ of the machine M on the closed subset $h(R)$ of S. This submachine of M is referred to as the *image* of the homomorphism h. In symbols, we have

$$\mathrm{Im}(h) = M \mid h(R).$$

PROPOSITION 4.3.   *A homomorphism* h *from the machine L into the machine M is an epimorphism iff*

$$\mathrm{Im}(h) = M.$$

Now let us establish the following theorem.

THEOREM 4.4.   *For every state* $a \in S$ *of a sequential machine*

$$M : S \times Q^n \to S$$

of n variables, there exists a unique homomorphism

$$h_a : T_n \to S$$

from the free sequential machine

$$F_n : T_n \times Q^n \to T_n$$

of n variables into the machine M satisfying the condition

$$h_a(\square) = a.$$

Furthermore, the image $\mathrm{Im}(h_a)$ *of this homomorphism* h_a *is the component machine* M_a *of M determined by the state* $a \in S$.

Proof. To establish the existence, let us define a function $h_a : T_n \to S$ by taking

$$h_a(\sigma) = a\sigma$$

for every input tape $\sigma \in T_n$. Then we have

$$h_a(\square) = a\square = a.$$

To prove that h_a is a homomorphism, let τ denote an arbitrary input tape in T_n. Then we have

$$h_a(\sigma\tau) = a(\sigma\tau) = (a\sigma)\tau = [h_a(\sigma)]\tau$$

for every $\sigma \in T_n$. Hence h_a is a homomorphism. This completes the existence proof of the first assertion.

To prove that $\operatorname{Im}(h_a)$ is the component machine M_a of M, it suffices to establish

$$h_a(T_n) = S_a.$$

For this purpose, let $\sigma \in T_n$ be arbitrarily given. Then we have

$$h_a(\sigma) = a\sigma \in S_a$$

by the definition of the component S_a of S. Hence we obtain

$$h_a(T_n) \subset S_a.$$

On the other hand, let b denote an arbitrary state in S_a. By the definition of S_a, there exists an input tape $\tau \in T_n$ with $a\tau = b$. Hence we obtain

$$b = a\tau = h_a(\tau) \in h_a(T_n).$$

Since b is any state in S_a, we have

$$S_a \subset h_a(T_n).$$

Combining these two inclusions, we obtain

$$h_a(T_n) = S_a,$$

thus proving the second assertion.

It remains to establish the uniqueness in the first assertion. For this purpose, let

$$k : T_n \to S$$

denote any homomorphism from the free sequential machine F_n into the given machine M satisfying

$$k(\square) = a.$$

We have to prove $k = h_a$. For this purpose, let σ denote an arbitrary input tape in T_n. Then we have

$$k(\sigma) = k(\square\sigma) = [k(\square)]\sigma = a\sigma = h_a(\sigma).$$

Since σ is any member of T_n, this proves $k = h_a$ and completes the proof of (4.4). ∥

The remainder of this section is devoted to the behaviors of homomorphic sequential machines. For this purpose, let us consider arbitrary output function

$$f : R \to Q, \qquad g : S \to Q$$

for the given sequential machines L and M, respectively. A homomorphism $h : R \to S$ from the machine L into the machine M is said to *preserve output* with respect to f and g iff

$$g[h(a)] = f(a)$$

holds for every state $a \in R$. In other words, the homomorphism h preserves output with respect to f and g iff the output function f is the composition of the functions h and g, in symbols,

$$g \circ h = f.$$

The practical interest of homomorphisms of sequential machines is raised by the following theorem.

THEOREM 4.5. *If a homomorphism* $h : R \to S$ *from the machine* L *into the machine* M *preserves output with respect to output function* $f : R \to Q$ *and* $g : S \to Q$, *then we have*

$$\beta(L, a, f) = \beta[M, h(a), g]$$

for every state $a \in R$.

Proof. Let $a \in R$ be arbitrarily given and denote

$$A = \beta(L, a, f), \qquad B = \beta[M, h(a), g].$$

We need to prove $A(\tau) = B(\tau)$ for every input tape τ in T_n. For this purpose, let $\tau \in T_n$ be arbitrarily given. Then we have

$$A(\tau) = f(a\tau) = g[h(a\tau)] = g[h(a)\tau] = B(\tau).$$

This completes the proof of (4.5). ∥

The following corollary is a direct consequence of (4.5) and (3.2).

COROLLARY 4.6. *For any homomorphism* h *from the machine* L *into the machine* M, L *behaves exactly as its image*

$$\mathrm{Im}(h) = M \mid h(R).$$

The cardinality of $h(R)$, that is, the numbers of states in $h(R)$, cannot exceed that of R. Consequently, the usually simpler machine $\mathrm{Im}(h)$ behaves exactly as the given machine L.

5. Quotient Machines

Consider an arbitrarily given sequential machine

$$L : R \times Q^n \to R$$

of n variables.

By an *equivalence relation* in R, we mean any relation in R which is reflexive, symmetric, and transitive as defined in [H2, p. 30]. An equivalence relation $\sim$ in R is said to be *invariant* with respect to the machine L iff, for any two states a and b in R, $a \sim b$ implies

$$L(a, w) \sim L(b, w)$$

for every $w \in Q^n$. The following proposition is obvious.

PROPOSITION 5.1. *An equivalence relation $\sim$ in R is invariant with respect to the machine L iff, for any two states a and b in R, $a \sim b$ implies*

$$a\tau \sim b\tau$$

for every input tape $\tau \in T_n$.

For an example of invariant equivalence relations in R, let us consider an arbitrarily given homomorphism

$$h : R \to S$$

from the given machine L into any sequential machine

$$M : S \times Q^n \to S$$

of n variables. Define a relation $\sim$ in R as follows: For any two states a and b in R, $a \sim b$ iff

$$h(a) = h(b).$$

This relation $\sim$ in R is obviously reflexive, symmetric, and transitive, [H2, p. 30, Example (3)]. Hence $\sim$ is an equivalence relation in R. To show that $\sim$ is invariant with respect to the machine L, let a and b denote any two states in R satisfying $a \sim b$. Then, for every input tape $\tau \in T_n$, we have

$$h(a\tau) = [h(a)]\tau = [h(b)]\tau = h(b\tau)$$

as a consequence of (4.1) and $a \sim b$. This implies

$$a\tau \sim b\tau.$$

By (5.1), this proves that $\sim$ is invariant with respect to the machine L. Hereafter, this relation $\sim$ in R will be referred to as the *invariant equivalence relation induced by the homomorphism h.*

To establish the converse, that every invariant equivalence relation $\sim$ in R is induced by some homomorphism, we need to introduce the concept of *quotient machines*. For this purpose, let us consider an arbitrarily given invariant equivalence relation $\sim$ in R with respect to the given sequential machine

$$L. : R \times Q^n \to R.$$

Since $\sim$ is an equivalence relation in R, it divides R into a collection R^* of disjoint subsets of R called the *equivalence classes* of R over $\sim$. These equivalence classes are characterized by the property that, for any two states a and b in R, $a \sim b$ iff a and b are contained in the same equivalence class. If the reader is not familiar with the concept of equivalence classes, he is strongly advised to read [H2, chap. i, sec. 8, pp. 29–33].

Now, R^* is a set whose members are the equivalence classes of R over $\sim$; in symbols,

$$R^* = R/\sim.$$

We propose to construct a sequential machine L^* of n variables with the members of R^* as states. For this purpose, let us consider an arbitrary member ξ of R^* and any input word $w \in Q^n$. The Cartesian product

$$\xi \times w = \{(a, w) \mid a \in \xi\}$$

is a subset of $R \times Q^n$ and, therefore, its image

$$L(\xi \times w) = \{L(a, w) \mid a \in \xi\}$$

is a subset of R. Since the equivalence relation $\sim$ in R is invariant, we have

$$L(a, w) \sim L(b, w)$$

for any two states a and b in ξ. It follows that $L(\xi \times w)$ is contained in a unique member η of R^*. This assignment $(\xi, w) \to \eta$ defines a function

$$L^* : R^* \times Q^n \to R^*.$$

By the definition given in §2, this function L^* is a sequential machine and will be referred to as the *quotient machine* of the given machine L over the invariant equivalence relation $\sim$ in R. In symbols, we have

$$L^* = L/\sim.$$

Next let us consider the *natural projection*

$$p : R \to R^*$$

which is the function defined for every state $a \in R$ by taking $p(a)$ as the member of R^* containing a.

LEMMA 5.2.   *The natural projection $p : R \to R^*$ is an epimorphism from the given machine L onto its quotient machine L^*.*

Proof.   Since p is obviously surjective ($=$ onto), it suffices to prove that p is a homomorphism. For this purpose, let $a \in R$ and $w \in Q^n$ be arbitrarily given. By definition of p, $p[L(a, w)]$ is the member of R^* which contains $L(a, w)$. By definition of L^*, $L^*[p(a), w]$ is also the member of R^* which contains $L(a, w)$. This proves

$$p[L(a, w)] = L^*[p(a), w].$$

Hence p is a homomorphism. ‖

This epimorphism p will be called the *natural projection* of the given machine L onto its quotient machine L^*.

LEMMA 5.3.   *The natural projection p of the machine L onto its quotient machine $L/\sim$ of L over an invariant equivalence relation $\sim$ in the set R of states of L induces $\sim$.*

Proof.   Let a and b denote any two states in R^*. By the definition of the natural projection $p : R \to R^*$, we have $p(a) = p(b)$ iff a and b are contained in the same equivalence class of R over $\sim$. Hence, $p(a) = p(b)$ iff $a \sim b$. This proves that $\sim$ is induced by p. ‖

The following corollary is a direct consequence of (5.3).

COROLLARY 5.4.   *Every invariant equivalence relation $\sim$ in the set R of states of a sequential machine L is induced by some homomorphism from L into a sequential machine M.*

Now let us consider an arbitrarily given homomorphism

$$h : R \to S$$

from a sequential machine $L : R \times Q^n \to R$ into a sequential machine $M : S \times Q^n \to S$. We propose to show that the image Im(h) of the homomorphism h can be identified with a quotient machine of L. For this purpose, we may assume without loss of generality that

$$\mathrm{Im}(h) = M;$$

hence, h is an epimorphism because it defines an epimorphism

$$h' : R \to h(R)$$

from L onto Im(h) by taking $h'(a) = h(a)$ for every $a \in R$. This homomorphism h induces an invariant equivalence relation $\sim$ in R which is defined by $a \sim b$ iff $h(a) = h(b)$ for any two states a and b in R. Consider the quotient machine

$$L^* = L/\sim \, : R^* \times Q^n \to R^*.$$

Let ξ denote an arbitrary member of R^*. Since ξ is an equivalence class in R over $\sim$, we have $a \sim b$ and hence $h(a) = h(b)$ for any two states in ξ. Hence the image

$$h(\xi) = \{h(a) \mid a \in \xi\}$$

is a singleton, that is, $h(\xi)$ consists of a single state in S. The assignment $\xi \to h(\xi) \in S$ defines a function

$$h^* : R^* \to S.$$

THEOREM 5.5. *For every epimorphism* $h : R \to S$ *from the machine* L *onto the machine* M, *the function* $h^* : R^* \to S$ *is an isomorphism from the quotient machine* L^* *onto the machine* M *satisfying*

$$h^* \circ p = h,$$

that is, $h^*[p(a)] = h(a)$ *holds for every state* $a \in R$.

Here p stands for the natural projection from the machine L onto its quotient machine L^*.

Proof. To prove that h^* is a homomorphism, let $\xi \in R^*$ and $\tau \in T_n$ be arbitrarily. Let $a \in \xi$. Then $\xi\tau$ is the member of R^* containing the state $a\tau \in R$. Since h is a homomorphism, we have

$$h^*(\xi\tau) = h(a\tau) = [h(a)]\tau = [h^*(\xi)]\tau.$$

Hence h^* is a homomorphism from the quotient machine L^* of L into M.

To prove that h^* is an epimorphism, let b denote an arbitrary state in S. Since h is an epimorphism, there exists a state a in R with $h(a) = b$. Let ξ denote the member of R^* that contains $a \in R$. Then we have

$$h^*(\xi) = h(a) = b.$$

This proves that h^* is an epimorphism.

To prove that h^* is a monomorphism let ξ and η denote any two members of R^* satisfying $h^*(\xi) = h^*(\eta)$. Let $a \in \xi$ and $b \in \eta$. Then we have

$$h(a) = h^*(\xi) = h^*(\eta) = h(b).$$

Since the equivalence relation $\sim$ in R is induced by h, this implies $a \sim b$. Since ξ and η are equivalence classes over $\sim$, this implies $\xi = \eta$. Hence, h^* is a monomorphism.

Combining the last three paragraphs, we conclude that h^* is an isomorphism from the quotient machine L^* onto the machine M.

It remains to prove $h^* \circ p = h$. For this purpose, let $a \in R$ be arbitrarily given. Let $\xi = p(a)$. Then ξ is the member of R^* that contains $a \in R$. Hence we have

$$(h^* \circ p)(a) = h^*[p(a)] = h^*(\xi) = h(a).$$

Since a is any state in R, this implies $h^* \circ p = h$ and completes the proof of (5.5). ‖

The following corollary is a direct consequence of (5.5).

COROLLARY 5.6. *Every homomorphic image of a sequential machine L is isomorphic to a quotient machine of L.*

A sequential machine $M : S \times Q^n \to S$ is said to be *connected* iff there exists a state $a \in S$ with

$$M_a = M.$$

Here M_a stands for the component machine of M defined in §3.

COROLLARY 5.7. *Every connected sequential machine of n variables is isomorphic to a quotient machine of the free sequential machine F_n of n variables.*

Proof. Let $M : S \times Q^n \to S$ denote any connected sequential machine. Then there exists a state $a \in S$ with $M_a = M$. According to (4.4), there exists a homomorphism

$$h : T_n \to S$$

from the free sequential machine F_n into the given machine M satisfying $h(\square) = a$. By the second assertion in (4.4), the image of h is $M_a = M$ and hence h is an epimorphism. By (5.5), M is isomorphic to a quotient machine of F_n. ‖

6. Admissible Homomorphisms

Consider any two sequential machines

$$L : R \times Q^n \to R, \qquad M : S \times Q^n \to S$$

of n variables and an arbitrarily given homomorphism

$$h : R \to S$$

from the machine L into the machine M. Then, for any given output function

$$g : S \to Q$$

for the machine M, the composition

$$f = g \circ h : R \to Q,$$

defined by $f(a) = g[h(a)]$ for every $a \in R$, is an output function for the machine L. According to our definition in §4, the homomorphism h preserves output with respect to f and g. By (4.5), this implies

$$\beta[L, a, f] = \beta[M, h(a), g]$$

for every state $a \in R$. Therefore, if h is an epimorphism, the machine L behaves exactly as the machine M.

In practice, we are more interested in the case where the roles of f and g are interchanged. Precisely, with an arbitrarily given output function

$$f : R \to Q$$

for the machine L, we want to construct an output function

$$g : S \to Q$$

for the machine M satisfying

$$g \circ h = f.$$

Obviously, this is not always possible, for, if h carries two states in R with different outputs into the same state in S, then we have

$$g \circ h \neq f$$

for every output function $g : S \to Q$ for the machine M. This suggests the following concept of admissible homomorphisms.

Let $f : R \to Q$ denote an arbitrarily given output function for the machine L. A homomorphism

$$h : R \to S$$

from the machine L into the machine M is said to be *admissible* for the output function f iff, for any two states a and b in R, $h(a) = h(b)$ implies $f(a) = f(b)$. In other words, the homomorphism h is admissible for the output function f iff all states in R which are carried by h into the same state in S have the same output.

LEMMA 6.1. *If $h : R \to S$ is an admissible homomorphism for the output function $f : R \to Q$, then there exists an output function $f : S \to Q$ satisfying*

$$g \circ h = f.$$

Proof. Let ξ denote an arbitrary state in the subset $h(R)$ of S and consider the nonempty inverse image

$$h^{-1}(\xi) = \{a \in R \mid h(a) = \xi\}.$$

Since h is admissible for f, the image $f[h^{-1}(\xi)]$ is a single element of the set Q. Hence we may define a function $g : S \to Q$ by setting

$$g(\xi) = \begin{cases} f[h^{-1}(\xi)], & \text{if } \xi \in h(R), \\ *, & \text{if } \xi \in S \backslash h(R). \end{cases}$$

Here, the don't care sign $*$ means that the value of $g(\xi)$ for these ξ's are immaterial and may be given either of the values 0 and 1.

It remains to verify the relation $g \circ h = f$. For this purpose, let a denote an arbitrary state in R. Let $\xi = h(a)$. Then we have $\xi \in h(R)$ and $a \in h^{-1}(\xi)$. Hence we obtain

$$(g \circ h)(a) = g[h(a)] = g(\xi) = f[h^{-1}(\xi)] = f(a).$$

Since a is any state in R, this implies $g \circ h = f$ and completes the proof of (6.1). ‖

COROLLARY 6.2. *If an epimorphism $h : R \to S$ from the machine L onto the machine M is admissible for the output function $f : R \to Q$, then there exists a unique output function $g : S \to Q$ satisfying $g \circ h = f$.*

Proof. Since the existence follows from (6.1), it remains to establish the uniqueness. For this purpose, let

$$g, k : S \to Q$$

denote any two output functions for M satisfying

$$g \circ h = f = k \circ h.$$

To prove $g = k$, let ξ denote any state in S. Since h is an epimorphism, there exists a state a in R with $h(a) = \xi$. Then we have

$$g(\xi) = g[h(a)] = f(a) = k[h(a)] = k(\xi).$$

Since ξ is any state in S, this implies $g = k$ and completes the proof of (6.2). ‖

The uniquely determined output function $g : S \to Q$ for the machine M in (6.2) will be referred to as the *output function induced from f by the epimorphism h* and will be denoted by

$$g = h(f).$$

The following corollary is a direct consequence of (4.5) and (6.2).

COROLLARY 6.3. *If an epimorphism $h : R \to S$ from the machine L onto the machine M is admissible for the output function $f : R \to Q$, then we have*

$$\beta(L, a, f) = \beta[M, h(a), h(f)]$$

or every state a in R.

The following two propositions are obvious.

PROPOSITION 6.4. *Every isomorphism $h : R \to S$ from the machine L onto the machine M is admissible for every output function $f : R \to Q$. Furthermore, we have*

$$h(f) = f \circ h^{-1},$$

where $h^{-1} : S \to R$ denotes the inverse function of h.

PROPOSITION 6.5. *If $h : R \to S$ is an admissible epimorphism from the machine L onto the machine M for an output function $f : R \to Q$ and if $j : S \to T$ is an admissible epimorphism from the machine M onto a machine N for the induced output function $g = h(f) : S \to Q$, then the composition*

$$k = j \circ h : R \to T$$

is an admissible epimorphism from the machine L onto the machine N for the output function $f : R \to Q$. Furthermore, we have

$$k(f) = j(g) = j[h(g)].$$

An invariant equivalence relation $\sim$ in the set R with respect to the machine L is said to *preserve output* with respect to $f : R \to Q$ iff, for any two states a and b in R, $a \sim b$ implies $f(a) = f(b)$.

The following two propositions are obvious from the definitions.

PROPOSITION 6.6. *A homomorphism $h : R \to S$ from the machine L into the machine M is admissible for the output function $f : R \to Q$ iff its induced invariant equivalence relation $\sim$ in the set R preserves output with respect to f.*

PROPOSITION 6.7. *An invariant equivalence relation $\sim$ in the set R with respect to the machine L preserves output with respect to $f : R \to Q$ iff the natural projection*

$$p : R \to R/\sim$$

from the machine L onto its quotient machine $L/\sim$ is admissible for f.

Let $f : R \to Q$ denote an arbitrarily given output function for the machine L. Define a relation

$$\underset{f}{\sim}$$

in the set R as follows: for any two states a and b, $a \underset{f}{\sim} b$ iff

$$f(a\sigma) = f(b\sigma)$$

holds for every input tape $\sigma \in T_n$.

LEMMA 6.8.   *This relation $\underset{f}{\sim}$ in R is an invariant equivalence relation with respect to the machine L and preserves output with respect to f.*

Proof. Since $\underset{f}{\sim}$ is clearly reflexive, symmetric, and transitive, it is an equivalence relation in the set R.

To prove that $\underset{f}{\sim}$ is invariant with respect to the machine L, let a and b denote any two states in R with $a \underset{f}{\sim} b$. We need to prove $a\tau \underset{f}{\sim} b\tau$ for every $\tau \in T_n$ according to (5.1). For this purpose, let $\tau \in T_n$ be arbitrarily given. Since $a \underset{f}{\sim} b$, we have

$$f[(a\tau)\sigma] = f[a(\tau\sigma)] = f[b(\tau\sigma)] = f[(b\tau)\sigma]$$

for every $\sigma \in T_n$. By definition of $\underset{f}{\sim}$, this implies $a\tau \underset{f}{\sim} b\tau$. Hence $\underset{f}{\sim}$ is invariant with respect to the machine L.

That $\underset{f}{\sim}$ preserves output with respect to $f : R \to Q$ is obvious from its definition. ‖

LEMMA 6.9.   *If an invariant equivalence relation $\sim$ in R with respect to the machine L preserves output with respect to $f : R \to Q$, then, for any two states a and b in R, $a \sim b$ implies $a \underset{f}{\sim} b$.*

Proof. Assume $a \sim b$. To prove $a \underset{f}{\sim} b$, let $\tau \in T_n$ be arbitrarily given. Since $\sim$ is invariant, $a \sim b$ implies $a\tau \sim b\tau$ according to (5.1). Since $\sim$ preserves output with respect to f, $a\tau \sim b\tau$ implies

$$f(a\tau) = f(b\tau).$$

According to the definition of $\underset{f}{\sim}$, this proves $a \underset{f}{\sim} b$. ‖

Because of (6.8) and (6.9), $\underset{f}{\sim}$ will be referred to as the *maximal invariant equivalence relation in R that preserves output with respect to $f : R \to Q$.* The quotient machine

$$L_f = L/\underset{f}{\sim}$$

will be called the *minimal quotient machine of L with respect to the output function $f : R \to Q$* because of the following theorem.

THEOREM 6.10.   *For an arbitrarily given admissible epimorphism*

$$h : R \to S$$

from the machine L onto the machine M with respect to an output function
$f : R \to Q$, *there exists a unique homomorphism*

$$k : S \to R/\underset{f}{\sim}$$

*from the machine M into the minimal quotient machine L_f of L with respect
to f such that the composition*

$$p = k \circ h : R \to R/\underset{f}{\sim}$$

*is the natural projection from the machine L onto its quotient machine L_f.
Furthermore, k is an epimorphism and is admissible for the output function*

$$g = h(f) : S \to Q.$$

Proof. Let $\sim$ denote the invariant equivalence relation in R induced
by the homomorphism h and consider the quotient machine

$$L^* = L/\sim$$

with $R^* = R/\sim$ as its set of states. Since h is an epimorphism, h induces
an isomorphism

$$i = h^* : R^* \to S$$

from the quotient machine L^* onto the machine M according to (5.5).

Since h is admissible for the output function $f : R \to Q$, it follows from
(6.6) that $\sim$ preserves output with respect to f. Then it follows from (6.9)
that, for any two states a and b in R, $a \sim b$ implies $a \underset{f}{\sim} b$. In other words,
every member ξ of $R^* = R/\sim$ is contained in a unique member $j(\xi)$ of
$R_f = R/\underset{f}{\sim}$. The assignment $\xi \to j(\xi)$ defines a function

$$j : R^* \to R_f.$$

To prove that j is a homomorphism, let $\xi \in R^*$ and $\tau \in T_n$ be arbitrarily
given. Select a state $a \in R$ that is contained in ξ. Then $\xi\tau$ is the member
of R^* which contains $a\tau \in R$. Since $a \in j(\xi)$, $[j(\xi)]\tau$ is the member of R_f
which contains $a\tau$. By the definition of the function j, we obtain

$$j(\xi\tau) = [j(\xi)]\tau.$$

This proves that j is a homomorphism from the machine L^* into the
machine L_f; therefore, the composition

$$k = j \circ i^{-1} : S \to R_f$$

of the inverse isomorphism $i^{-1} : S \to R^*$ with j is a homomorphism from
the machine M into the machine L_f.

To prove the relation $p = k \circ h$, let a denote an arbitrary state in R.
Since i is the isomorphism induced by h, $i^{-1}[h(a)]$ is the member of R^*

which contains the state $a \in R$. Hence, $j\{i^{-1}[h(a)]\}$ is the member of R_f which contains the state a. This implies

$$k[h(a)] = j\{i^{-1}[h(a)]\} = p(a).$$

Since this is true for every $a \in R$, we have $k \circ h = p$. This completes the existence proof for the first assertion.

To establish the uniqueness, let

$$k, l : S \to R_f$$

denote any two homomorphisms from the machine M into the machine L_f satisfying

$$k \circ h = p = l \circ h.$$

We need to prove $k = l$. For this purpose, let b denote any state in S. Since h is an epimorphism, there exists a state $a \in R$ with $h(a) = b$. Hence we obtain

$$k(b) = k[h(a)] = p(a) = l[h(a)] = l(b).$$

Since this is true for every $b \in S$, we have $k = l$. This completes the proof of the first assertion.

To prove the second assertion, we observe that i^{-1} is an isomorphism and that j is an epimorphism. Hence, their composition $k = j \circ i^{-1}$ must be an epimorphism.

It remains to show that k is admissible for the output function g. For this purpose, let x and y denote any two states in S with $k(x) = k(y)$. Since h is an epimorphism, there exist two states a and b in R with $h(a) = x$ and $h(b) = y$. Then we have

$$p(a) = k[h(a)] = k(x) = k(y) = k[h(b)] = p(b).$$

This implies $a \underset{f}{\sim} b$ and hence $f(a) = f(b)$. Since $g = h(f)$, we have $g \circ h = f$. This implies

$$g(x) = g[h(a)] = f(a) = f(b) = g[h(b)] = g(y).$$

Hence k is admissible for g. This completes the proof of (6.10). ‖

7. Minimal Machines

Throughout the present section, let

$$A : T_n \to Q$$

denote an arbitrarily given automaton of n variables.

According to (2.2), this automaton A can be realized by the free sequential machine F_n of n variables with $\square$ as initial state and A itself as output function. In symbols, we have

$$A = \beta(F_n, \square, A).$$

In view of (5.7), the free sequential machine F_n is the most complicated connected sequential machines of n variables. Consequently, it is of practical interest to look for simpler sequential machines that can realize the given automaton A. For this purpose, let us consider T_n as the set of states for the free sequential machine F_n and the given automaton A as an output function for the machine F_n. Then the maximal invariant equivalence relation $\underset{A}{\sim}$ in T_n is defined in §6 as follows. For any two input tapes ξ and η in T_n, we have

$$\xi \underset{A}{\sim} \eta$$

iff

$$A(\xi\tau) = A(\eta\tau)$$

holds for every input tape $\tau \in T_n$. Let

$$S_A = T_n/\underset{A}{\sim}$$

denote the set of all equivalence classes in T_n over the equivalence relation $\underset{A}{\sim}$. Then the minimal quotient machine

$$M_A = F_n/\underset{A}{\sim} : S_A \times Q^n \to S_A$$

of the free sequential machine F_n with respect to the output function $A : T_n \to Q$ as defined in §6 will be called the *minimal sequential machine* for the given automaton A.

This terminology can be justified as follows. Since $\underset{A}{\sim}$ preserves output with respect to $A : T_n \to Q$, it follows from (6.7) that the natural projection

$$p_A : T_n \to S_A$$

is an admissible epimorphism for the output function $A : T_n \to Q$. According to (6.2), p_A induces a uniquely determined output function

$$f_A = p_A(A) : S_A \to Q$$

for the machine M_A satisfying

$$f_A \circ p_A = A.$$

Let $a = p_A(\square) \in S_A$. Then it follows from (6.3) that we have

$$\beta(M_A, a, f_A) = \beta(F_n, \square, A) = A.$$

Hence the machine M_A realizes the given automaton A by means of the initial state $a \in S_A$ and the output function $f_A : S_A \to Q$.

Next let us consider any sequential machine

$$M : S \times Q^n \to S$$

which realizes the given automaton A by means of initial state $a \in S$ and output function $f : S \to Q$. In symbols, we have

$$A = \beta(M, a, f).$$

By (3.2) the component machine M_a of M can realize the automaton A exactly as M itself. Hence we may assume without loss of generality that

$$M_a = M.$$

According to (4.4), there exists a unique epimorphism

$$h_a : T_n \to S$$

from the free sequential machine F_n onto the machine M satisfying

$$h_a(\square) = a.$$

In the proof of (4.4), one can find that

$$h_a(\tau) = a\tau$$

for every input tape $\tau \in T_n$. Because of $A = \beta(M, a, f)$, we obtain

$$A(\tau) = f(a\tau) = f[h_a(\tau)]$$

for every input tape $\tau \in T_n$. This proves

$$A = f \circ h_a.$$

Hence h_a is an admissible epimorphism for the output function $A : T_n \to Q$ with

$$h_a(A) = f.$$

According to (6.10) with $L = F_n$, there exists a uniquely determined epimorphism

$$k : S \to S_A$$

from the machine M onto the machine M_A satisfying

$$k \circ h_a = p_A.$$

Furthermore, k is admissible for the output function $f = h_a(A)$. By (6.5), we also have

$$k(f) = k[h_a(A)] = p_A(A) = f_A.$$

Consequently, we obtain

$$f_A \circ k = f.$$

Since k sends S onto S_A, the cardinality of S_A (i.e., the number of states in S_A) can never be larger than that of S. This justifies our terminology "the minimal sequential machine for the given automaton A" for the machine M_A constructed above.

Now let us continue our investigation of the sequential machine M which realizes the given automaton A by means of the initial state $a \in S$ and the output function $f : S \to Q$. Recall our assumption $M_a = M$ and consider the minimal quotient machine

$$M_f = M/\underset{f}{\sim}$$

of the machine M with respect to the output function f as defined in §6. Applying (6.10) to the epimorphism

$$k : S \to S_A$$

from the given machine M onto the minimal machine M_A for A obtained above, we deduce the existence of a uniquely determined epimorphism

$$i : S_A \to S_f = S/\underset{f}{\sim}$$

from M_A onto the minimal quotient machine M_f such that the composition

$$p_f = i \circ k : S \to S_f$$

is the natural projection from the machine M onto its quotient machine M_f. Furthermore, i is admissible for the output function

$$f_A = k(f) : S_A \to Q.$$

Let $b = p_f(a) \in S_f$ and let

$$g : S_f \to Q$$

denote the output functions induced from $f_A : S_A \to Q$ by the admissible epimorphism i. By (6.5), we have

$$p_f(f) = i[k(f)] = i(f_A) = g.$$

Hence it follows from (4.5) that

$$\beta(M_f, b, g) = \beta(M, a, f) = A.$$

In words, this asserts that the machine M_f realizes the given automaton A by means of the initial state b and the output function g.

Now let us establish the following important lemma.

LEMMA 7.1. *The epimorphism*

$$i : S_A \to S_f$$

*from the minimal sequential machine M_A for A onto the minimal quotient
machine M_f of M is an isomorphism.*

Proof. As above, there exists a uniquely determined admissible
epimorphism

$$h_b : T_n \twoheadrightarrow S_f$$

from the free sequential machine F_n onto the machine M_f satisfying

$$h_b(\square) = b, \qquad A = g \circ h_b.$$

By the definitions of h_a, h_b, and p_f, one can easily see

$$h_b = p_f \circ h_a.$$

According to (6.10) with $L = F_n$, there exists a uniquely determined
epimorphism

$$j : S_f \twoheadrightarrow S_A$$

from the machine M_f onto the machine M_A satisfying

$$j \circ h_b = p_A.$$

Now consider the composition

$$d = j \circ i : S_A \twoheadrightarrow S_A$$

of the two functions $i : S_A \twoheadrightarrow S_f$ and $j : S_f \twoheadrightarrow S_A$. According to (6.5), d
is an epimorphism from the machine M_A onto itself. Furthermore, we have

$$d \circ p_A = j \circ i \circ k \circ h_a$$
$$= j \circ p_f \circ h_a = j \circ p_b = p_A.$$

On the other hand, the identity function

$$e : S_A \twoheadrightarrow S_A,$$

defined by $e(x) = x$ for every $x \in S_A$, is also an epimorphism from the
machine M_A onto itself satisfying

$$e \circ p_A = p_A.$$

It follows from the uniqueness part of (6.10) with

$$L = F_n, \qquad M = M_A, \qquad h = p_A = p,$$

that $d = e$.

To prove that the epimorphism i is an isomorphism, it remains to show
that i is injective, that is, one-to-one. For this purpose, let ξ and η denote
any two members of the set S_A satisfying $i(\xi) = i(\eta)$. Then we have

$$\xi = e(\xi) = d(\xi) = j[i(\xi)] = j[i(\eta)] = d(\eta) = e(\eta) = \eta.$$

Hence $\xi = \eta$, implying that i is injective and completing the proof of (7.1). ∥

Note that, if S_A is a finite set, (7.1) follows immediately from the fact that the number of states in S_A can never be larger than that in S_f.

The following theorem is a restatement of (7.1) in words.

THEOREM 7.2. *If a sequential machine*

$$M : S \times Q^n \to S$$

of n variables realizes an arbitrarily given automaton

$$A : T_n \to Q$$

by means of an initial state $a \in S$ and an output function $f : S \to Q$ and if $M_a = M$, then the minimal quotient machine M_f of M with respect to f is isomorphic to the minimal sequential machine M_A for the given automaton A.

Since isomorphic sequential machines are essentially the same machine, (7.2) shows that the minimal sequential machine M_A for an arbitrarily given automaton $A : T_n \to Q$ can be constructed from any sequential machine M that realizes A.

8. Finite Machines

A sequential machine $M : S \times Q^n \to S$ of n variables is said to be *finite* iff S is a finite set. In other words, M is finite iff it operates on a finite number of states. A sequential machine M of n variables is said to be *infinite* iff M is not finite. For example, the free sequential machine F_n of n variables is infinite for every $n \geq 1$.

PROPOSITION 8.1. *Every submachine of a finite sequential machine M of n variables is finite.*

PROPOSITION 8.2. *Every quotient machine of a finite sequential machine M of n variables is finite.*

In particular, for an arbitrary finite sequential machine

$$M : S \times Q^n \to S,$$

its component machine M_a is finite for every state $a \in S$, and its minimal quotient machine M_f is finite for every output function $f : S \to Q$.

An automaton $A : T_n \to Q$ is said to be *finite* iff it can be realized by a finite sequential machine. In other words, A is finite iff there exists a finite sequential machine $M : S \times Q^n \to S$ such that

$$\beta(M, a, f) = A$$

holds for some state $a \in S$ and some output function $f : S \to Q$. An automaton $A : T_n \to Q$ is said to be *infinite* iff it is not finite.

Most automata of n variables are infinite. In fact, we have the following two propositions.

PROPOSITION 8.3.   *The set of all finite automata of n variables is countable.*

Proof.   For every positive integer p, let Φ_p denote the set of all automata of n variables which can be realized by a sequential machine with p states. Let S denote a set that consists of p distinct members. Then there are precisely

$$p^{p \times 2^n} = p^{p2^n}$$

sequential machines of the form

$$M : S \times Q^n \to S.$$

There are p states in S and 2^p output functions of the form $f : S \to Q$. Since isomorphic sequential machines behave alike, Φ_p consists of not more than

$$p^{p2^n} \times p \times 2^p$$

automata of n variables. As the union

$$\Phi = \Phi_1 \cup \Phi_2 \cup \cdots \cup \Phi_p \cup \cdots$$

of a countable collection of finite sets, the set Φ of all finite automata of n variables is a countable set. This completes the proof of (8.3). ‖

PROPOSITION 8.4.   *The set of all automata of n variables is uncountable.*

Proof.   Let Ω denote the set of all automata of n variables. To prove (8.4) by contradiction, let us assume that Ω were countable. By the usual definition of countably infinite sets [H2, p. 37], the members of Ω could be arranged in the form of an infinite sequence

$$\Omega = \{A_1, A_2, \cdots, A_k, \cdots\}.$$

Let v_0 denote the origin $00 \cdots 0$ of the n-cube Q^n. For every positive integer k, let τ_k denote the input tape of length k which consists of k v_0's as its input words. Define an automaton

$$A : T_n \to Q$$

by taking, for every $\tau \in T_n$,

$$A(\tau) = \begin{cases} 1 - A_k(\tau), & \text{(if } \tau = \tau_k \text{ for some } k), \\ 0, & \text{(if } \tau \neq \tau_k \text{ for each } k). \end{cases}$$

Since $A \neq A_k$ for every $k = 1, 2, \cdots$, A cannot be in Ω. This contradiction proves (8.4). ‖

The following corollary is a direct consequence of (8.3) and (8.4).

COROLLARY 8.5. *The set of all infinite automata of n variables is uncountable.*

As a necessary and sufficiency condition for an automaton to be finite, we have the following theorem.

THEOREM 8.6. *An automaton $A : T_n \rightarrow Q$ of n variables is finite iff its minimal sequential machine*

$$M_A : S_A \times Q^n \rightarrow S_A$$

defined in §7 is finite.

Proof. Since M_A realizes A, the condition is clearly sufficient. To establish the necessity of the condition, let us assume that A is finite. Then, by definition, there exists a finite sequential machine

$$M : S \times Q^n \rightarrow S$$

which realizes A by means of an initial state $a \in A$ and an output function $f : S \rightarrow Q$. According to §7, the cardinality of S_A can never be larger than that of S. Since S is finite, so must be S_A. This proves that M_A is a finite sequential machine and completes the proof of (8.6). ‖

By the *rank* of an automaton $A : T_n \rightarrow Q$ of n variables, we mean the cardinality $rk(A)$ of the set S_A of states in the minimal sequential machine M_A for A.

The following corollary is a restatement of (8.6).

COROLLARY 8.7. *An automaton $A : T_n \rightarrow Q$ of n variables is finite iff it is of finite rank.*

PROPOSITION 8.8. *If a finite automaton A of n variables is realized by a sequential machine M with precisely $rk(A)$ states, then M is isomorphic to the minimal sequential machine M_A for A.*

Proof. Let $M : S \times Q^n \rightarrow S$ realize A by means of an initial state $a \in S$ and an output function $f : S \rightarrow Q$. Since S has the minimum number $rk(A)$ of states, we must have $M_a = M$. Applying (6.10) with $L = F_n$, we obtain an epimorphism

$$k : S \rightarrow S_A$$

from the machine M onto the minimal machine M_A. Since S and S_A are finite and have the number $rk(A)$ of states, this epimorphism k must be an isomorphism. ‖

Therefore, any finite automaton A of n variables can be realized by an essentially unique sequential machine M with minimum number $rk(A)$ of states.

Let n denote an arbitrary positive integer. Hereafter, let us denote the set of all automata of n variables by the symbol Ω_n, and the set of all finite automata of n variables by the symbol Φ_n. Since most of the automata of n variables are infinite, we like to know how the set Φ_n behaves in the containing set Ω_n. For this purpose, let us first study the structure of the set Ω_n. As the collection of all functions from a set T_n into the set $Q = \{0, 1\}$, Ω_n forms a Boolean algebra with respect to two binary operations, the *conjunction* $\wedge$ and the *disjunction* $\vee$, and a unary operation, the *complementation* $'$, defined as follows. For any two automata $A, B \in \Omega_n$, the automata $A \wedge B$, $A \wedge B$, and A are defined by

$$(A \wedge B)(\tau) = \wedge[A(\tau), B(\tau)],$$
$$(A \vee B)(\tau) = \vee[A(\tau), B(\tau)],$$
$$A'(\tau) = c[A(\tau)]$$

for every input tape $\tau \in T_n$. Here, the symbols $\wedge$, $\vee$, and c on the right sides of the equations denote the conjunction function $\wedge : Q^2 \rightarrow Q$, the disjunction function $\vee : Q^2 \rightarrow Q$, and the complementation function $c : Q \rightarrow Q$. One can easily verify the laws of a Boolean algebra as in (I, §4). Now let us establish the following theorem.

THEOREM 8.9. Φ_n *is a Boolean subalgebra of the Boolean algebra* Ω_n, *that is, the following two statements are true:*
(1) *The constant automata* 0 *and* 1 *of* n *variables are finite.*
(2) *If* A *and* B *are finite automata of* n *variables, then so are* $A \wedge B$, $A \vee B$, *and* A'.

Proof.   To prove (1), let us consider any finite sequential machine

$$M : S \times Q^n \rightarrow S.$$

After choosing any initial state $a \in S$, we have

$$\beta(M, a, 0) = 0, \qquad \beta(M, a, 1) = 1,$$

where the 0 and 1 within the parentheses are the constant output functions for the machine M. This proves (1). In fact, we have proved that every sequential machine can realize each of the two constant automa 0 and 1. To prove (2), let us assume that the finite sequential machines

$$L : R \times Q^n \rightarrow R, \qquad M : S \times Q^n \rightarrow S$$

with behaviors

$$\beta(L, a, f) = A, \qquad \beta(M, b, g) = B,$$

where $a \in R, b \in S, f : R \to Q$, and $g : S \to Q$. Considering the Cartesian product $R \times S$ of all pairs (x, y) with $x \in R$ and $y \in S$, we define a function

$$N : (R \times S) \times Q^n \to R \times S$$

by taking

$$N[(x, y), w] = [L(x, w), M(y, w)]$$

for every $(x, y) \in R \times S$ and every $w \in Q^n$. Then N is a sequential machine with the members of $R \times S$ as states and is called the *direct product* of the machines L and M; in symbols, we have

$$N = L \times M.$$

Considering the output functions

$$f \wedge g, f \vee g : R \times S \to Q$$

for the machine $N = L \times M$ defined by

$$(f \wedge g)(x, y) = \wedge[f(x), g(y)],$$
$$(f \vee g)(x, y) = \vee[f(x), g(y)]$$

for every $(x, y) \in R \times S$. Then we have

$$\beta[N, (a, b), f \wedge g] = A \wedge B,$$
$$\beta[N, (a, b), f \vee g] = A \vee B.$$

Since $R \times S$ is a finite set, these prove that the automa $A \wedge B$ and $A \vee B$ are finite.

Finally, let $f' : S \to Q$ denote the output function for M defined by

$$f'(x) = c[f(x)] = 1 - f(x)$$

for every $x \in S$. Then we have

$$\beta(M, a, f') = A'.$$

This implies that A' is finite and completes the proof of (8.9). ‖

To conclude the present section, we give a few propositions which, together with (8.9), will be useful in determining whether a particular automaton is finite.

PROPOSITION 8.10. *For an arbitrarily given input tape* $\sigma \in T_n$, *the automaton*

$$B_\sigma : T_n \to Q,$$

defined by

$$B_\sigma(\tau) = \begin{cases} 1, & (\text{if } \tau = \sigma), \\ 0, & (\text{if } \tau \neq \sigma), \end{cases}$$

is finite.

Proof. Let $\sigma \in T_n$ be the input tape $(w_1, \cdots, w_q)$ with length $q \geq 0$. Here we understand $\sigma = \square$ if $q = 0$. Considering a set S with $q + 2$ distinct members, say

$$S = \{a_0, a_1, \cdots, a_q, a_{q+1}\},$$

we define a function

$$M : S \times Q^n \to S$$

by taking

$$M(a, w) = \begin{cases} a_i, & (\text{if } a = a_{i-1},\ w = w_i,\ i = 1, 2, \cdots, q), \\ a_{q+1}, & (\text{otherwise}). \end{cases}$$

Then M is a finite sequential machine. Let $f : S \to Q$ denote the output function for the machine M defined by

$$f(a) = \begin{cases} 1, & (\text{if } a = a_q), \\ 0, & (\text{if } a \neq a_q). \end{cases}$$

Then we have

$$\beta(M, a_0, f) = B_\sigma.$$

This proves (8.10). ‖

The following corollary is a direct consequence of (8.9) and (8.10).

COROLLARY 8.11. *An automaton* $A : T_n \to Q$ *is finite if either its on-set* $A^{-1}(1)$ *is finite or its off-set* $A^{-1}(0)$ *is finite.*

PROPOSITION 8.12. *If an automaton* $A : T_n \to Q$ *is finite, then so is the automaton*

$$A^* : T_n \to Q$$

defined by setting $A^*(\tau) = 1$ *for an arbitrarily given input tape* $\tau \in T_n$ *iff* τ *can be decomposed into a product*

$$\tau = \tau_1 \tau_2 \cdots \tau_k$$

of input tapes $\tau_1, \tau_2, \cdots, \tau_k$ *satisfying*

$$A(\tau_i) = 1, \qquad (i = 1, 2, \cdots, k).$$

Proof. Consider a finite sequential machine

$$M : S \times Q^n \to S$$

that realizes the automaton A by means of an initial state $a \in S$ and an output function $f : S \to S$. Let

$$S^* = 2^S$$

denote the set of all subsets of the finite set S. Then S^* is a finite set. Define a function

$$M^* : S^* \times Q^n \to S^*$$

as follows. Let $E \in S^*$ and $w \in Q^n$ be arbitrarily given. Then E is a subset of S and, therefore, $E \times w$ is a subset of the Cartesian product $S \times Q^n$. Consider the image $M(E \times w)$ in S. Let $M^*(E, w)$ denote the subset of S defined by

$$M^*(E, w) = \begin{cases} M(E \times w), & \text{if } M(E \times w) \subset f^{-1}(0), \\ [M(E \times w) \cap f^{-1}(0)] \cup \{a\}, & \text{otherwise.} \end{cases}$$

As a subset of S, $M^*(E, w)$ is a member of S^*. The assignment $(E, w) \to M^*(E, w)$ defines the function M^*. This function M^* is a finite sequential machine.

Let $a^* \in S^*$ denote the singleton subset $a^* = \{a\}$ of S and let

$$f^* : S^* \to Q$$

denote the output function for M^* defined by setting $f^*(E) = 1$ for an arbitrarily given member E of S^* iff

$$E \cap f^{-1}(1) \neq \square.$$

Then one can easily verify

$$\beta(M^*, a^*, f^*) = A^*.$$

This completes the proof of (8.12). ∥

PROPOSITION 8.13. *If the automata* $A : T_n \to Q$ *and* $B : T_n \to Q$ *are finite, then so is the automaton*

$$A*B : T_n \to Q$$

defined by setting $(A*B)(\tau) = 1$ *for an arbitrarily given input tape* $\tau \in T_n$ *iff* τ *can be decomposed into a product*

$$\tau = \xi\eta$$

of input tapes $\xi, \eta \in T_n$ *satisfying*

$$A(\xi) = 1, \qquad B(\eta) = 1.$$

Proof. Consider finite sequential machines

$$L : R \times Q^n \to R, \qquad M : S \times Q^n \to S$$

that realize the automata A and B, respectively, by means of the initial states $a \in R$, $b \in S$ and the output functions

$$f : R \to Q, \qquad g : S \to Q.$$

Assume $R \cap S = \square$ and consider the set

$$P = 2^{R \cup S}$$

of all subsets of the union $R \cup S$. Then P is a finite set. Define a function

$$N : P \times Q^n \to P$$

as follows. Let $E \in P$ and $w \in Q^n$ be arbitrarily given. Then E is a subset of $R \cup S$. Consider the subsets $L[(E \cap R) \times w]$ and $M[(E \cap S) \times w]$ of R and S, respectively. If $L[(E \cap R) \times w] \subset f^{-1}(0)$, we define

$$N(E, w) = L[(E \cap R) \times w] \cup M[(E \cap S) \times w];$$

otherwise, we define

$$N(E, w) = \{L[(E \cap R) \times w] \cap f^{-1}(0)\} \cup \{b\} \cup M[(E \cap S) \times w].$$

This completes the definition of the function N. This function N is a finite sequential machine.

Use the singleton subset $\{a\}$ of $R \cup S$ as the initial state of N and let

$$h : P \to Q$$

denote the output function for N defined by setting $h(E) = 1$ for an arbitrarily given member E of P iff

$$E \cap g^{-1}(1) \neq \square.$$

Then one can easily verify

$$\beta(N, \{a\}, h) = A*B.$$

This completes the proof of (8.13). ∥

The automaton $A*B$ in (8.13) is defined for any two automata A and B of n variables and will be referred to as the *transition product* of A and B. One can easily verify that the transition product is associative, that is,

$$(A*B)*C = A*(B*C)$$

holds for arbitrary automata A, B, C of n variables; however, the transition product is clearly not always commutative.

9. Minimization

Let us consider an arbitrarily given automaton

$$A : T_n \to Q$$

of n variables. According to §7, this automaton A can be realized by its minimal sequential machine

$$M_A : S_A \times Q^n \to S_A$$

which operates on the minimum number of states. By definition, M_A is the minimal quotient machine of the free sequential machine F_n with respect to $A : T_n \to Q$ as its output function. This section is devoted to an algorithm for constructing M_A. The algorithm shall be finite at least where the given automaton A is finite.

For this purpose, consider any sequential machine

$$M : S \times Q^n \to S$$

that realizes the given automaton A by means of an initial state $a \in S$ and an output function

$$f : S \to Q.$$

In symbols, we have

$$\beta(M, a, f) = A.$$

This means that

$$f(a\tau) = A(\tau)$$

holds for every input tape $\tau \in T_n$.

In particular, we may take

$$M = F_n, \qquad a = \square \in T_n, \qquad f = A.$$

If A is finite, we may assume that so is M. In fact, we can usually construct a finite sequential machine M to realize A by means of either the methods given in the proofs of (8.9)–(8.13) or other methods as used in [Mc, pp. 224–237]. Because of (3.2) and (3.4), we may assume

$$M_a = M.$$

It then follows from (7.2) that the minimal sequential machine M_A for A is isomorphic to the minimal quotient machine

$$M_f : S_f \times Q^n \to S_f$$

of M with respect to the output function $f : S \to Q$. This reduces the problem of constructing M_A to that of constructing M_f.

In order to construct M_f, we need to effectively construct its set S_f of states. By definition, S_f is the set of all equivalence classes in S with respect to the equivalence relation $\underset{f}{\sim}$. Here, for any two states $x, y \in S$, we have

$$x \underset{f}{\sim} y$$

iff

$$f(x\tau) = f(y\tau)$$

holds for every input tape τ in T_n. The difficulty lies in the fact that T_n is an infinite set and that it is physically impossible to check infinitely many equations one-by-one. To solve this difficulty at least for the case where M is a finite machine, we shall introduce a sequence

$$E_i \qquad (i = 0, 1, 2, \cdots)$$

of equivalence relations in S as follows. For any two states $x, y \in S$, we define

$$xE_i y$$

iff $f(x\tau) = f(y\tau)$ holds for every input tape $\tau \in T_n$ with length

$$\lg(\tau) \leq i.$$

Note that there are only a finite number of input tapes in T_n with length not exceeding i; precisely, the number of these input tapes in T_n is

$$K_i = \sum_{j=0}^{i} 2^{nj}.$$

The elementary properties of these equivalence relations in S are given by the following proposition.

PROPOSITION 9.1. *For any two states x and y in S, the following statements are true:*

(a) $xE_i y$ *implies* $xE_j y$ *for every* $j \leq i$.
(b) $x \underset{f}{\sim} y$ *iff* $xE_i y$ *holds for every* $i \geq 0$.
(c) $xE_{i+1} y$ *iff* $xE_i y$ *and* $M(x, w)E_i M(y, w)$ *for every* $w \in Q^n$.

Proof. (a) and (b) are obvious from the definition. It remains to prove (c). To establish the necessity of (c), let us assume $xE_{i+1} y$. By (a), this implies $xE_i y$. Next, let $w \in Q^n$ be arbitrarily given and let τ denote any input tape in Q^n with $\lg(\tau) \leq i$. Then $w\tau$ is an input tape in T_n with $\lg(w\tau) \leq i + 1$. Since $xE_{i+1} y$, we have

$$f[M(x, w)\tau] = f[x(w\tau)] = f[y(w\tau)] = f[M(y, w)\tau].$$

This proves $M(x, w)E_i M(y, w)$ and establishes the necessity of (c).

To establish the sufficiency of (c), let τ denote any input tape in T_n with $\lg(\tau) \leq i + 1$. We need to prove

$$f(x\tau) = f(y\tau).$$

Since $xE_i y$, we may assume $\lg(\tau) = i + 1$. Then τ can be decomposed into the product $\tau = w\sigma$ of a $w \in Q^n$ and an input tape $\sigma \in T_n$ with $\lg(\sigma) = i$. Since $M(x, w)E_i M(y, w)$, we have

$$f(x\tau) = f[M(x, w)\sigma] = f[M(y, w)\sigma] = f(y\tau).$$

This implies $xE_{i+1} y$ and completes the proof of (9.1). ‖

Next let us establish the important property of these equivalence relations as stated in the following lemma.

LEMMA 9.2. $E_i = \underset{f}{\sim}$ iff $E_i = E_{i+1}$.

Proof. By (a) and (b) in (9.1), the necessity of (9.2) is obvious. It remains to prove its sufficiency. For this purpose, assume $E_i = E_{i+1}$. Let x and y denote any two states in S satisfying $xE_{i+1}y$. By (c) of (9.1), this implies

$$M(x, w)E_iM(y, w)$$

for every $w \in Q^n$. Since $E_i = E_{i+1}$, we have

$$M(x, w)E_{i+1}M(y, w)$$

for every $w \in Q^n$. Since $xE_{i+1}y$, it follows from (c) of (9.1) that this implies

$$xE_{i+2}y.$$

Since x and y are any two states in S satisfying $xE_{i+1}y$, we obtain

$$E_i = E_{i+1} = E_{i+2}.$$

By a simple mathematical induction, one can prove

$$E_i = E_j$$

for every integer $j \geq i$. In view of (a) and (b) in (9.1), this implies

$$E_i = \underset{f}{\sim}$$

and completes the proof of (9.2). ‖

According to the usual definition of relation as given in [H2, p. 29], the relation E_i in the set S means the subset

$$E_i = \{(x, y) \in S^2 \mid xE_iy\}$$

of the Cartesian square $S^2 = S \times S$ of all ordered pairs (x, y) of members of S. It follows from (a) and (b) of (9.1) that we have

$$E_0 \supset E_1 \supset E_2 \supset \cdots \supset E_i \supset E_{i+1} \supset \cdots \supset \underset{f}{\sim},$$

where the symbol $\supset$ stands for the word "contains."

Because of (9.2) and (c) in (9.1), these inclusions suggest an algorithm for computing the relation $\underset{f}{\sim}$ in S and hence its set S_f of equivalence classes as follows. The subset E_0 of S^2 can be constructed by deleting the pairs $(x, y) \in S^2$ with

$$f(x) \neq f(y).$$

Having constructed E_0, we may construct E_1 by deleting the pairs $(x, y) \in E_0$ such that there exists a $w \in Q^n$ with

$$(xw, yw) \notin E_0.$$

If $E_1 = E_0$, then we obtain

$$\underset{f}{\sim} = E_0$$

according to (9.2). Otherwise, we go ahead to construct E_2. In general, let $i \geq 0$ and assume that E_i has already been constructed. Then we may construct E_{i+1} by deleting the pairs $(x, y) \in E_i$ such that there exists a $w \in Q^n$ with

$$(xw, yw) \notin E_i.$$

If $E_{i+1} = E_i$, then we obtain

$$\underset{f}{\sim} = E_i$$

according to (9.2). Otherwise, we go ahead to construct E_{i+2}. Hence this algorithm will either terminate after a finite number of operations or continue indefinitely. In the former case, it gives

$$\underset{f}{\sim} = E_i$$

for some integer $i \geq 0$. In the latter case, we obtain $\underset{f}{\sim}$ as the intersection

$$\underset{f}{\sim} = E_0 \cap E_1 \cap \cdots \cap E_i \cap \cdots$$

of all the relations E_i, $i = 0, 1, 2, \cdots$.

The catch to this algorithm is the following theorem.

THEOREM 9.3. *For any finite sequential machine M, the algorithm terminates. Precisely, if M has k states, then there exists a nonnegative integer*

$$i \leq k - 2$$

such that $\underset{f}{\sim} = E_i$.

Proof. If $E_j \neq E_{j-1}$, then the set-theoretic difference $E_j \backslash E_{j-1}$ contains at least one pair $(x, y) \in S^2$. Since the subsets

$$E_j \backslash E_{j-1}, \quad j = 1, 2, \cdots,$$

of S^2 are disjoint and since S^2 has only a finite number, namely k^2, of pairs, there exists a nonnegative i such that

$$E_i = E_{i+1}.$$

This proves that the algorithm terminates with

$$\underset{f}{\sim} = E_i.$$

It remains to prove $i \leq k - 2$. For this purpose, we may assume that the output function f is not constant for, otherwise, we have

$$E_0 = \underset{f}{\gamma} = S^2.$$

Denote by r_j the number of equivalence classes in S with respect to E_j. Assume $E_j \neq E_{j+1}$. Then we must have

$$2 = r_0 < r_1 < \cdots < r_j < r_{j+1} \leq k.$$

This implies

$$j + 1 \leq k - 2$$

and hence $j \leq k - 3$. This implies $i \leq k - 2$ and completes the proof of (9.3). ‖

The remainder of this section is devoted to the technical details of the algorithm for finite sequential machines. These will be given by means of an illustrative example. For this purpose, let $S = \{1, 2, 3, 4, 5, 6\}$ and consider the sequential machine

$$M : S \times Q^2 \to S$$

of two variables defined by Table IV-9-1. Our problem is to construct the minimal quotient machine M_f of M with respect to the output function

$$f : S \to Q$$

defined by

$$f^{-1}(1) = \{1, 3, 6\}, \qquad f^{-1}(0) = \{2, 4, 5\}.$$

TABLE IV-9-1

$M(x, w)$ x	w 00	01	11	10
1	1	5	1	2
2	3	2	2	2
3	3	4	3	2
4	1	4	6	4
5	1	5	3	5
6	6	5	6	2

TABLE IV-9-2

1						
2						
3						
4						
5						
6						
	1	2	3	4	5	6

According to the algorithm described above, we shall construct the subsets $E_j, j = 0, 1, 2, \cdots$, of the Cartesian square`

$$S^2 = S \times S.$$

The members of S^2 can be conveniently represented by the vacant cells in Table IV-9-2. Here, the cell located at the i-th row and the j-th column represents the member (i, j) of S^2. Since every equivalence relation is reflexive and symmetric, we may consider only those cells in Table IV-9-2 which lie below the principal diagonal. Thus we obtain Table IV-9-3.

To construct E_0, we simply cross out those cells (i, j) in Table IV-9-3 such that

$$f(i) \neq f(j).$$

TABLE IV-9-3

2					
3					
4					
5					
6					
	1	2	3	4	5

TABLE IV-9-4

	1	2	3	4	5
2	✕				
3		✕			
4	✕		✕		
5	✕		✕		
6		✕		✕	✕

Thus we obtain Table IV-9-4. The vacant cells in Table IV-9-4 represent the essential pairs in the equivalence relation E_0. Therefore, we have

$$E_0 = \{(3, 1), (4, 2), (5, 2), (5, 4), (6, 1), (6, 3)\}.$$

To construct E_1 from E_0, we need to operate each $w \in Q^2$ on every pair $(x, y) \in E_0$ and obtain the pair

$$(xw, yw) \in S^2.$$

If any one of the three equations

$$xw = yw, \qquad (xw, yw) = (x, y), \qquad (xw, yw) = (y, x)$$

is satisfied, this pair (xw, yw) is to be replaced by the don't care sign $*$. If $xw < yw$, this pair (xw, yw) is to be replaced by (yw, xw). Thus we obtain Table IV-9-5 from Table IV-9-1.

Observe the rows in Table IV-9-5. If a row (x, y) contains a pair (i, j) whose corresponding cell in Table IV-9-4 is crossed, the cell in Table IV-9-4 which represents (x, y) is to be crossed. Thus the two cells $(4, 2)$ and $(5, 2)$ are to be crossed and we obtain Table IV-9-6.

The vacant cells in Table IV-9-6 represent the essential pairs in the equivalence relation E_1; therefore, we have

$$E_1 = \{(3, 1), (5, 4), (6, 1), (6, 3)\}.$$

To construct E_2 from E_1, we need to investigate every pair $(x, y) \in E_1$. If the row (x, y) in Table IV-9-5 contains a pair (i, j) whose corresponding in Table IV-9-6 is crossed, the cell in Table IV-9-6 which represents (x, y)

TABLE IV-9-5

(xw, yw) w (x, y)	00	01	11	10
(3, 1)	*	(5, 4)	*	*
(4, 2)	(3, 1)	*	(6, 2)	*
(5, 2)	(3, 1)	*	(3, 2)	*
(5, 4)	*	*	(6, 3)	*
(6, 1)	*	*	*	*
(6, 3)	*	(5, 4)	*	*

is to be crossed. For our present example, it happens that no vacant cell in Table IV-9-6 is to be crossed. This means

$$E_2 = E_1$$

and, therefore, we obtain

$$\underset{f}{\sim} = E_1 = \{(3, 1), (5, 4), (6, 1), (6, 3)\}.$$

This equivalence relation in S gives three equivalence classes, namely,

$$a = \{1, 3, 6\}, \qquad b = \{2\}, \qquad c = \{4, 5\}.$$

TABLE IV-9-6

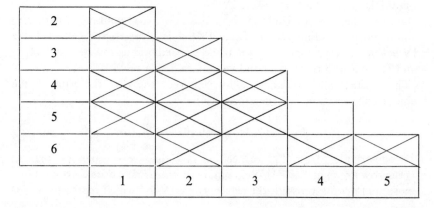

Hence $S_f = \{a, b, c\}$ and the minimal quotient machine

$$M_f : S_f \times Q^2 \to S_f$$

is given by Table IV-9-7.
The output function

$$g = p(f) : S_f \to Q$$

for M_f induced by the natural projection $p : S \to S_f$ is defined by

$$g^{-1}(1) = \{a\}, \qquad g^{-1}(0) = \{b, c\}.$$

This completes the minimization problem for the given example.

For the purpose of quick practice, one can combine the operations of computing all E_i, $i = 1, 2, \cdots$, into one process described as follows: While we are computing the rows of Table IV-9-5 in the lexicographical

TABLE IV-9-7

$M_f(x, w)$ $\diagdown$ w x	00	01	11	10
a	a	c	a	b
b	a	b	b	b
c	a	c	a	c

order of the pairs in E_0, we do the following operation. Assume that we have just computed the row (x, y) in Table IV-9-5. If this row (x, y), contains no pair (i, j) whose corresponding cell in Table IV-9-4 is crossed, we enter the symbol (x, y) into every cell of Table IV-9-4 whose symbol appears in this row (x, y). Otherwise, cross the cell (x, y) with a rule that, while we cross any cell (u, v), we have to cross all cells whose symbols have been entered into the cell (u, v). After we have done this for all members (x, y) of E_0 and have crossed all cells according to the rule described above, Table IV-9-4 becomes Table IV-9-8.

The uncrossed cells in Table IV-9-8 represent the essential pairs in the equivalence relation $\underset{f}{\sim}$. It is not difficult to see this process is correct for any given finite sequential machine M.

TABLE IV-9-8

	1	2	3	4	5
2	✕				
3	✕	✕			
4	✕	✕	✕		
5	✕	✕	✕	(3, 1) (6, 3)	
6	✕	✕	(5, 4)	✕	✕

10. Synthesis of Finite Machines

Consider an arbitrarily given finite sequential machine

$$M : S \times Q^n \to S$$

together with an output function

$$f : S \to Q.$$

This section is devoted to the construction of switching circuits that will mechanize both the machine M and the output function f. This process is described by means of an illustrative example.

For this purpose, let $S = \{a, b, c\}$ and consider the sequential machine

$$M : S \times Q^2 \to S$$

defined by Table IV-10-1 together with an output function

$$f : S \to Q$$

defined by

$$f^{-1}(1) = \{a\}, \qquad f^{-1}(0) = \{b, c\}.$$

(Note that M and f in this example are the results of the example of the minimization algorithm in the preceding section.)

The states S of the machine M can be taken care of by internal variables. Since k 2-valued internal variables have 2^k combinations of values and since S has three states, we need two internal variables, say v_1 and v_2.

TABLE IV-10-1

$M(x, w)$ $\quad w$ x	00	01	11	10
a	a	c	a	b
b	a	b	b	b
c	a	c	a	c

Let $v = v_1 v_2$ denote an arbitrary combination of value. Then $v \in Q^2$. To represent the states in S, we need to assign three distinct members of Q^2 to the three states a, b, c in S. There are

$$P_3^4 = 4 \times 3 \times 2 = 24$$

different ways to carry out this assignment, one of which is

$$a = 00, \qquad b = 01, \qquad c = 10.$$

Table IV-10-1 is usually called the *state table* for the machine M. In this table, let us replace every a by 00, every b by 01, and every c by 10. Furthermore, since 11 is not used in this assignment, we enter a row of don't care signs * headed by 11. Thus we obtain Table IV-10-2. Table IV-10-2 is traditionally called a *transition table* for the machine M.

TABLE IV-10-2

$M(v, w)$ $\quad w$ v	00	01	11	10
00	00	10	00	01
01	00	01	01	01
11	*	*	*	*
10	00	10	00	10

TABLE IV-10-3

x	x_1	x_2	$f(x)$
0	0	0	0
1	0	1	0
2	1	0	0
3	1	1	*

On the other hand, the given output function becomes a switching function

$$f : Q^2 \to Q^*$$

with don't care point and defined by Table IV-10-3.

The two coordinates of the matrix $M(v, w)$ in Table IV-10-2 determine two switching functions

$$e_1, e_2 : Q^4 \to Q^*$$

of four variables, with don't care points and defined by Tables IV-10-4 and IV-10-5.

These two switching functions e_1 and e_2 are usually called the *excitation functions* of the machine M. Now the machine M, together with its output function f, can be mechanized by the circuit shown in Figure IV-10-6. Here, the symbol i stands for the identity function $i : Q \to Q$. In practice, a delaying device is built in each of the two boxes indicated by i to make sure that the inner states change at the right time.

Theoretically, this solves the problem. In practice, one must realize the three switching functions f, e_1 and e_2 by means of standard logical devices.

TABLE IV-10-4

$e_1(vw)$ v \ w	00	01	11	10
00	0	1	0	0
01	0	0	0	0
11	*	*	*	*
10	0	1	0	1

TABLE IV-10-5

$e_2(vw)$ v \ w	00	01	11	10
00	0	0	0	1
01	0	1	1	1
11	*	*	*	*
10	0	0	0	0

FIGURE IV-10-6

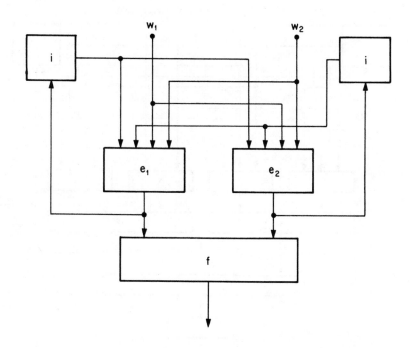

This depends on what logical devices are to be used and how many levels have been allowed for each of these switching functions.

If the classical 2-level circuits of AND and OR gates are desired, then one should apply the methods given in Chapter II to these switching functions. From Table IV-10-3, one observes that f can be realized by the NOR function

$$\vee' = c \circ \vee : Q^2 \to Q,$$

where $c : Q \to Q$ denotes the complementation function. As to e_1 and e_2, Tables IV-10-4 and IV-10-5 are already in the form of their Karnaugh maps. Therefore, one can easily obtain their minimal Boolean expressions

$$e_1 = v_2' w_1' w_2 \vee v_1 w_1 w_2',$$

$$e_2 = v_2 w_2 \vee v_1' w_1 w_2'.$$

Thus the circuit in Figure IV-10-6 is realized by the circuit shown in the diagram of Figure IV-10-7.

FIGURE IV-10-7

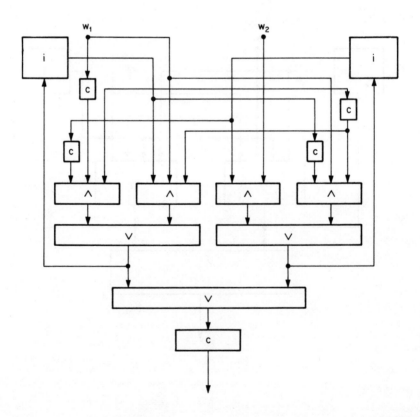

If other logical devices are to be used, then we should apply the methods given in Chapter III to the three switching functions f, e_1 and e_2 to obtain a circuit with the desired logical devices as components.

Early in this section, we observed that there are 24 different ways of assigning three distinct members of Q^2 to the three states a, b, and c. We selected arbitrarily one of these 24 ways, namely

$$a = 00, \qquad b = 01, \qquad c = 10.$$

If some other way of assignment were chosen, the resulting circuit might be essentially different from the one we constructed above. As to the problem of looking for the assignment that gives rise to the most economic circuit, see [Mc, pp. 263–267] and the references cited there.

Exercises

1. Consider the finite sequential machine M of two variables defined by Table IV-E-1 together with an output function defined by $f^{-1}(1) = \{a, c\}$ and $f^{-1}(0) = \{b, d\}$. Prove that this machine M is minimal

TABLE IV-E-1

$M(x, w)$ w x	00	01	11	10
a	a	b	d	c
b	a	b	d	c
c	b	c	c	c
d	d	d	d	c

with respect to f and design a circuit with $\wedge$, $\vee$, c as component devices to realize both M and f.

2. Consider the finite sequential machine M of three variables defined by Table IV-E-2 together with an output function defined by $f^{-1}(1) = \{a, d, e\}$ and $f^{-1}(0) = \{b, c\}$. Prove that this machine M is minimal with respect to f and design a circuit with $\wedge$, $\vee$, c as component devices to realize both M and f.

3. Consider the electronic gadget G described as follows. G has two input leads that receive signals in the form of pulses and one output indicator that reads 0 or 1. The pulse signals never overlap and never

TABLE IV-E-2

M(x, w) ＼ w ＼ x	000	001	010	011	100	101	110	111
a	a	b	a	*	e	*	*	*
b	b	a	c	*	b	*	*	*
c	c	d	b	*	c	*	*	*
d	d	c	e	*	d	*	*	*
e	e	e	d	*	a	*	*	*

arrive on the input leads simultaneously. The output reading changes only when some pulse arrives on the input leads. The output indicator will read 0 as long as the pulses arrive alternately on the two input leads and will read 1 whenever two or more successive pulses are received by the same input lead.

(a) Determine the automaton $A : T_2 \to Q^*$ by which this gadget G behaves.

(b) Prove that A is finite.

(c) Find a finite sequential machine $M : S \times Q^2 \to S$, an initial state $a \in S$, and an output function $f : S \to Q$ to realize the automaton A.

(d) Find the minimal quotient machine $M_f : S_f \times Q^2 \to S_f$ of M with respect to f and the output function $g : S_f \to Q$ induced from f by the natural projection $p : S \to S_f$.

(e) Construct a circuit of classical $\wedge$, $\vee$, c devices to mechanize both M_f and g.

(f) Construct a circuit of threshold devices to mechanize both M_f and g.

4. Let the members of the n-cube Q^n be denoted by the integers $0, 1, \cdots, 2^n - 1$ as usual. By the $mod\ 2^n\ adder$, we mean the sequentiat machine

$$M : Q^n \times Q^n \to Q^n$$

defined by

$$M(x, y) \equiv x + y \bmod 2^n$$

for every $x \in Q^n$ and every $y \in Q^n$, together with n output functions

$$f_i : Q^n \to Q, \qquad (i = 1, 2, \cdots, n),$$

defined by

$$f_i(x) \equiv [x/2^{n-i}] \bmod 2$$

for every $x \in Q^n$. Here $[t]$ denotes the largest integer not exceeding t.

(a) Prove that, for every $x \in Q^n$, the binary representation of the integer x is
$$x = f_1(x)f_2(x) \cdots f_n(x).$$

(b) Prove that the machine M is minimal with respect to f_1.

(c) For $n = 2$, construct a circuit of classical $\wedge$, $\vee$, c devices to mechanize both the machine M and the output functions f_1 and f_2.

5. Let p denote any positive integer and let n denote the least integer satisfying $p \leq 2^n$. By the *mod p adder*, we mean the sequential machine
$$M : Q^n \times Q^n \rightarrow Q^n$$
defined for any $(x, y) \in Q^n \times Q^n$ by
$$M(x, y) = \begin{cases} x + y \bmod p, & \text{(if } x < p \text{ and } y < p\text{)}, \\ *, & \text{(otherwise)}, \end{cases}$$

together with the n output functions $f_1, \cdots, f_n$ in the preceding exercise. For $p = 3$ and hence $n = 2$, construct a circuit of classical $\wedge$, $\vee$, c devices to mechanize both the machine M and the output functions f_1 and f_2.

6. Let p and n be positive integers as in the preceding exercise. By the *mod p multiplier*, we mean the sequential machine
$$M : Q^n \times Q^n \rightarrow Q^n$$
defined for any $(x, y) \in Q^n \times Q^n$ by
$$M(x, y) = \begin{cases} xy, & \text{(if } x < p \text{ and } y < p\text{)}, \\ *, & \text{(otherwise)}, \end{cases}$$

together with the n output functions $f_1, \cdots, f_n$ in Exercise 4. For $p = 3$ and hence $n = 2$, construct a circuit of classical $\wedge$, $\vee$, c devices to mechanize both the machine M and the output functions f_1 and f_2.

7. Consider any finite semigroup S as defined in [H2, p. 96]. To avoid confusion with the multiplication of integers, we shall denote the binary operation in S by the symbol $\otimes$. Let p denote the order of S (i.e., S has p distinct members). Let n be the least integer satisfying $p \leq 2^n$. Since we can label the members of S by p distinct integers in Q^n, we may consider S as a subset of Q^n. Consider the sequential machine
$$M : Q^n \times Q^n \rightarrow Q^n$$
defined for every $(x, y) \in Q^n \times Q^n$ by
$$M(x, y) = \begin{cases} x \otimes y, & \text{(if } x \in S \text{ and } y \in S\text{)}, \\ *, & \text{(otherwise)}. \end{cases}$$

Together with the n output functions, this machine realizes the semigroup S. Construct sequential machines realizing the groups of order not exceeding 4 and construct circuits of classical $\wedge, \vee, c$ devices to mechanize these machines.

8. A sequential machine $M : S \times Q^n \to S$ is said to be *connected* iff there exists a state $a \in S$ with $M_a = M$. The machine M is said to be *strongly connected* iff $M_a = M$ holds for every $a \in S$. Prove that every homomorphic image of a connected machine is connected and every homomorphic image of a strongly connected machine is strongly connected.

9. Prove that the automorphisms of any sequential machine

$$M : S \times Q^n \to S$$

form a subgroup $A(M)$ of the group $P(S)$ of all permutations of the set S.

10. Consider any sequential machine $M : S \times Q^n \to S$. For every input tape $\tau \in T_n$, define a function

$$\phi_\tau : S \to S$$

by taking $\phi_\tau(a) = a\tau$ for every $a \in S$. Prove that the set

$$\Phi = \{\phi_\tau \mid \tau \in T_n\}$$

form a submonoid of the monoid of all functions from S into itself. Prove that the assignment $\tau \to \phi_\tau$ defines a homomorphism $h : T_n \to \Phi$ from the free monoid T_n generated by Q^n onto Φ.

11. In the set T_n of all input tapes of n variables, define a relation $\sim$ by setting, for any two input tapes $\xi, \eta \in T_n$, $\xi \sim \eta$ iff $\lg(\xi) = \lg(\eta)$. Prove that $\sim$ is an invariant equivalence relation in T_n with respect to the free sequential machine F_n of n variables. Study the quotient machine $F_n/\sim$.

12. By the *transpose* of an input tape $\tau \in T_n$, we mean the input tape $\tau^\# \in T_n$ obtained from τ by reversing the order of the input words in τ. Thus, if $\tau = (w_1, \cdots, w_q)$, then we have $\tau^\# = (w_q, \cdots, w_1)$. Prove:

(a) $\square^\# = \square$,

(b) If $\tau \in Q^n$, then $\tau^\# = \tau$.

(c) For any two $\sigma, \tau \in T_n$, we have $(\sigma\tau)^\# = \tau^\#\sigma^\#$.

(d) For any $\tau \in T_n$, we have $(\tau^\#)^\# = \tau$. By the *transpose* of an automaton $A : T_n \to Q$, we mean the automaton $A^\# : T_n \to Q$ defined by

$$A^\#(\tau) = A(\tau^\#)$$

for every $\tau \in T_n$. Prove that the transpose of every finite automaton is finite.

13. By a *Mealy machine*, we mean a sequential machine

$$M : S \times Q^n \to S$$

together with a function

$$f : S \times Q^n \to Q.$$

The latter may be called a Mealy output function for the sequential machine M. Consider the Cartesian product

$$S^* = S \times Q.$$

Define a sequential machine

$$M^* : S^* \times Q^n \to S^*$$

by taking

$$M^*[(x, t), w] = [M(x, w), f(x, w)]$$

for every $(x, t) \in S^*$ and every $w \in Q^n$. Define a (Moore) output function

$$f^* : S^* \to Q$$

by taking $f^*(x, t) = t$ for every $(x, t) \in S^*$. Prove that (M, f) is equivalent to (M^*, f^*), that is to say, they have the same behavior over $T_n \backslash \{\Box\}$. Generalize the minimization method in §9 to sequential machines with Mealy output functions.

14. Consider any given sequential machine $M : S \times Q^n \to S$. Let $a \in S$ and $w \in Q^n$. The state a is said to be *stable* under w iff $M(a, w) = a$. The machine M is said to be *stable* iff $M(a, w)$ is stable under w for every $a \in S$ and every $w \in Q^n$. The machine M is said to be *fundamental* iff, for every $a \in S$ and every $w \in Q^n$, there exists a positive integer k, which may depend on a and w, such that aw^k is stable under w. For any fundamental machine M, the assignment $(a, w) \to aw^k$ defines a stable machine

$$\bar{M} : S \times Q^n \to S.$$

Prove:

(a) A stable machine M can be operated in *fundamental mode, pulse mode*, or any other mode in the sense of [Mc, pp. 183–207]. The behavior of M does not depend on the mode in which it is operated.

(b) A sequential machine M can be operated in the fundamental mode iff M is fundamental.

(c) When a fundamental machine M is operated in the fundamental mode, it behaves the same as its corresponding stable machine $\bar{M}$.

This bibliography has been reduced to the minimum essential to the text and the exercises. For comprehensive lists, see [Ha, pp. 473–490], [Holst 1, pp. 638–655], and [Kautz 1, pp. 184–204].

Books

[Ca] Caldwell, S. H. *Switching Circuits and Logical Design*. New York: Wiley, 1958.

[Cu] Curtis, H. A. *A New Approach to the Design of Switching Circuits*. Princeton, N.J.: Van Nostrand, 1962.

[Gil] Gill, A. *Introduction to the Theory of Finite-State Machines*. New York: McGraw-Hill, 1962.

[Gin] Ginsburg, S. *An Introduction to Mathematical Machine Theory*. Reading, Mass.: Addison-Wesley Publishing Co., 1962.

[Ha] Harrison, M. A. *Introduction to Switching and Automata Theory*. New York: McGraw-Hill, 1965.

[H-S] Hartmanis, J., and R. E. Stearns. *Algebraic Structure Theory of Sequential Machines*. Englewood Cliffs, N.J.: Prentice-Hall, 1966.

[Ho] Hohn, F. E. *Applied Boolean Algebra*. New York: Macmillan, 1960.

[H1] Hu, S.-T. *Threshold Logic*. Berkeley and Los Angeles: University of California Press, 1965.

[H2] Hu, S.-T. *Introduction to Contemporary Mathematics*. San Francisco: Holden-Day, 1966.

[H3] Hu, S.-T. *Elements of Modern Algebra*. San Francisco: Holden-Day, 1965.

[Mc] McCluskey, E. J. *Introduction to the Theory of Switching Circuits*. New York: McGraw-Hill, 1965.

[Mi] Miller, R. E. *Switching Theory*. New York: Wiley, 1965. 2 vols.

Papers

Ashenhurst, R. L.
1. *Non-Disjoint Decomposition*. Harvard Computation Laboratory Report No. BL-4, Sec. IV (1953).
2. "The Decomposition of Switching Functions." Proc. of an International Symposium on the Theory of Switching, April 2–5, 1957. *Annals of the Harvard Computational Laboratory* (Harvard University Press, 1959), XXIX, 74–116.

Glover, F.
1. *An All-Integer Integer Programming Algorithm*. ONR Research Memo No. 116 (Dec., 1963).

Gomory, R. E.
1. "Outline of an Algorithm for Integer Solutions to Linear Programs," *Bulletin of the American Mathematical Society*, 64 (Sept., 1958), 275–278.
2. *An Algorithm for Integer Solutions to Linear Programs*. Princeton-I.B.M. Mathematics Research Project, Technical Report No. 1 (Nov., 1958).

Holst, P. A.
1. "Bibliography on Switching Circuits and Logical Algebra," *IRE Transactions on Electronic Computers*, Vol. EC-10 (Dec., 1961), pp. 638–661.

Hu, S.-T.
1. *On the Decomposition of Switching Functions*. LMSC Technical Report 6-90-61-15 (June, 1961). 28 pp.
2. *Duality Theory of Switching Functions*. LMSC Technical Report 6-90-61-17 (July, 1961). 52 pp.

Huffman, D. A.
1. "The Synthesis of Sequential Switching Circuits," *Journal of Franklin Institute*, 257 (March–April, 1954), 161–190, 275–303.

Karp, R. M.
1. "Functional Decomposition and Switching Circuit Design," *Journal of the Society of Industrial Applied Mathematics*, 11 (June, 1963), 291–335.

Kautz, W. H.
1. "A Survey and Assessment of Progress in Switching Theory and Logical Design in the Soviet Union," *IEEE Transactions on Electronic Computers*, Vol. EC-15 (April, 1966), pp. 164–204.

Moore, E. F.
1. "Gedanken-Experiments on Sequential Machines," in *Automata Studies* (Princeton University Press, 1956), pp. 129–153.
Pólya, G.
1. "Kombinatorische Anzahlbestimmungen für Gruppen, Graphen, und Chemische Verbindungen," *Acta Math.*, 68 (1939), 145–253.
Povarov, G. N.
1. "A Mathematical Theory for the Synthesis of Contact Networks with One Input and *k* Outputs," Proc. of an International Symposium on the Theory of Switching, April 2–5, 1957. *Annals of the Harvard Computational Laboratory* (Harvard University Press, 1959), Pt. II, pp. 74–94.
Pyne, I. B., and E. J. McCluskey, Jr.
1. "An Essay on Prime Implicant Tables," *Journal of the Society of Industrial Applied Mathematics*, 9 (Dec., 1961), 604–631.
Roth, J. P.
1. "Algebraic Topological Methods for the Synthesis of Switching System I," *Transactions of the American Mathematics Society*, 88 (July, 1958), 301–326.
2. "Algebraic Topological Methods in Synthesis," *Annals of the Harvard Computational Laboratory*, XXIX (1959) 57–73.
3. "Minimization over Boolean Trees," *IBM Journal of Research and Development*, 4 (Nov., 1960), 543–558.
Roth, J. P., and R. M. Karp
1. "Minimization over Boolean Graphs," *IBM Journal of Research and Development*, 6 (April, 1962), 227–238.
Roth, J. P., and E. G. Wagner
1. "Algebraic Topological Methods for the Synthesis of Switching Systems, III: Minimization of Nonsingular Boolean Trees," *IBM Journal of Research and Development*, 4 (Oct., 1959), 1–19.
Shannon, C. E.
1. "A Symbolic Analysis of Relay and Switching Circuits," *Transactions of the AIEE*, 57 (1938), 713–723.
2. "The Synthesis of Two-Terminal Switching Circuits, *Bell System Technical Journal*, 28 (Jan., 1949), 59–98.
Szwarc, W.
1. *The Mixed Integer Linear Programming Problem When the Integer Variables Are Zero or One.* Research Project on Planning and Control of Industrial Operations. Pittsburgh: Carnegie Institute of Technology, May, 1963.

Todd, J. A.
1. "The Group of Symmetries of the Regular Polytopes," *Proceedings of the Cambridge Philosophical Society*, 27 (1931), 212–231.

Young, A.
1. "On Quantitative Substitutional Analysis," *Proceedings of the London Mathematics Society*, ser. 2, vol. 31 (1930), pp. 273–288.

Young, R. D.
1. *A Primal (All-Integer) Integer Programming Algorithm: Antecedents, Description, Proof of Finiteness, Exemplification.* Working Paper No. 52, Graduate School of Business, Stanford University, Dec., 1964.

INDEX